Solutions Manual

IMPACT MATHEMATICS

Algebra and More

Course 3

Developed by
Education Development Center, Inc.

McGraw Hill **Glencoe**

New York, New York   Columbus, Ohio   Chicago, Illinois   Peoria, Illinois   Woodland Hills, California

Glencoe

The *McGraw·Hill* Companies

The algebra content for *Impact Mathematics* was adapted from the series, *Access to Algebra*, by Neville Grace, Jayne Johnston, Barry Kissane, Ian Lowe, and Sue Willis. Permission to adapt this material was obtained from the publisher, Curriculum Corporation of Level 5, 2 Lonsdale Street, Melbourne, Australia.

Send all inquiries to:
Glencoe/McGraw-Hill
8787 Orion Place
Columbus, OH 43240-4027

ISBN 0-07-861324-8

Impact Mathematics, Course 3,
Solutions Manual

Printed in the United States of America.

1 2 3 4 5 6 7 8 9 10 045 12 11 10 09 08 07 06 05 04

CONTENTS

Chapter 1   Linear Relationships 1

Chapter 2   Quadratic and Inverse Relationships 27

Chapter 3   Exponents and Exponential Variation 48

Chapter 4   Solving Equations 75

Chapter 5   Transformational Geometry 106

Chapter 6   Working with Expressions 130

Chapter 7   Solving Quadratic Equations 154

Chapter 8   Functions and Their Graphs 183

Chapter 9   Probability 201

Chapter 10 Modeling with Data 217

Appendix: Trigonometric Ratios 231

Chapter 1 Linear Relationships

1-1 Direct Variation

1.

		150 + 350 = 500
150 · 2 = 300		300 + 350 = 650
150 · 3 = 450		450 + 350 = 800
150 · 4 = 600		600 + 350 = 950
150 · 5 = 750		750 + 350 = 1,100
150 · 6 = 900		900 + 350 = 1,250

Hours Worked on Sunday, h	0	1	2	3	4	5	6
Sunday Deliveries, s	0	150	300	450	600	750	900
Total Deliveries, t	350	500	650	800	950	1,100	1,250

2a. 150 · 2 = 300 yes
300 · 2 = 600 yes

2b. 350 · 2 = 700 no
650 · 2 = 1,300 no

2c. 150 · 3 = 450 yes
300 · 3 = 900 yes

2d. 500 · 3 = 1,500 no
650 · 3 = 1,950 no

3.
$0 = 150 \cdot 0$
$150 = 150 \cdot 1$
$300 = 150 \cdot 2$
$450 = 150 \cdot 3$
$600 = 150 \cdot 4$
$750 = 150 \cdot 5$
$900 = 150 \cdot 6$
$s = 150h$

4.
$350 = 150 \cdot 0 + 350$
$500 = 150 \cdot 1 + 350$
$650 = 150 \cdot 2 + 350$
$800 = 150 \cdot 3 + 350$
$950 = 150 \cdot 4 + 350$
$1,110 = 150 \cdot 5 + 350$
$1,250 = 150 \cdot 6 + 350$
$t = 150h + 350$

Page 8 Problem Set B

1.

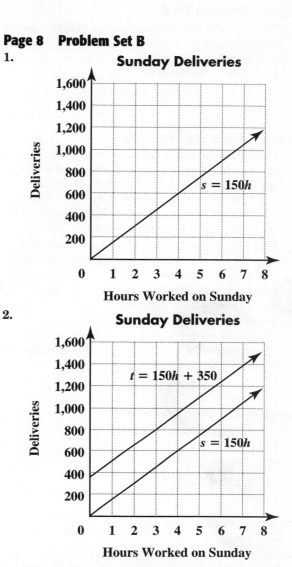

Sunday Deliveries

$s = 150h$

2.

Sunday Deliveries

$t = 150h + 350$

$s = 150h$

3. They are lines with the same steepness, but the graph of Sunday deliveries passes through the origin, while the graph of total deliveries passes through (0, 350).

4a. Because before Mikayla started working on Sunday, she had made 0 Sunday deliveries.

4b. Because before Mikayla started working on Sunday, she had made 350 deliveries already.

5. Possible answer: The graphs change at the same rate, but the t values are always 350 more than the corresponding s values. Since s and t can never be the same for any value of h, the graphs can't intersect.

6a. Mikayla's delivery rate per hour

6b. It would make the graph less steep.

6c. It would make the graph steeper.

7. Yes; Possible explanations: There is no fixed starting amount. *Or*, the equation for a direct variation can be written in the form $y = mx$. Since (0, 0) satisfies this equation, the graph must pass through the origin.

Page 9 Problem Set C

1. Batai's, Cal's, and Daniela's; their graphs have the same steepness.

2. Alison's, Daniela's, and Evan's; their graphs are lines passing through the origin.

3. Batai's and Cal's; their graphs do not pass through the origin.

Page 9 Share and Summarize

1. Possible answer: If a car travels at a constant rate of 60 mph, the relationship between the time it travels and the distance traveled is a direct variation. If a taxi charges a fixed fee of $3.00 plus $1.50 per mile, the relationship between miles and cab fare is not a direct variation.

2. Possible answer: The graph of distance versus time for the car will be a line through the origin. The graph of dollar versus miles for the taxi will be a line; if miles traveled is on the x-axis, the line will go through the point (0, 3).

3. Possible answer: The equation for time vs. distance a car travels has no starting amount. The equation for cab fare vs. number of miles has a starting amount of 3.

Pages 10–11 Problem Set D

1. $1{,}000 - 350 = 650$

2. $650 - 150 = 500$
   $500 - 150 = 350$
   $350 - 150 = 200$
   $200 - 150 = 50$

Hours Worked on Sunday, h	0	1	2	3	4
Pamphlets Remaining, r	650	500	350	200	50

3. $650 = 650 - 150 \cdot 0$
   $500 = 650 - 150 \cdot 1$
   $350 = 650 - 150 \cdot 2$
   $200 = 650 - 150 \cdot 3$
   $50 = 650 - 150 \cdot 4$
   $r = 650 - 150h \text{ or } r = {}^-150h + 650$

4. $4\frac{1}{3}$ h; Possible explanation: The table shows that after 4 h, she had 50 pamphlets left. She delivers 150 per hour, so she can deliver 50 in $\frac{1}{3}$ of an hour.

5.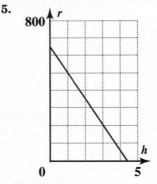

The relationship is linear.

6. The line slants downward from left to right. The situation is about a quantity that becomes smaller instead of larger.

7. No; the graph does not pass through the origin.

8a. The number of pamphlets is decreasing by 150 per hour. For every hour of delivery, the total remaining drops by 150. This causes the graph to slant downward. Every increase of 1 in h corresponds to a decrease of 150 in r.

8b. Mikayla started Sunday with 650 pamphlets; when she started, $h = 0$, and the number of pamphlets remaining was 650. The 650 determines where the graph crosses the vertical axis, at (0, 650).

9. She starts Sunday with $1{,}000 - 200 = 800$ pamphlets.
   $r = 800 - 100h \text{ or } r = {}^-100h + 800$

Page 11 Problem Set E

1a. Possible situation: Lydia owes her parents $15.00. She plans to give them $2.50 per week until her debt is paid.

1b. Possible table:

Weeks, w	1	2	3	4	5	6
Debt Remaining, d	$12.50	$10.00	$7.50	$5.00	$2.50	$0

1c. $12.50 = {}^-2.50 \cdot 1 + 15$
   $10.00 = {}^-2.50 \cdot 2 + 15$
   $7.50 = {}^-2.50 \cdot 3 + 15$
   $5.00 = {}^-2.50 \cdot 4 + 15$
   $2.50 = {}^-2.50 \cdot 5 + 15$
   $0 = {}^-2.50 \cdot 6 + 15$

   Possible equation: $d = {}^-2.50w + 15.00$

1d. Possible graph:

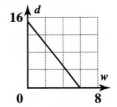

2. Possible situation: A submarine started at sea level and descended 100 ft per minute.

Page 12 Share and Summarize

Possible answer: decreasing relationships (Lines a, b, c, f) vs. increasing relationships (Lines d, e); direct variation (Lines a, c, e) vs. variation that is not direct (Lines b, d, f)

Page 13 Problem Set F

1a. a direct variation

1b. The relationship involves a constant change and no fixed starting amount.

1c. at 0 weeks: $0

after 1 week: $25 \cdot 1 = \$25$

after 2 weeks: $25 \cdot 2 = \$50$

after 3 weeks: $25 \cdot 3 = \$75$

after w weeks: $25 \cdot w = \$25w$

$a = 25w$

2a. linear but not a direct variation

2b. The relationship involves a constant change and a starting amount.

2c. at 0 weeks: $150

after 1 week: $25 \cdot 1 + 150 = \$175$

after 2 weeks: $25 \cdot 2 + 150 = \$200$

after 3 weeks: $25 \cdot 3 + 150 = \$225$

after w weeks: $25 \cdot w + 150 = 25w + 150$

$a = 25w + 150$

3a. nonlinear

3b. The relationship does not involve a constant change; the amount withdrawn lessens each week.

4a. linear but not a direct variation

4b. There is a constant change, and there is also a starting amount.

4c. at the beginning of school: $150

after 1 week: $150 - 25 \cdot 1 = \$125$

after 2 weeks: $150 - 25 \cdot 2 = \$100$

after 3 weeks: $150 - 25 \cdot 3 = \$75$

after w weeks: $150 - 25 \cdot w = 150 - 25w$

$a = 150 - 25w$ or $a = {}^{-}25w + 150$

Page 14   Problem Set G

1. linear but not a direct variation; line that does not go through the origin

2. a direct variation; line that goes through the origin

3. nonlinear; not a line

4. linear but not a direct variation; line that does not go through the origin

5. nonlinear; not a line

6. linear but not a direct variation; line that does not go through the origin

Page 14   Problem Set H

1. a direct variation; constant rate of change with no constant, or number, added

2. linear but not a direct variation; constant rate of change with a constant added

3. a direct variation; constant rate of change with no constant added

4. linear but not a direct variation; constant rate of change with a constant added

5. nonlinear; as s increases, t changes in greater amounts

6. linear but not a direct variation; constant rate of change with a constant added

7. a direct variation; constant rate of change with no constant added

8. nonlinear; as p increases, y changes in smaller amounts

Page 15   Problem Set I

1a. As x increases by 1, y increases by 4.

Yes; constant change in x results in constant change in y.

1b. As x doubles from 2 to 4, y goes from 7 to 15 and does not double.

Not a direct variation; when x doubles, y does not.

2a. As u increases by 1, w increases by 2, 6, 22, and 54.

No; constant change in u does not result in constant change in w.

3a. As p increases by 2, q increases by 20.

Yes; constant change in p results in constant change in q.

3b. As p doubles from 2 to 4, q changes from 26 to 46 and does not double.

Not a direct variation; when p doubles, q does not.

4a. As t increases by 4, r increases by 12.

Yes; constant change in t results in constant change in r.

4b. As t triples from 2 to 6, r triples from 6 to 18.

A direct variation; when t triples, r triples too.

Page 15   Share and Summarize

Relationship	Words	Graph	Equation	Table
nonlinear	doesn't have a constant rate of change	not a line	can't be represented in the form $y = mx + b$ (even with m or b equal to 0)	as x values change by a constant amount, differences in y values are not constant
direct variation	has a constant rate of change and no added constant	a line that passes through the origin	can be represented in the form $y = mx$	constant difference in y values as x changes by a constant amount; doubling or tripling one quantity doubles or triples the other
linear but not a direct variation	has a constant rate of change and an added constant	a line that does not go through the origin	can be represented in the form $y = mx + b$ with $b \neq 0$	y value not equal to 0 when x is equal to 0; one is not a constant multiple of the other

1a. $0 \cdot 20 = 0$
$1 \cdot 20 = 20$
$2 \cdot 20 = 40$
$3 \cdot 20 = 60$
$4 \cdot 20 = 80$
$5 \cdot 20 = 100$
$6 \cdot 20 = 120$
$7 \cdot 20 = 140$

Possible table:

Hours Worked, h	0	1	2	3	4	5	6	7
Posters Made, p	0	20	40	60	80	100	120	140

1b.

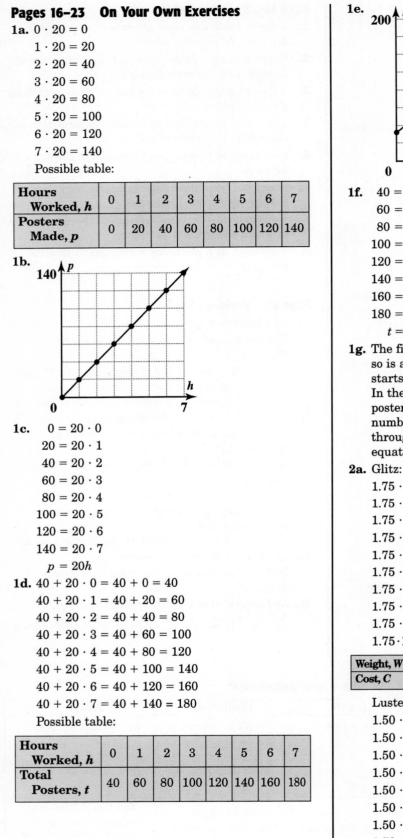

1c. $0 = 20 \cdot 0$
$20 = 20 \cdot 1$
$40 = 20 \cdot 2$
$60 = 20 \cdot 3$
$80 = 20 \cdot 4$
$100 = 20 \cdot 5$
$120 = 20 \cdot 6$
$140 = 20 \cdot 7$
$p = 20h$

1d. $40 + 20 \cdot 0 = 40 + 0 = 40$
$40 + 20 \cdot 1 = 40 + 20 = 60$
$40 + 20 \cdot 2 = 40 + 40 = 80$
$40 + 20 \cdot 3 = 40 + 60 = 100$
$40 + 20 \cdot 4 = 40 + 80 = 120$
$40 + 20 \cdot 5 = 40 + 100 = 140$
$40 + 20 \cdot 6 = 40 + 120 = 160$
$40 + 20 \cdot 7 = 40 + 140 = 180$

Possible table:

Hours Worked, h	0	1	2	3	4	5	6	7
Total Posters, t	40	60	80	100	120	140	160	180

1e.

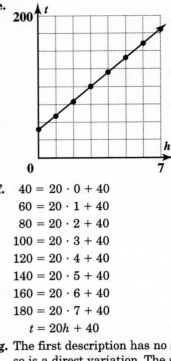

1f. $40 = 20 \cdot 0 + 40$
$60 = 20 \cdot 1 + 40$
$80 = 20 \cdot 2 + 40$
$100 = 20 \cdot 3 + 40$
$120 = 20 \cdot 4 + 40$
$140 = 20 \cdot 5 + 40$
$160 = 20 \cdot 6 + 40$
$180 = 20 \cdot 7 + 40$
$t = 20h + 40$

1g. The first description has no starting amount and so is a direct variation. The second description starts with 40 posters and is linear but not direct. In the first table, when $h = 0$, the number of posters is 0; in the second table, when $h = 0$, the number of posters is 40. The first graph passes through the origin; the second does not. The first equation has no added constant; the second does.

2a. Glitz:
$1.75 \cdot 1 = 1.75$
$1.75 \cdot 2 = 3.50$
$1.75 \cdot 3 = 5.25$
$1.75 \cdot 4 = 7.00$
$1.75 \cdot 5 = 8.75$
$1.75 \cdot 6 = 10.50$
$1.75 \cdot 7 = 12.25$
$1.75 \cdot 8 = 14.00$
$1.75 \cdot 9 = 15.75$
$1.75 \cdot 10 = 17.50$

Weight, W	1	2	3	4	5	6	7	8	9	10
Cost, C	1.75	3.50	5.25	7.00	8.75	10.50	12.25	14.00	15.75	17.50

Lusterless:
$1.50 \cdot 1 + 1.25 = 2.75$
$1.50 \cdot 2 + 1.25 = 4.25$
$1.50 \cdot 3 + 1.25 = 5.75$
$1.50 \cdot 4 + 1.25 = 7.25$
$1.50 \cdot 5 + 1.25 = 8.75$
$1.50 \cdot 6 + 1.25 = 10.25$
$1.50 \cdot 7 + 1.25 = 11.75$
$1.50 \cdot 8 + 1.25 = 13.25$
$1.50 \cdot 9 + 1.25 = 14.75$
$1.50 \cdot 10 + 1.25 = 16.25$

Weight, W	1	2	3	4	5	6	7	8	9	10
Cost, C	2.75	4.25	5.75	7.25	8.75	10.25	11.75	13.25	14.75	16.25

2b. Glitz: $C = 1.75W$

Lusterless: $C = 1.25 + 1.50W$

2c.

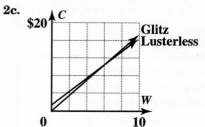

2d. Glitz is better for weights up to 5 lb; Lusterless is better for weights greater than 5 lb.

2e. The graphs show that the shipping charge for Glitz is below that for Lusterless for weights up to 5 lb, and above it for weights over 5 lb.

2f. They would have to stop charging $1.25 for every order and charge only by weight.

3a. $s = 200h$

3b. $t = 200h + 400$

4. Graphs b and c; they slant downward to the right—in other words, y decreases as x increases.

5. Tables A and C; the y values decrease as x increases.

6. Equations a and c; the negative number multiplied by x indicates that the values of y decrease as the values of x increase.

7.

Business	Equation Number	Table Number	Graph Number	Type of Relationship
Rent You Wrecks	ii	iii	iii	not direct
Get You There	iii	ii	iv	not direct
Internet Cafe	i	iv	i	not direct
Talk-a-Lot	v	i	v	not direct
Walk 'em All	iv	v	ii	direct

8a.

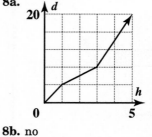

8b. no

9a. yes

9b. $d = 400h$

Flight Distance vs. Time

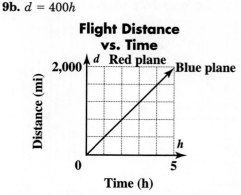

9c. No; it is not traveling at a constant rate.

9d.

Flight Distance vs. Time

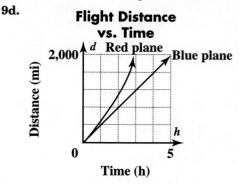

10a.

Vehicle Distance vs. Time

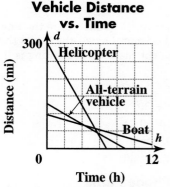

10b. helicopter: from hour 0 to about hour $6\frac{2}{3}$; all-terrain vehicle: from about hour $6\frac{2}{3}$ to about hour $8\frac{2}{3}$; boat: from hour $8\frac{2}{3}$ on (boat arrives after 12.5 h)

10c. helicopter: $d = 300 - 45h$

all-terrain vehicle: $d = 130 - 15h$

boat: $d = 100 - 8h$

11a. after 1 hour: $d = 4 \cdot 1 = 4$ miles

after 2 hours: $d = 4 \cdot 2 = 8$ miles

after 3 hours: $d = 4 \cdot 3 = 12$ miles

after h hours: $d = 4h$

$d = 4h$

11b.

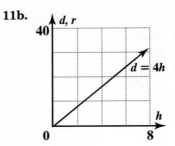

11c. $30 = 4h$

$7.5 = h$

7.5 hours

11d. after 1 hour: $r = 30 - 4 \cdot 1 = 26$ miles

after 2 hours: $r = 30 - 4 \cdot 2 = 22$ miles

after 3 hours: $r = 30 - 4 \cdot 3 = 18$ miles

after h hours: $r = 30 - 4h$

$r = 30 - 4h$

11e.

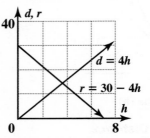

11f. The solution is at the point where the line touches the horizontal axis—the hours that have elapsed when the distance remaining is 0.

12a. i. $c = 50$

ii. $c = 0.20t$

iii. $c = 0.10t + 30$

12b. i. $m = 0$, $b = 50$

ii. $m = 0.20$, $b = 0$

iii. $m = 0.10$, $b = 30$

12c. **Cellular Phone Plans**

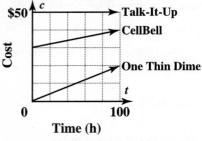

12d. i. $m = 0$ indicates that the line has no steepness, so the line is parallel to the horizontal axis; $b = 50$ tells where the line hits the vertical axis.

ii. $m = 0.20$ means as t changes by 1 unit, c increases by 0.2 unit; $b = 0$ means the graph starts at the origin.

iii. $m = 0.10$ means as t changes by 1 unit, c increases by 0.1 unit; $b = 30$ tells where the line hits the vertical axis.

13a. area of a circle: $A = \pi r^2$

nonlinear; Possible explanation: The formula $A = \pi r^2$ can't be written in the form $y = mx + b$.

13b. circumference of a circle: $C = 2\pi r$

linear; Possible explanation: The formula $C = 2\pi r$ is in the form $y = mx + b$, with $m = 2\pi$ and $b = 0$.

13c. area of a square: $A = s^2$

nonlinear; Possible explanation: The formula $A = s^2$ can't be written in the form $y = mx + b$.

13d. perimeter of a square: $P = 4s$

linear; Possible explanation: The formula $P = 4s$ is in the form $y = mx + b$, with $m = 4$ and $b = 0$.

14. $az + 2az^2$

15. $ab^3 - 0.4a^3b^2$

16. $\dfrac{-4}{c} - 2c^3$

17. $\dfrac{q}{p} - q^2$

18. $^{-}20y$

19. $0.8mn^2$

20. $\dfrac{-1}{b}$

21. $4 + \dfrac{a^2}{n^2}$

22. $20.5a = 61.5$

$a = 3$

23. $\pi \cdot (3k)^2 = 56.25\pi$

$9\pi k^2 = 56.25\pi$

$k^2 = 6.25$

$k = 2.5$

24a. 2 units in the x direction, $^{-}6$ units in the y direction

24b. $^{-}5$ units in the x direction, 2 units in the y direction

24c. $^{-}3$ units in the x direction, 5 units in the y direction

24d. 6 units in the x direction, $^{-}1$ unit in the y direction

25.

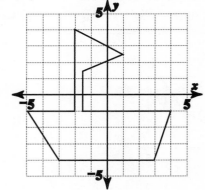

Page 23 In Your Own Words

Possible answer: You know a linear relationship is a direct variation from a description in words if the description suggests a constant rate of change in one variable with respect to another. In addition, it suggests no fixed starting value, so that when one variable has a value of zero, the other variable is also zero. A direct variation has an equation of the form $y = mx$ and its graph is a line that passes through the point $(0, 0)$.

1-2 | Slope

Pages 25–26   Problem Set A

1a. 100 mm, 40 mm

1b.

Points	A to B	A to C	B to C	A to D	B to D	D to E	O to E
Rise	20	40	20	60	40	20	100
Run	8	16	8	24	16	8	40

1c. $\dfrac{20}{8} = \dfrac{5}{2}$

$\dfrac{40}{16} = \dfrac{5}{2}$

$\dfrac{60}{24} = \dfrac{5}{2}$

$\dfrac{100}{40} = \dfrac{5}{2}$

All ratios will be $\dfrac{5}{2}$.

1d. $\dfrac{5}{2}$, or 2.5; It is the same as the ratios in the table.

2. Each pair of points gives the same $\dfrac{\text{rise}}{\text{run}}$, $\dfrac{8}{4}$, or 2.

3. $\dfrac{5}{2} > 2$

The first ratio is greater; the first ladder is steeper.

4. $\dfrac{\text{rise}}{\text{run}} = \dfrac{11}{4}$

$\dfrac{11}{4} > \dfrac{5}{2} > 2$

It would be greater.

5. Possible answer: Yes; the steeper the ladder, the greater its $\dfrac{\text{rise}}{\text{run}}$ ratio.

Page 26   Problem Set B

1. about $\dfrac{2}{3}$; about $\dfrac{3}{1}$; about $\dfrac{5}{4}$; They have different ratios.

2. A ladder has the same $\dfrac{\text{rise}}{\text{run}}$ between any pair of points on the line. For a curved cable, $\dfrac{\text{rise}}{\text{run}}$ between two points depends on the points chosen. A ladder has a constant ratio (steepness); a curved cable does not.

Pages 27–28   Problem Set C

1. (1, 6) and (4, 12)

2. rise: $12 - 6 = 6$

run: $4 - 1 = 3$

slope $= \dfrac{\text{rise}}{\text{run}} = \dfrac{6}{3} = 2$

3a. $12 - 6 = 6$

3b. $4 - 1 = 3$

3c. $\dfrac{6}{3} = 2$

4. rise $= 6 - 12 = {}^{-}6$

run $= 1 - 4 = {}^{-}3$

slope $= \dfrac{\text{rise}}{\text{run}} = \dfrac{{}^{-}6}{{}^{-}3} = 2$

Yes; rise $= {}^{-}6$ and run $= {}^{-}3$, so slope $= \dfrac{{}^{-}6}{{}^{-}3} = 2$.

5. No; the slope between any pair of points on the line is 2.

6. He subtracted Point R's y-coordinate from Point S's, but Point S's x-coordinate from Point R's.

7. Possible answer: Yes; you can subtract the y-coordinate of Point R from the y-coordinate of Point S, or you can subtract the y-coordinate of Point S from the y-coordinate of Point R, but whatever order you use for the y-coordinates you must use for the x-coordinates.

8. rise $= 4 - 2 = 2$

run $= {}^{-}3 - {}^{-}7 = 4$

slope $= \dfrac{\text{rise}}{\text{run}} = \dfrac{2}{4} = \dfrac{1}{2}$

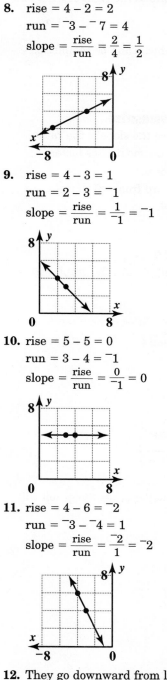

9. rise $= 4 - 3 = 1$

run $= 2 - 3 = {}^{-}1$

slope $= \dfrac{\text{rise}}{\text{run}} = \dfrac{1}{{}^{-}1} = {}^{-}1$

10. rise $= 5 - 5 = 0$

run $= 3 - 4 = {}^{-}1$

slope $= \dfrac{\text{rise}}{\text{run}} = \dfrac{0}{{}^{-}1} = 0$

11. rise $= 4 - 6 = {}^{-}2$

run $= {}^{-}3 - {}^{-}4 = 1$

slope $= \dfrac{\text{rise}}{\text{run}} = \dfrac{{}^{-}2}{1} = {}^{-}2$

12. They go downward from left to right.

13. It is horizontal.

14. Possible answer: Starting at (4, 5), I move down 2 and right 3 to (7, 3). From (7, 3), I move down 2 and right 3 to (10, 1).

15a.

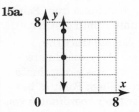

a vertical line, 2 units to the right of the y-axis

15b. rise $= 7 - 4 = 3$

run $= 2 - 2 = 0$

slope $= \dfrac{\text{rise}}{\text{run}} = \dfrac{3}{0}$, which can't be computed.

15c. 2

15d. $x = 2$

Page 29 Share and Summarize

1. Possible answer: Since the slope is the ratio $\dfrac{\text{rise}}{\text{run}}$, a greater slope means it rises faster, which means it's steeper.

2. The line goes downward from left to right.

3. The line is horizontal.

4. Answers will vary.

Page 30 Problem Set D

1a. If the y-axis has a large scale, the graph will appear to rise slowly.

equation: $y = 10x$

Possible graph:

CD Purchases

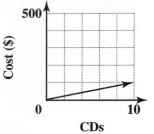

1b. If the y-axis has a smaller scale, the graph will appear to rise quickly.

equation: $y = 10x$

Possible graph:

CD Purchases

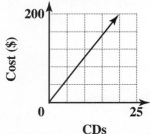

2a. the amount of money decreases $5 each week

rise $= {}^-5$

run $= 1$

slope $= \dfrac{\text{rise}}{\text{run}} = \dfrac{{}^-5}{1} = {}^-5$

2b. If the x-axis has a large scale, the graph will appear to decrease quickly.

equation: $y = {}^-5x$

Possible graph:

Bank Account

2c. If the y-axis has a large scale, the graph will appear to decrease slowly.

equation: $y = {}^-5x$

Possible graph:

Bank Balance

Page 30 Problem Set E

1.

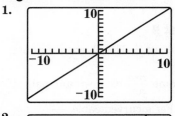

2.

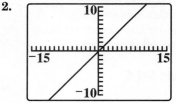

3. Possible answer: With the square setting, the line appears to be at a 45° angle to both axes. With the standard setting, it looks less steep.

4. Possible settings: Xmin $= {}^-20$, Xmax $= 20$, Ymin $= {}^-10$, Ymax $= 10$

5. Possible settings: Xmin $= {}^-10$, Xmax $= 10$, Ymin $= {}^-30$, Ymax $= 30$

Page 31 Share and Summarize

1. To make the graph look steep, use a large range for x or a small range for y. To make it look not steep, use a small range for x or a large range for y.

2. Possible answer: A large range of x values makes 1 unit on the x-axis small, so the run seems small, which makes the ratio $\frac{\text{rise}}{\text{run}}$ seem large. A small range of y values makes 1 unit on the y-axis large, which makes $\frac{\text{rise}}{\text{run}}$ seem large.

Page 33   Problem Set F

1. $y = 4x + b$
$5 = 4(1) + b$
$5 = 4 + b$
$1 = b$
$y = 4x + 1$

2. $y = 3x + b$
$4 = 3(2) + b$
$4 = 6 + b$
$^-2 = b$
$y = 3x - 2$

3. $y = {}^-2x + b$
$^-12 = {}^-2(8) + b$
$^-12 = {}^-16 + b$
$4 = b$
$y = {}^-2x + 4$

4. $y = 0x + b$
$5 = 0(3) + b$
$5 = 0 + b$
$5 = b$
$y = 0x + 5$
$y = 5$

Page 33   Problem Set G

1. rise $= 11 - 3 = 8$
run $= 3 - 1 = 2$
slope $= \frac{\text{rise}}{\text{run}} = \frac{8}{2} = 4$

2. $m =$ slope $= 4$

3. $y = 4x + b$
$3 = 4(1) + b$
$3 = 4 + b$
$^-1 = b$

4. $y = 4x - 1$

5. Answers will vary.
Possible answer:
$y = 4x - 1$
$3 = 4 \cdot 1 - 1$
$3 = 4 - 1$
$3 = 3 ✓$
$y = 4x - 1$
$11 = 4 \cdot 3 - 1$
$11 = 12 - 1$
$11 = 11 ✓$
Both points satisfy the equation.

Page 34   Problem Set H

1. rise $= 12 - 7 = 5$
run $= 8 - 3 = 5$
slope $= \frac{\text{rise}}{\text{run}} = \frac{5}{5} = 1$
$y = 1x + b$
$7 = 1(3) + b$
$7 = 3 + b$
$4 = b$
$y = 1x + 4$
$y = x + 4$

2. rise $= 17 - 11 = 6$
run $= 18 - 6 = 12$
slope $= \frac{\text{rise}}{\text{run}} = \frac{6}{12} = 0.5$
$y = 0.5x + b$
$11 = 0.5(6) + b$
$11 = 3 + b$
$8 = b$
$y = 0.5x + 8$

3. rise $= 100 - 0 = 100$
run $= 100 - 0 = 100$
slope $= \frac{\text{rise}}{\text{run}} = \frac{100}{100} = 1$
$y = 1x + b$
$0 = 1(0) + b$
$0 = 0 + b$
$0 = b$
$y = 1x + 0$
$y = x$

4. rise $= 5 - 5 = 0$
run $= {}^-1 - 3 = {}^-4$
slope $= \frac{\text{rise}}{\text{run}} = \frac{0}{{}^-4} = 0$
$y = 0x + b$
$5 = 0(3) + b$
$5 = 0 + b$
$5 = b$
$y = 0x + 5$
$y = 5$

Pages 34–35   Problem Set I

1. Possible graph:

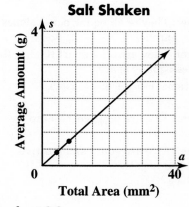

Salt Shaken

Average Amount (g) / Total Area (mm²)

2. about 0.6 g

3. $A = \pi r^2$

$A = \pi \cdot 1.1^2$

$A \approx 3.8 \text{ mm}^2$

about 3.8 mm²

4. $3.8 \cdot 10 = 38 \text{ mm}^2$

about 3.1 g

5. about 5 mm²

6. rise $= 0.73 - 0.45 = 0.28$

run $= 8 - 4.5 = 3.5$

slope $= \dfrac{\text{rise}}{\text{run}} = \dfrac{0.28}{3.5} = 0.08$

$s = 0.08a + b$

$0.45 = 0.08(4.5) + b$

$0.45 = 0.36 + b$

$0.09 = b$

$s = 0.08a + 0.09$

7a. $s = 0.08(2.7) + 0.09$

$s = 0.216 + 0.09$

$s = 0.306$

about 0.31 g

7b. $s = 0.08(44.7) + 0.09$

$s = 3.576 + 0.09$

$s = 3.666$

about 3.67 g

Page 35   Share and Summarize

1. The equation of a line can be written as $y = mx + b$. Substitute the slope for m in the equation. Then use the x-coordinate of the point for x and the y-coordinate of the point for y in the equation, and solve for b.

2. Compute the slope as $\dfrac{\text{rise}}{\text{run}}$. Since you now have the slope and two points, use the method in the answer to Question 1, with either point.

Pages 36–37   Lab

1. Possible equations: $y = 2x$, $y = 0.5x$, $y = {}^-2x$, $y = {}^-0.5x$

2. Possible answer: They're all 0.

3. Possible answer: Two are positive and two are negative.

4. Possible equations: $y = x$, $y = x + 2$, $y = x + 4$, $y = x + 6$

5. Possible answer: They're all equal; equal slopes make the lines parallel.

6. Possible answer: They are all 2 apart (0, 2, 4, 6); it makes the lines equally spaced.

7. Possible equations: $y = x + 5$, $y = x - 5$, $y = {}^-x + 5$, $y = {}^-x - 5$

8. Possible answer: Two are positive; two are negative.

9. Possible answer: Two are equal and positive; two are equal and negative.

10. Reports will vary.

1a.

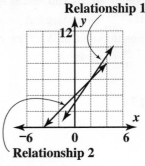

Relationship 1

Relationship 2

1b. Relationship 1: (2, 6), (4, 9)

rise $= 9 - 6 = 3$

run $= 4 - 2 = 2$

slope $= \dfrac{\text{rise}}{\text{run}} = \dfrac{3}{2} = 1.5$

Relationship 2: (1, 5), (3, 7)

rise $= 7 - 5 = 2$

run $= 3 - 1 = 2$

slope $= \dfrac{\text{rise}}{\text{run}} = \dfrac{2}{2} = 1$

1c. Choices will vary; if the graphs are accurate, the table and the graphs represent the same information.

1d. Relationship 1: (1, 4.5), (3, 7.5)

rise $= 7.5 - 4.5 = 3$

run $= 3 - 1 = 2$

slope $= \dfrac{\text{rise}}{\text{run}} = \dfrac{3}{2} = 1.5$

Relationship 2: ($^-$3, 1), ($^-$1, 3)

rise $= 3 - 1 = 2$

run $= {}^-1 - {}^-3 = 2$

slope $= \dfrac{\text{rise}}{\text{run}} = \dfrac{2}{2} = 1$

2a. Answers will vary. Barn X has the steepest roof.

2b. Barn X: $\dfrac{22 - 8}{18} = \dfrac{7}{9} \approx 0.78$

Barn Y: $\dfrac{16 - 8}{24} = \dfrac{1}{3} \approx 0.33$

Barn Z: $\dfrac{10}{15} = \dfrac{2}{3} \approx 0.67$

3a–c. Answers will vary.

4. (0, 0), (1, 3)

rise $= 3 - 0 = 3$

run $= 1 - 0 = 1$

slope $= \dfrac{\text{rise}}{\text{run}} = \dfrac{3}{1} = 3$

5. (0, 4), (1, 5)

rise $= 5 - 4 = 1$

run $= 1 - 0 = 1$

slope $= \dfrac{\text{rise}}{\text{run}} = \dfrac{1}{1} = 1$

6. (0, 1), (2, 2)

rise $= 2 - 1 = 1$

run $= 2 - 0 = 2$

slope $= \dfrac{\text{rise}}{\text{run}} = \dfrac{1}{2}$

7. (4, 0), (5, 1)

rise $= 1 - 0 = 1$

run $= 5 - 4 = 1$

slope $= \dfrac{\text{rise}}{\text{run}} = \dfrac{1}{1} = 1$

8. Possible points: (2, 3.5), (4, 4.5), (5, 5)

9. Possible points: (1, 6), (3, 4), (4, 3)

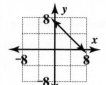

10. Possible points: (0, 2), (1, 5), (3, 11)

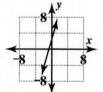

11. Possible points: (0, 4), (8, 6), (12, 7)

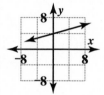

12a. The steepness of each graph is less on one grid than on the other.

12b. Possible answer: the intersections with the x- and y-axes; the fact that the $3x$ graph is steeper than the $2x$ graph; the relationship between x and y for any point on either graph; the values of the slopes

13a. Lines i and j, Lines k and m, Lines l and n

13b. Line i: (⁻3, 0), (⁻2, ⁻3)
rise: ⁻3 − 0 = ⁻3
run: ⁻2 − ⁻3 = 1
slope = $\frac{\text{rise}}{\text{run}} = \frac{^-3}{1} = ^-3$
Line j: (0, 0), (1, ⁻3)
rise: ⁻3 − 0 = ⁻3
run: 1 − 0 = 1
slope = $\frac{\text{rise}}{\text{run}} = \frac{^-3}{1} = ^-3$
Line k: (0, 2), (3, 3)
rise: 3 − 2 = 1
run: 3 − 0 = 3
slope = $\frac{\text{rise}}{\text{run}} = \frac{1}{3}$
Line l: (0, 2), (3, 1)
rise: 1 − 2 = ⁻1
run: 3 − 0 = 3
slope = $\frac{\text{rise}}{\text{run}} = \frac{^-1}{3}$

Line m: (4, ⁻1), (1, ⁻2)
rise: ⁻2 − ⁻1 = ⁻1
run: 1 − 4 = ⁻3
slope = $\frac{\text{rise}}{\text{run}} = \frac{^-1}{^-3} = \frac{1}{3}$
Line n: (⁻2, ⁻1), (1, ⁻2)
rise: ⁻2 − ⁻1 = ⁻1
run: 1 − ⁻2 = 3
slope = $\frac{\text{rise}}{\text{run}} = \frac{^-1}{3}$

14. $y = ^-1x + b$
$4 = ^-1(1) + b$
$4 = ^-1 + b$
$5 = b$
$y = ^-1x + 5$
$y = ^-x + 5$

15. $y = \frac{1}{3}x + b$
$3 = \frac{1}{3}(3) + b$
$3 = 1 + b$
$2 = b$
$y = \frac{1}{3}x + 2$

16. $y = ^-2x + b$
$6 = ^-2(3) + b$
$6 = ^-6 + b$
$12 = b$
$y = ^-2x + 12$

17. rise = 8 − 4 = 4
run = 7 − 3 = 4
slope = $\frac{\text{rise}}{\text{run}} = \frac{4}{4} = 1$
$y = 1x + b$
$4 = 1(3) + b$
$4 = 3 + b$
$1 = b$
$y = 1x + 1$
$y = x + 1$

18. rise = 6 − 7 = ⁻1
run = 6 − 2 = 4
slope = $\frac{\text{rise}}{\text{run}} = \frac{^-1}{4} = ^-0.25$
$y = ^-0.25x + b$
$7 = ^-0.25(2) + b$
$7 = ^-0.5 + b$
$7.5 = b$
$y = ^-0.25x + 7.5$

19. rise = 9 − 5 = 4
run = 9 − 3 = 6
slope = $\frac{\text{rise}}{\text{run}} = \frac{4}{6} = \frac{2}{3}$
$y = \frac{2}{3}x + b$
$5 = \frac{2}{3}(3) + b$
$5 = 2 + b$
$3 = b$
$y = \frac{2}{3}x + 3$

20a. Make a table of values:

x	y
⁻1	⁻1
0	0
1	1

Difference in y values:

$0 - {}^-1 = 1$

$1 - 0 = 1$

As x increases by 1, the constant difference between the y values is 1.

20b. Make a table of values:

x	y
2	2
0	0
⁻2	⁻2

Difference in y values:

$0 - 2 = {}^-2$

${}^-2 - 0 = {}^-2$

As x decreases by 2, the constant difference between the y values is ⁻2.

21a. Make a table of values:

x	y
⁻1	1
0	2
1	3

Difference in y values:

$2 - 1 = 1$

$3 - 2 = 1$

As x increases by 1, the constant difference between the y values is 1.

21b. Make a table of values:

x	y
2	4
0	2
⁻2	0

Difference in y values:

$2 - 4 = {}^-2$

$0 - 2 = {}^-2$

As x decreases by 2, the constant difference between the y values is ⁻2.

22a. Make a table of values:

x	y
⁻1	⁻6
0	⁻3
1	0

Difference in y values:

${}^-3 - {}^-6 = 3$

$0 - {}^-3 = 3$

As x increases by 1, the constant difference between the y values is 3.

22b. Make a table of values:

x	y
2	3
0	⁻3
⁻2	⁻9

Difference in y values:

${}^-3 - 3 = {}^-6$

${}^-9 - {}^-3 = {}^-6$

As x decreases by 2, the constant difference between the y values is ⁻6.

23a. Make a table of values:

x	y
⁻1	14
0	12
1	10

Difference in y values:

$12 - 14 = {}^-2$

$10 - 12 = {}^-2$

As x increases by 1, the constant difference between the y values is ⁻2.

23b. Make a table of values:

x	y
2	8
0	12
⁻2	16

Difference in y values:

$12 - 8 = 4$

$16 - 12 = 4$

As x decreases by 2, the constant difference between the y values is 4.

24a. Make a table of values:

x	y
⁻1	⁻5
0	0
1	5

Difference in y values:

$0 - {}^-5 = 5$

$5 - 0 = 5$

As x increases by 1, the constant difference between the y values is 5.

24b. Make a table of values:

x	y
2	10
0	0
⁻2	⁻10

Difference in y values:

$0 - 10 = {}^-10$

${}^-10 - 0 = {}^-10$

As x decreases by 2, the constant difference between the y values is ⁻10.

25a. Make a table of values:

x	y
$^-1$	$-\frac{1}{2}$
0	0
1	$\frac{1}{2}$

Difference in y values:

$0 - \dfrac{-1}{2} = \dfrac{1}{2}$

$\dfrac{1}{2} - 0 = \dfrac{1}{2}$

As x increases by 1, the constant difference between the y values is $\dfrac{1}{2}$.

25b. Make a table of values:

x	y
2	1
0	0
$^-2$	$^-1$

Difference in y values:

$0 - 1 = {}^-1$

$^-1 - 0 = {}^-1$

As x decreases by 2, the constant difference between the y values is $^-1$.

26a. Make a table of values:

x	y
$^-1$	$^-41$
0	$^-18$
1	5

Difference in y values:

$^-18 - {}^-41 = 23$

$5 - {}^-18 = 23$

As x increases by 1, the constant difference between the y values is 23.

26b. Make a table of values:

x	y
2	28
0	$^-18$
$^-2$	$^-64$

Difference in y values:

$^-18 - 28 = {}^-46$

$^-64 - {}^-18 = {}^-46$

As x decreases by 2, the constant difference between the y values is $^-46$.

27a. Make a table of values:

x	y
$^-1$	1
0	0
1	$^-1$

Difference in y values:

$0 - 1 = {}^-1$

$^-1 - 0 = {}^-1$

As x increases by 1, the constant difference between the y values is $^-1$.

27b. Make a table of values:

x	y
2	$^-2$
0	0
$^-2$	2

Difference in y values:

$0 - {}^-2 = 2$

$^-2 - 0 = 2$

As x decreases by 2, the constant difference between the y values is 2.

28a. Make a table of values:

x	y
$^-1$	8
0	6
1	4

Difference in y values:

$6 - 8 = {}^-2$

$4 - 6 = {}^-2$

As x increases by 1, the constant difference between the y values is $^-2$.

28b. Make a table of values:

x	y
2	2
0	6
$^-2$	10

Difference in y values:

$6 - 2 = 4$

$10 - 6 = 4$

As x decreases by 2, the constant difference between the y values is 4.

29a. $\dfrac{10}{14} \approx 0.714$

29b. step rise:

10 ft $\cdot$ 12 = 120 inches

$\dfrac{120}{18} = \dfrac{20}{3} = 6\dfrac{2}{3}$ inches

step run:

14 ft $\cdot$ 12 = 168 inches

$\dfrac{168}{18} = \dfrac{28}{3} = 9\dfrac{1}{3}$ inches

$\dfrac{\text{step rise}}{\text{step run}} = \dfrac{6\frac{2}{3}}{9\frac{1}{3}} = \dfrac{20}{28} = \dfrac{5}{7} \approx 0.714$

29c. Possible answer: The ratio $\frac{\text{rise}}{\text{run}}$ is the same for the total staircase as for each step, because you divide the total run and the total rise by the same number, 18, to determine $\frac{\text{rise}}{\text{run}}$ for each step.

30. Possible answer: 24 steps with a height of 7 in., a run of 10 in., $\frac{\text{step rise}}{\text{step run}}$ of 0.7, a total run of 20 ft, and $\frac{\text{total rise}}{\text{total run}}$ of 0.7.

31a. Account B, because the line representing Account B is steeper

31b. Account A, because the line representing Account A has a greater y-intercept

31c. No; if the two accounts are graphed on the same grid, you are using the same scale, so you can compare them.

32a.

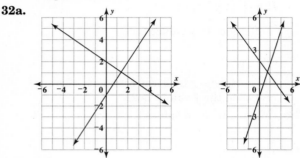

32b. no

32c. He assumed the scales were the same for the two axes.

33. slope 2, y-intercept 0.25

34. slope ⁻1, y-intercept 5

35. slope 1, y-intercept ⁻3

36. slope ⁻2, y-intercept 0

37. slope $\frac{1}{2}$, y-intercept $\frac{3}{4}$

38. slope 3, y-intercept 0

39a.

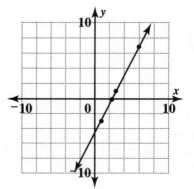

39b. yes

(3, 1), (6, 7)

rise = 7 − 1 = 6

run = 6 − 3 = 3

slope = $\frac{\text{rise}}{\text{run}} = \frac{6}{3} = 2$

$y = 2x + b$

$1 = 2(3) + b$

$1 = 6 + b$

$⁻5 = b$

$y = 2x − 5$

39c. ⁻9; check: $y = 2\,(⁻2) − 5 = ⁻9$

39d. 1.5; check: $y = 2(1.5) − 5 = ⁻2$

39e. $x = 0$: $y = 2(0) − 5 = ⁻5$

$x = ⁻1$: $y = 2(⁻1) − 5 = ⁻7$

$x = ⁻1.5$: $y = 2(⁻1.5) − 5 = ⁻8$

$x = ⁻2.5$: $y = 2(⁻2.5) − 5 = ⁻10$

⁻5, ⁻7, ⁻8, ⁻10; The points (0, ⁻5), (⁻1, ⁻7), (⁻1.5, ⁻8), and (⁻2.5, ⁻10) are all on the line.

40a.

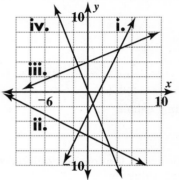

40b. Line i: 2; Line ii: $\frac{⁻1}{2}$; Line iii: $\frac{2}{5}$; Line iv: $\frac{⁻5}{2}$

40c. Both pairs appear to intersect at right angles.

40d. Possible answers: The slopes of the lines in each pair are negative reciprocals. *Or*, the product of each pair of slopes is ⁻1.

40e. Possible answer: If two lines are perpendicular, their slopes are reciprocals, but with different signs.

40f. Possible answer: Lines with slopes of ⁻3 and $\frac{1}{3}$; yes.

40g. $m = ⁻3$ since $⁻3 \cdot \frac{1}{3} = ⁻1$

$y = ⁻3x + b$

$4 = ⁻3(⁻1) + b$

$4 = 3 + b$

$1 = b$

$y = ⁻3x + 1$

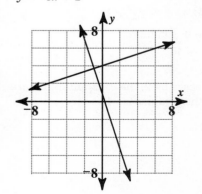

41. $2^3 + 3^2 = 8 + 9 = 17$

42. $\left(\frac{2}{3} + 2\right)^2 = \left(\frac{2}{3} + \frac{6}{3}\right)^2 = \left(\frac{8}{3}\right)^2 = \frac{64}{9} \approx 7.1$

43. $3^2 \cdot 3^2 = 9 \cdot 9 = 81$

44a. Line m

44b. Line j

44c. Line l

44d. Line i

44e. Line k

45a. Lines k, l, m

45b. Lines i, k

45c. Line m

45d. Line i

45e. Line l

45f. none

46a. July 22, 2009

46b. <u>duration:</u>

Convert to seconds and order.

42, 100, 117, 124, 147, 242, 247, 296, 320, 399

median = $(147 + 242) \div 2 = 194.5$ s = 3 min, 14.5 s

<u>width:</u>

17, 36, 54, 112, 118, 125, 157, 160, 164, 338

median = $(118 + 125) \div 2 = 121.5$ mi

46c.

Solar Eclipses

46d. Nov 23, 2003

Page 43 In Your Own Words

Possible answer: To determine the slope of a line from a graph, choose two points on the graph and find the vertical distance (rise) and the horizontal distance (run) between them. The slope of the line is then written as the ratio $\frac{\text{rise}}{\text{run}}$. If you are given the slope of a line, you also need to know one point on the line before you can graph the line.

1-3 More Explorations with Lines

Page 47 Problem Set A

1. They are parallel.

2. They are parallel. Possible explanation: If they have the same slope, they rise at the same rate. Every unit of change in x gives the same change in y for both lines, so they always stay the same distance apart.

3. Equation a is a line with slope 2.

Equation b is not a line.

Equation c is a line with slope 2.

Equation d is a line with slope 5.

Equations a and c; their graphs would be lines with the same slope.

4a. The value of m is 5.

4b. $y = 5x + 0$

$y = 5x$

4c. $y = 5x + 3$

4d. $y = 5x + b$

$11 = 5(2) + b$

$11 = 10 + b$

$1 = b$

$y = 5x + 1$

5. $y = 3x + b$

$4 = 3(3) + b$

$4 = 9 + b$

$^-5 = b$

$y = 3x - 5$

6a.

6b. $y = 0x + b$

$6 = 0(3) + b$

$6 = 0 + b$

$6 = b$

$y = 0x + 6$

$y = 6$

Page 48 Problem Set B

1. Possible answer: Find the line through two of the points, and then check whether the third point is on that line. If they're on the same line, all three points will satisfy the equation.

2. Set A:

$(^-4, ^-3), (1, 2)$

rise $= 2 - ^-3 = 5$

run $= 1 - ^-4 = 5$

slope $= \dfrac{\text{rise}}{\text{run}} = \dfrac{5}{5} = 1$

$y = 1x + b$

$2 = 1(1) + b$

$2 = 1 + b$

$1 = b$

$y = 1x + 1$

$y = x + 1$

Check $(7, 7)$.

$7 = 1(7) + 1$

$7 = 7 + 1$

$7 \neq 8$

$(^-4, ^-3)$ and $(1, 2)$ are on the line $y = x + 1$.

$(7, 7)$ is not on that line.

The points in Set A are not collinear.

Set B:

$(^-1, 1), (0, ^-1)$

rise $= ^-1 - 1 = ^-2$

run $= 0 - ^-1 = 1$

slope $= \dfrac{\text{rise}}{\text{run}} = \dfrac{^-2}{1} = ^-2$

The point $(0, ^-1)$ lies on the y-axis, so $b = ^-1$.

$y = ^-2x - 1$

Check $(2, ^-5)$.

$^-5 = ^-2(2) - 1$

$^-5 = ^-4 - 1$

$^-5 = ^-5$

$(^-1, 1), (0, ^-1)$, and $(2, ^-5)$ are on the line $y = ^-2x - 1$.

The points in Set B are collinear.

3a. $(^-3, ^-2), (0, 4)$

rise $= 4 - ^-2 = 6$

run $= 0 - ^-3 = 3$

slope $= \dfrac{\text{rise}}{\text{run}} = \dfrac{6}{3} = 2$

The point $(0, 4)$ lies on the y-axis, so $b = 4$.

$y = 2x + 4$

Check $(1.5, 7)$.

$7 = 2(1.5) + 4$

$7 = 3 + 4$

$7 = 7$

collinear

3b. $(1.25, 1.37), (1.28, 1.48)$

rise $= 1.48 - 1.37 = 0.11$

run $= 1.28 - 1.25 = 0.03$

slope $= \dfrac{\text{rise}}{\text{run}} = \dfrac{0.11}{0.03} = \dfrac{11}{3}$

$y = \dfrac{11}{3}x + b$

$1.37 = \dfrac{11}{3}(1.25) + b$

$1.37 = 4.58 + b$

$^-3.21 = b$

$y = \dfrac{11}{3}x - 3.21$

Check $(1.36, 1.70)$.

$1.70 = \dfrac{11}{3}(1.36) - 3.21$

$1.70 = 4.99 - 3.21$

$1.70 \neq 1.78$

$(1.25, 1.37)$ and $(1.28, 1.48)$ are on the line

$y = \dfrac{11}{3}x - 3.21$.

$(1.36, 1.70)$ is not on that line.

not collinear

Page 49   Share and Summarize

1. Find the slope of the line through Points A and B. Use that slope for m and the coordinates of C to solve the equation $y = mx + b$ for b. The equation is then $y = mx + b$ using the values you found for m and b.

2. Possible answer: Find an equation for the line through points A and B. Then substitute the x- and y-coordinates for Point D into the equation to see whether it is true. If it is, Point D is on the line.

Page 49   Problem Set C

1. $3y = \dfrac{x}{2} - 8$

$y = \dfrac{x}{6} - \dfrac{8}{3}$

linear; $m = \dfrac{1}{6}, b = \dfrac{^-8}{3}$

2. $y = 3$

$y = 0x + 3$

linear; $m = 0, b = 3$

3. $y = \dfrac{2}{x}$

Nonlinear; it can't be written in the form $y = mx + b$.

4. $5y - 7x = 10$

$5y = 7x + 10$

$y = \dfrac{7}{5}x + 2$

linear; $m = \dfrac{7}{5}, b = 2$

5. $2y = 10 - 2(x + 3)$

$2y = 10 - 2x - 6$

$2y = ^-2x + 4$

$y = ^-x + 2$

linear; $m = ^-1, b = 2$

6. $y = x(x - 1) - 2(1 - x)$

$y = x^2 - x - 2 + 2x$

$y = x^2 + x - 2$

Nonlinear; it can't be written in the form $y = mx + b$.

7. $y = 2x + \dfrac{1}{2}(3x + 1) + \dfrac{1}{4}(2x + 8)$

$y = 2x + \dfrac{3}{2}x + \dfrac{1}{2} + \dfrac{1}{2}x + 2$

$y = 4x + 2.5$

linear; $m = 4, b = 2.5$

Page 50   Problem Set D

1a. $p = 2q + 4$

1b. $p - 2q = 4$

  $p = 2q + 4$

1c. $p - 2q + 4 = 0$

  $p = 2q - 4$

1d. $0.5p = q + 2$

  $p = 2q + 4$

1e. $p - 4 = 2q$

  $p = 2q + 4$

1f. $2p = 8 + 4q$

  $p = 4 + 2q$

  $p = 2q + 4$

  all except Equation c

2. $y - 1 = 2x$

  $y = 2x + 1$

3. $2y - 4x = 3$

  $2y = 4x + 3$

  $y = 2x + 1.5$

4. $2x + 4y = 3$

  $4y = {}^-2x + 3$

  $y = {}^-0.5x + 0.75$

5. $6y - 12x = 0$

  $6y = 12x$

  $y = 2x$

6. $x = 2y - 3$

  $x + 3 = 2y$

  $0.5x + 1.5 = y$

  $y = 0.5x + 1.5$

7. $y + 4 = {}^-2$

  $y = {}^-6$

8. Equations 2, 3, and 5 have slope of 2, so the graphs are parallel.

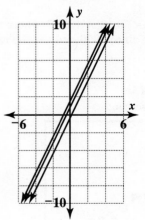

9a. $y = (2x - 7) - 3$

  $y = 2x - 10$

  slope = 2

9b. $y + 5 + 2x = 5$

    $y = {}^-2x$

  slope = $^-2$

9c. $y = 30 + 4(x - 7)$

  $y = 30 + 4x - 28$

  $y = 4x + 2$

  slope = 4

9d. $4y - 5x = 3x - 2$

   $4y = 3x + 5x - 2$

   $4y = 8x - 2$

   $y = 2x - 0.5$

  slope = 2

9e. $y + 3(10 - x) = x$

  $y + 30 - 3x = x$

     $y = 4x - 30$

  slope = 4

9f. $y = 5x + 3(10 - x)$

  $y = 5x + 30 - 3x$

  $y = 2x + 30$

  slope = 2

9g. $y = 8x - \frac{1}{3}(12x - 30)$

  $y = 8x - 4x + 10$

  $y = 4x + 10$

  slope = 4

9h. $y = 1 + \frac{1}{2}(2 - 4x)$

  $y = 1 + 1 - 2x$

  $y = {}^-2x + 2$

  slope = $^-2$

9i. $y - 3 = {}^-2x$

    $y = {}^-2x + 3$

  slope = $^-2$

9j. $2y = {}^-4(3 - x)$

  $2y = {}^-12 + 4x$

   $y = {}^-6 + 2x$

   $y = 2x - 6$

  slope = 2

The lines for Equations a, d, f and j are parallel; Equations b, h, and i are parallel; and Equations c, e, and g are parallel.

Page 50   Share and Summarize

Possible answer: Move everything that doesn't involve y to one side of the equation, add or subtract numbers in the expression, add or subtract values of x and y that are in the expression, and eliminate grouping symbols by using the distributive property.

Pages 52–53   Problem Set E

1a. Possible line:

Exercise Results

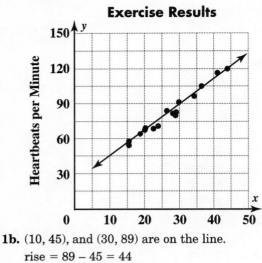

1b. (10, 45), and (30, 89) are on the line.

rise = 89 – 45 = 44

run = 30 – 10 = 20

slope = $\dfrac{\text{rise}}{\text{run}} = \dfrac{44}{20} = 2.2$

$y = 2.2x + b$

$45 = 2.2(10) + b$

$45 = 22 + b$

$23 = b$

Possible equation: $y = 2.2x + 23$

2a. $432 \div 16 = 27$ breaths per minute

$1,318 \div 16 = 82.375$ heartbeats per minute

2b. Possible line:

Exercise Results

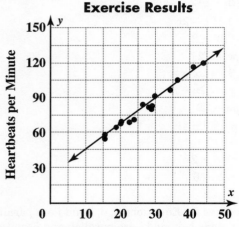

3. (10, 45), and (27, 82.375) are on the line.

rise = 82.375 – 45 = 37.375

run = 27 – 10 = 17

slope = $\dfrac{\text{rise}}{\text{run}} = \dfrac{37.375}{17} \approx 2.2$

$y = 2.2x + b$

$45 = 2.2(10) + b$

$45 = 22 + b$

$23 = b$

$y = 2.2x + 23$

Possible answer: $y = 2.2x + 23$; someone else may think the line should pass through different points, so that line would have a different slope.

4. Answers will vary. Possible answer using $y = 2.2x + 23$:

$y = 2.2(35) + 23$

$y = 77 + 23$

$y = 100$

100 beats per minute

Comparisons will vary, but all answers should be fairly close.

5. Possible answer using $y = 2.2x + 23$:

$y = 2.2(100) + 23$

$y = 220 + 23$

$y = 243$

243 beats per minute; probably not, because 100 breaths is so far beyond what we have data for, we can't be sure the relationship will still be linear. It seems unlikely a person's heart would be beating 240 times a minute.

Page 54   Problem Set F

1. (28, 47.5)

2. Possible answer: It was the first Olympiad after World War II, and people may not have been in training for the usual length of time.

3. $672 \div 12$

The line passes through the points (40, 44.2) and (60, 41.7).

rise = 41.7 – 44.2 = ⁻2.5

run = 60 – 40 = 20

slope = $\dfrac{\text{rise}}{\text{run}} = \dfrac{^{-}2.5}{20} = ^{-}0.125$

$y = ^{-}0.125x + b$

$44.2 = ^{-}0.125(40) + b$

$44.2 = ^{-}0.5 + b$

$49.2 = b$

$y = ^{-}0.125x + 49.2$

$t = ^{-}0.125n + 49.2$

Possible equation: $t = ^{-}0.125n + 49.2$, where n is the number of years since 1920 and t is the race time in seconds

Page 55   Problem Set G

1a. Possible calculator screen:

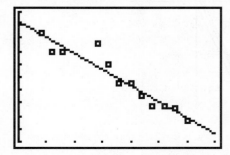

Possible calculator screen:

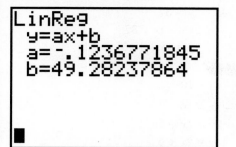

```
LinReg
 y=ax+b
 a=-.1236771845
 b=49.28237864
■
```

Possible equation: $y = {}^-0.124x + 49.3$

(Equations will vary depending on the calculator.)

1b. Answers will vary.

Comparing $y = {}^-0.124x + 49.3$ to
$t = {}^-0.125n + 49.2$, the slope and y-intercepts
are very similar.

2. No; there will be a physical limit to how quickly
people can run.

3. Possible answer using $y = {}^-0.124x + 49.3$ from
problem 1a:

1984: $x = 64$

$y = {}^-0.124(64) + 49.3 \approx 41.36$ s

1988: $x = 68$

$y = {}^-0.124(68) + 49.3 \approx 40.87$ s

1992: $x = 72$

$y = {}^-0.124(72) + 49.3 \approx 40.37$ s

1996: $x = 76$

$y = {}^-0.124(76) + 49.3 \approx 39.88$ s

4. Answers will vary. The 1984 time will probably be
somewhat close; the others probably will not be.

5a. Using the equation $y = {}^-0.124x + 49.3$ from
problem 1a:
Possible answer:

$0 = {}^-0.124n + 49.3$

$^-49.3 = {}^-0.124n$

$398 \approx n$

5b. $1920 + 398 = 2318$

Possible answer: 2318

Page 55 Share and Summarize

Answers will vary.

Pages 56–63 On Your Own Exercises

1. All four lines are parallel because they have the
same slope.

2. All four lines pass through the origin because
none has an added constant.

3. All four lines are parallel because they have the
same slope.

4. All four lines have negative slopes and pass
through the point (0, 1) because the equations all
have 1 as the y-intercept.

5a–d. Answers will vary.

6a.

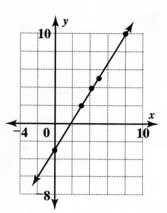

6b. Possible answer: All the points except (4, 4) look
like they might be on the line.

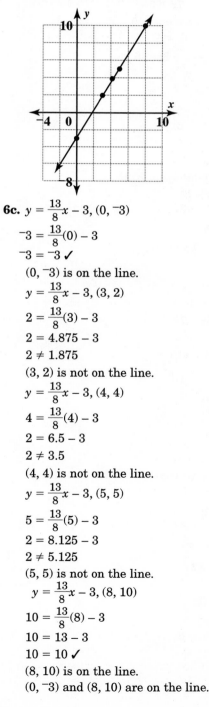

6c. $y = \dfrac{13}{8}x - 3$, $(0, {}^-3)$

$^-3 = \dfrac{13}{8}(0) - 3$

$^-3 = {}^-3$ ✓

$(0, {}^-3)$ is on the line.

$y = \dfrac{13}{8}x - 3$, $(3, 2)$

$2 = \dfrac{13}{8}(3) - 3$

$2 = 4.875 - 3$

$2 \neq 1.875$

$(3, 2)$ is not on the line.

$y = \dfrac{13}{8}x - 3$, $(4, 4)$

$4 = \dfrac{13}{8}(4) - 3$

$2 = 6.5 - 3$

$2 \neq 3.5$

$(4, 4)$ is not on the line.

$y = \dfrac{13}{8}x - 3$, $(5, 5)$

$5 = \dfrac{13}{8}(5) - 3$

$2 = 8.125 - 3$

$2 \neq 5.125$

$(5, 5)$ is not on the line.

$y = \dfrac{13}{8}x - 3$, $(8, 10)$

$10 = \dfrac{13}{8}(8) - 3$

$10 = 13 - 3$

$10 = 10$ ✓

$(8, 10)$ is on the line.

$(0, {}^-3)$ and $(8, 10)$ are on the line.

7. $y = 5x + \frac{1}{3}(6x + 12)$

$y = 5x + 2x + 4$

$y = 7x + 4$

slope $= 7$, y-intercept $= 4$

8. $y = \frac{1}{5}(10x + 5) - 5 + 7x$

$y = 2x + 1 - 5 + 7x$

$y = 9x - 4$

slope $= 9$, y-intercept $= {}^-4$

9. $3x + 2(x + 1) = \frac{{}^-1}{2}(4x + 6) + y$

$3x + 2x + 2 = {}^-2x - 3 + y$

$5x + 2 = {}^-2x - 3 + y$

$7x + 2 = {}^-3 + y$

$7x + 5 = y$

$y = 7x + 5$

slope $= 7$, y-intercept $= 5$

10. $3x^2 - y = 3x + 5$

$3x^2 = y + 3x + 5$

$3x^2 - 3x - 5 = y$

$y = 3x^2 - 3x - 5$

nonlinear

11. $y - 19 = {}^-2(x - 3)$

$y = {}^-2x + 6 + 19$

$y = {}^-2x + 25$

slope $= {}^-2$, y-intercept $= 25$

12a. $y = 3x - 5(x + 3)$

$y = 3x - 5x - 15$

$y = {}^-2x - 15$

slope $= {}^-2$

12b. $\frac{x - 2y}{2} = 7$

$x - 2y = 7 \cdot 2$

${}^-2y = {}^-x + 14$

$y = 0.5x - 7$

slope $= 0.5$

12c. $y = 17 - 3(3 + x) + x$

$y = 17 - 9 - 3x + x$

$y = 8 - 2x$

$y = {}^-2x + 8$

slope $= {}^-2$

12d. $3x + 2y = 4$

$2y = {}^-3x + 4$

$y = {}^-1.5x + 2$

slope $= {}^-1.5$

12e. $y = \frac{{}^-x}{2} + 2\left(6 - \frac{x}{2}\right)$

$y = \frac{{}^-x}{2} + 12 - x$

$y = {}^-1.5x + 12$

slope $= {}^-1.5$

12f. $x - y + 3 = 0$

$x + 3 = y$

$y = x + 3$

slope $= 1$

12g. $4x - 2y - 17 = 20$

$4x - 2y = 37$

${}^-2y = {}^-4x + 37$

$y = 2x - 18.5$

slope $= 2$

12h. $4\left(\frac{y}{2} - x\right) = 10$

$2y - 4x = 10$

$2y = 4x + 10$

$y = 2x + 5$

slope $= 2$

12i. $y + x = 4x + 5 - 2(4 + x)$

$y + x = 4x + 5 - 8 - 2x$

$y + x = 2x - 3$

$y = x - 3$

slope $= 1$

12j. $y = \frac{3x + 4}{2} - \frac{7 + 2x}{2}$

$2y = 3x + 4 - (7 + 2x)$

$2y = 3x + 4 - 7 - 2x$

$2y = x - 3$

$y = 0.5x - 1.5$

slope $= 0.5$

Parallel pairs: a and c, slope $= {}^-2$; b and j, slope $= 0.5$; d and e, slope $= {}^-1.5$; f and i, slope $= 1$; g and h, slope $= 2$

13a. $4x - 2y = 4$

${}^-2y = {}^-4x + 4$

$y = 2x - 2$

13b. $2y - 4x = 4$

$2y = 4x + 4$

$y = 2x + 2$

13c. $2x - y = 2$

$2x = y + 2$

$2x - 2 = y$

$y = 2x - 2$

13d. $y - 2x = 2$

$y = 2x + 2$

13e. $y - 2x = {}^-2$

$y = 2x - 2$

13f. $y = 2x - 2$

13g. $y = 2x + 2$

13h. $4x + 2y = 4$

$2y = {}^-4x + 4$

$y = {}^-2x + 2$

Equations a, c, e, and f are all the same as $y = 2x - 2$; Equations b, d, and g are all the same as $y = 2x + 2$; Equation h, $y = {}^-2x + 2$, does not match any of the others.

14a.

Animal Gestation vs. Lifespan

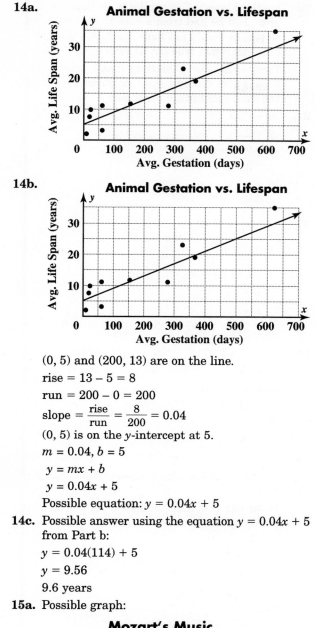

14b.

Animal Gestation vs. Lifespan

(0, 5) and (200, 13) are on the line.

rise = 13 − 5 = 8

run = 200 − 0 = 200

slope = $\dfrac{\text{rise}}{\text{run}} = \dfrac{8}{200} = 0.04$

(0, 5) is on the y-intercept at 5.

$m = 0.04$, $b = 5$

$y = mx + b$

$y = 0.04x + 5$

Possible equation: $y = 0.04x + 5$

14c. Possible answer using the equation $y = 0.04x + 5$ from Part b:

$y = 0.04(114) + 5$

$y = 9.56$

9.6 years

15a. Possible graph:

Mozart's Music

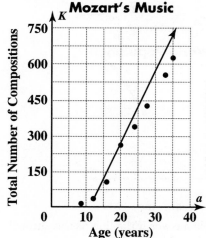

15b. Except for the first point, the data appear to be linear.

Possible answer:

$\dfrac{551 - 45}{32 - 12} = \dfrac{506}{20} = 25.3$

The rate is about 25 compositions per year.

15c. mean age: $174 \div 8 = 21.75$

mean composition number: $2{,}384 \div 8 = 298$

Using the means of the data, the line passes through (21.75, 298).

Possible graph:

Mozart's Music

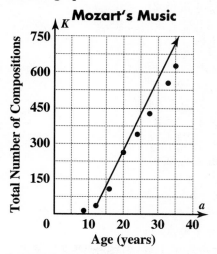

15d. Possible answer using (21.75, 298) and (12, 45) as points the line passes through:

rise = 298 − 45 = 253

run = 21.75 − 12 = 9.75

slope = $\dfrac{\text{rise}}{\text{run}} = \dfrac{253}{9.75} \approx 26$

$y = 26x + b$

$298 = 26(21.75) + b$

$298 = 565.5 + b$

$^{-}267.5 = b$

$y = 26x - 267.5$

Possible equation: $K = 26a - 267.5$

15e. Answers will vary; it may not be reasonable to assume that Mozart would have kept producing at the same rate throughout his life.

15f. $K = 26(0) - 267.6 = {}^{-}267.5$

$^{-}267.5$; This means that at birth, Mozart composed $^{-}267.5$ pieces. This makes no sense, and tells us that the linear model may not be a good one for data points far outside those given.

16a.

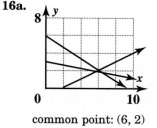

common point: (6, 2)

16b. $y = \frac{x}{2} - 1$, $(6, 2)$

$2 = \frac{6}{2} - 1$

$2 = 3 - 1$

$2 = 2$ ✓

$y = \frac{^-2x}{3} + 6$, $(6, 2)$

$2 = \frac{^-2(6)}{3} + 6$

$2 = ^-4 + 6$

$2 = 2$ ✓

$y = \frac{^-x}{6} + 3$, $(6, 2)$

$2 = \frac{^-6}{6} + 3$

$2 = ^-1 + 3$

$2 = 2$ ✓

17. $(2, 8)$, $(4, 12)$

rise $= 12 - 8 = 4$

run $= 4 - 2 = 2$

slope $= \frac{\text{rise}}{\text{run}} = \frac{4}{2} = 2$

$y = 2x + b$, $(2, 8)$

$8 = 2(2) + b$

$8 = 4 + b$

$4 = b$

$y = 2x + 4$

slope 2, y-intercept 4, equation $y = 2x + 4$

18. $(^-8, 26)$, $(^-3, 11)$

rise $= 11 - 26 = ^-15$

run $= ^-3 - ^-8 = 5$

slope $= \frac{\text{rise}}{\text{run}} = \frac{^-15}{5} = ^-3$

$y = ^-3x + b$, $(^-8, 26)$

$26 = ^-3(^-8) + b$

$26 = 24 + b$

$2 = b$

$y = ^-3x + 2$

slope $^-3$, y-intercept 2, equation $y = ^-3x + 2$

19. $(9, 5)$, $(7, 4)$

rise $= 4 - 5 = ^-1$

run $= 7 - 9 = ^-2$

slope $= \frac{\text{rise}}{\text{run}} = \frac{^-1}{^-2} = \frac{1}{2}$

$y = \frac{1}{2}x + b$, $(9, 5)$

$5 = \frac{1}{2}(9) + b$

$5 = 4.5 + b$

$\frac{1}{2} = b$

$y = \frac{1}{2}x + \frac{1}{2}$

slope $\frac{1}{2}$, y-intercept $\frac{1}{2}$, equation $y = \frac{1}{2}x + \frac{1}{2}$

20a. Answers will vary. Hoshi's conjecture is true only for lines whose slopes are 1 and $^-1$ (and when drawn on a grid in which the scales are the same).

20b. Pairs of lines with slopes other than 1 and $^-1$ do not cross at right angles, so Hoshi's conjecture is not true for all lines.

20c. He tried "special" examples with slopes of 1 and $^-1$. If he had tried a pair of lines with other slopes, he would not have concluded that his conjecture was true for all lines.

21. Possible answer: Equations that involve x^2 or higher powers and equations for which x is in the denominator are nonlinear.

22. $m = 2$, $(3, 0)$

$y = 2x + b$

$0 = 2(3) + b$

$0 = 6 + b$

$^-6 = b$

$y = 2x - 6$

23. $m = \frac{^-1}{2}$, $(^-2, 0)$

$y = \frac{^-1}{2}x + b$

$0 = \frac{^-1}{2}(^-2) + b$

$0 = 1 + b$

$^-1 = b$

$y = \frac{^-1}{2}x - 1$

24. $m = ^-6$, $(3, 0)$

$y = ^-6x + b$

$0 = ^-6(1) + b$

$0 = ^-6 + b$

$6 = b$

$y = ^-6x + 6$

25. There will be no slope when $\frac{\text{rise}}{\text{run}}$ is undefined.

A fraction is undefined when the denominator is 0.

If the run is 0, then the line is vertical and all points on the line have an x value of 3.

$x = 3$

26a. $Ax + By = C$

$By = ^-Ax + C$

$y = \frac{^-Ax + C}{B}$

$y = \frac{^-A}{B}x + \frac{C}{B}$

26b. slope $\frac{^-A}{B}$, y-intercept $\frac{C}{B}$

27a.

World Population

Years since 1900

(y-axis: Population (billions), 0 to 6; x-axis: 0 to 120)

27b. Possible answer if the line passes through $(40, 1.7)$ and $(80, 4.5)$:

rise $= 4.5 - 1.7 = 2.8$

run $= 80 - 40 = 40$

slope $= \frac{\text{rise}}{\text{run}} = \frac{2.8}{40} = 0.07$

$y = 0.07x + b$

$1.7 = 0.07(40) + b$

$1.7 = 2.8 + b$

$^-1.1 = b$

Possible equation: $y = 0.07x - 1.1$

27c. Possible answer using the equation from Part b:

$y = 0.07x - 1.1$

$y = 0.07(110) - 1.1$

$y = 7.7 - 1.1$

$y = 6.6$

6.6 billion

27d. Possible answer using the equation from Part b:

$y = 0.07x - 1.1$

$y = 0.07(0) - 1.1$

$y = 0 - 1.1$

$y = ^-1.1$

$^-1.1$ billion; no, world population could not be negative.

27e. Possible answer: The prediction for 1900 is way off; the prediction for 2010 is relatively close to the UN prediction. We probably can't trust the predictions for times much beyond those in the data set on which it is based.

28a.

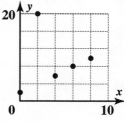

28b. (2, 20)

28c. mean of x values: $20 \div 5 = 4$

mean of y values: $46 \div 5 = 9.2$

28d. Possible answers:

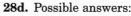

The line passes through (0, 5.2) and (4, 9.2).

rise = $9.2 - 5.2 = 4$

run = $4 - 0 = 4$

slope = $\dfrac{\text{rise}}{\text{run}} = \dfrac{4}{4} = 1$

$y = x + 5.2$

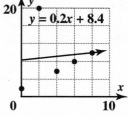

The line passes through (0, 8.4), and (4, 9.2).

rise = $9.2 - 8.4 = 0.8$

run = $4 - 0 = 4$

slope = $\dfrac{\text{rise}}{\text{run}} = \dfrac{0.8}{4} = 0.2$

$y = 0.2x + 8.4$

28e. mean of x values: $18 \div 4 = 4.5$;

mean of y values: $26 \div 4 = 6.5$

28f. The line passes through (4.5, 6.5) and (0, 2).

rise = $6.5 - 2 = 4.5$

run = $4.5 - 0 = 4.5$

slope = $\dfrac{\text{rise}}{\text{run}} = 1$

Possible equation: $y = x + 2$

28g. Answers will vary. Some students may think $y = x + 2$ is a good fit since the line goes through all the points except one, which is an outlier. Some may think there may be a reason that one data point is so far off, so the line should be adjusted accordingly.

29a. (7, 0)

$0 = 2(7) - 14$

$0 = 0$

29b. ($^-2$, 0)

$0 = (^-2)^2 - 4$

$0 = 4 - 4$

$0 = 0$

29c. ($^-1$, 0.9)

$0.9 = 0.1(^-1) + (^-1)^2$

$0.9 = ^-0.1 + 1$

$0.9 = 0.9$

29d. ($^-1$, $^-1$)

$^-1 = (^-1)^3$

$^-1 = ^-1$

29e. ($^-1$, 1)

$1 = ^-(^-1)^3$

$1 = ^-(^-1)$

$1 = 1$

29f. (10, 1)

$1 = 10^2 - 99$

$1 = 100 - 99$

$1 = 1$

30a. $V = \pi r^2 h$

$V = \pi m^2 m$

$8\pi = \pi m^3$

$m^3 = 8$

$m = 2$

30b. $V = \pi r^2 h$

$108\pi = \pi n^2 \cdot 4n$

$108\pi = 4\pi n^3$

$n^3 = 27$

$n = 3$

30c.
$$V = \pi r^2 h$$
$$0.125\pi = \pi \left(\frac{k}{2}\right)^2 \cdot 2k$$
$$0.125\pi = \frac{1}{2}\pi k^2$$
$$k^2 = 0.25$$
$$k = 0.5$$

31a.
$$a^2 + b^2 = c^2$$
$$3^2 + (2k)^2 = 5^2$$
$$9 + 4k^2 = 25$$
$$4k^2 = 16$$
$$k^2 = 4$$
$$k = 2$$

31b.
$$a^2 + b^2 = c^2$$
$$6^2 + 8^2 = (20m)^2$$
$$36 + 64 = 400m^2$$
$$100 = 400m^2$$
$$m^2 = 0.25$$
$$m = 0.5$$

31c.
$$a^2 + b^2 = c^2$$
$$(2.5p)^2 + (6p)^2 = 13^2$$
$$6.25p^2 + 36p^2 = 169$$
$$42.25p^2 = 169$$
$$p^2 = 4$$
$$p = 2$$

32a.
$$V = \pi r^2 h$$
$$V = \pi \cdot 4^2 \cdot 15 \approx 754$$
$$V = \pi \cdot 5^2 \cdot 15 \approx 1{,}178$$
$$V = \pi \cdot 6^2 \cdot 15 \approx 1{,}696$$
$$V = \pi \cdot 7^2 \cdot 15 \approx 2{,}309$$
$$V = \pi \cdot 8^2 \cdot 15 \approx 3{,}016$$
$$V = \pi \cdot 9^2 \cdot 15 \approx 3{,}817$$

Radius (m)	4	5	6	7	8	9
Volume (m³)	754	1,178	1,696	2,309	3,016	3,817

32b.

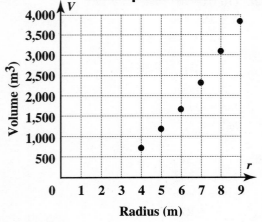

Tank Specifications

32c. about 8.6 m

Possible answer: A line of best fit can be useful in working with data. This line can be used to make predictions or to solve problems relating to the data.

---

1 Review and Self-Assessment

Pages 64–66   Strategies and Applications

1. Linear but not a direct variation; the constant rate of change, $1.25 per ride, indicates that the relationship is linear. The nonzero starting value, $2.50, indicates that it is not direct.

2. Nonlinear; the rate of change is not constant.

3. A direct variation; 65 is the constant rate, and $d = 0$ when $t = 0$.

4. Linear but not a direct variation; $^-12$ is the constant rate, and the y value is not 0 when $x = 0$.

5. As x increases by 10, y increases by 50.
   Linear but not a direct variation; as x increases by a constant amount, so does y. The y value is not 0 when $x = 0$.

6. As x increases by 5, y increases by 23.
   A direct variation; as x increases by a constant amount, so does y. When $x = 0$, $y = 0$.

7a. $y = 300 - 30x$
   The slope changes from $^-25$ to $^-30$.
   It would make the line steeper.

7b. $y = 300 - 20x$
   The slope changes from $^-25$ to $^-20$.
   It would make the line less steep.

7c. $y = 300 + 25x$
   The slope changes from $^-25$ to 25.
   It would change the direction of the line, since the slope is now positive.

7d. $y = ^-100 - 30x$
   The y-intercept changes from 300 to $^-100$.
   The line would now cross the y-axis at $^-100$.

8. Find the equation of the line that passes through $(^-2, 8)$ and $\left(\frac{1}{3}, 1\right)$.
$$\text{rise} = 1 - 8 = ^-7$$
$$\text{run} = \frac{1}{3} - ^-2 = 2\frac{1}{3} = \frac{7}{3}$$
$$\text{slope} = \frac{\text{rise}}{\text{run}} = \frac{^-7}{\frac{7}{3}} = ^-3$$
$$y = mx + b, \, m = ^-3, (^-2, 8)$$
$$8 = ^-3(^-2) + b$$
$$8 = 6 + b$$
$$2 = b$$
$$y = mx + b, \, m = ^-3, b = 2$$
$$y = ^-3x + 2$$
   Check to see that the line passes through $(5, ^-13)$.
$$^-13 = ^-3(5) + 2$$
$$^-13 = ^-15 + 2$$
$$^-13 = ^-13 \checkmark$$

collinear; Possible explanation: The line through the first two points has the equation $y = {}^-3x + 2$, and $(5, {}^-13)$ satisfies the equation.

9. Find the equation of the line that passes through $\left(2, \frac{7}{2}\right)$ and $(6, 6)$

rise $= 6 - \frac{7}{2} = \frac{5}{2}$

run $= 6 - 2 = 4$

slope $= \frac{\text{rise}}{\text{run}} = \frac{\frac{5}{2}}{4} = \frac{5}{8}$

$y = mx + b, m = \frac{5}{8}, (6, 6)$

$6 = \frac{5}{8}(6) + b$

$6 = \frac{15}{4} + b$

$2\frac{1}{4} = b$

$y = mx + b, m = \frac{5}{8}, b = 2\frac{1}{4}$

$y = \frac{5}{8}x + 2\frac{1}{4}$

Check to see that the line passes through $\left({}^-3, \frac{3}{2}\right)$.

$\frac{3}{2} = \frac{5}{8}({}^-3) + 2\frac{1}{4}$

$\frac{3}{2} = \frac{{}^-15}{8} + \frac{18}{8}$

$\frac{3}{2} \neq \frac{3}{8}$

not collinear; Possible explanation: The line through the first two points has the equation $y = \frac{5}{8}x + 2\frac{1}{4}$, and since $\frac{5}{8}({}^-3) + 2\frac{1}{4} \neq \frac{3}{2}$, the third point can't be on that line.

10. Find the equation of the line that passes through $({}^-6, {}^-3)$ and $\left(8, \frac{5}{3}\right)$.

rise $= \frac{5}{3} - {}^-3 = \frac{14}{3}$

run $= 8 - {}^-6 = 14$

slope $= \frac{\text{rise}}{\text{run}} = \frac{\frac{14}{3}}{14} = \frac{1}{3}$

$y = mx + b, m = \frac{1}{3}, ({}^-6, {}^-3)$

${}^-3 = \frac{1}{3}({}^-6) + b$

${}^-3 = {}^-2 + b$

${}^-1 = b$

$y = mx + b, m = \frac{1}{3}, b = {}^-1$

$y = \frac{1}{3}x - 1$

Check to see that the line passes through $(0, {}^-1)$.

${}^-1 = \frac{1}{3}(0) - 1$

${}^-1 = 0 - 1$

${}^-1 = {}^-1$ ✓

collinear; Possible explanation: The line through the first two points has the equation $y = \frac{1}{3}x - 1$, and $(0, {}^-1)$ satisfies the equation.

11. The slope of the line $y = {}^-3x + 1$ is ${}^-3$.

$m = {}^-3, ({}^-4, 1)$

$y = mx + b$

$1 = {}^-3({}^-4) + b$

$1 = 12 + b$

${}^-11 = b$

$y = mx + b, m = {}^-3, b = {}^-11$

$y = {}^-3x - 11$

12a.
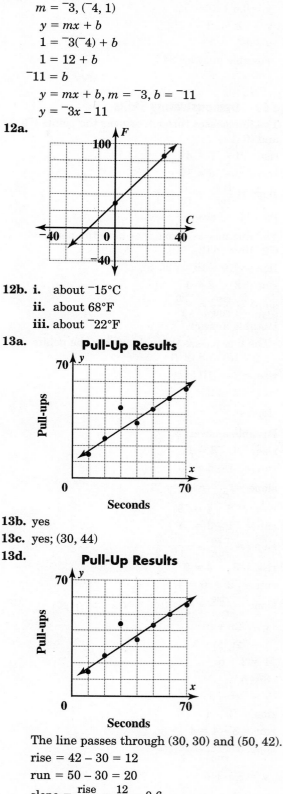

12b. i.   about ${}^-15$°C
     ii. about 68°F
     iii. about ${}^-22$°F

13a.

Pull-Up Results

13b. yes
13c. yes; $(30, 44)$
13d.

Pull-Up Results

The line passes through $(30, 30)$ and $(50, 42)$.

rise $= 42 - 30 = 12$

run $= 50 - 30 = 20$

slope $= \frac{\text{rise}}{\text{run}} = \frac{12}{20} = 0.6$

$y = mx + b, m = 0.6, (30, 30)$

$30 = 0.6(30) + b$

$30 = 18 + b$

$12 = b$

$y = mx + b, m = 0.6, b = 12$

Possible equation: $y = 0.6x + 12$

13e. 2 minutes = 120 seconds = x

$y = 0.6(120) + 12$

$y = 72 + 12$

$y = 84$

Possible answer: 84

Page 67   Demonstrating Skills

14. The line passes through or near the points $(^-6, ^-3)$ and $(6, 1)$.

rise $= 1 - ^-3 = 4$

run $= 6 - ^-6 = 12$

slope $= \dfrac{\text{rise}}{\text{run}} = \dfrac{4}{12} = \dfrac{1}{3}$

Possible answer: $\dfrac{1}{3}$

15. The line passes through or near the points $(^-2, 10)$ and $(2, ^-10)$.

rise $= ^-10 - 10 = ^-20$

run $= 2 - ^-2 = 4$

slope $= \dfrac{\text{rise}}{\text{run}} = \dfrac{^-20}{4} = ^-5$

Possible answer: $^-5$

16. The line passes through or near the points $(^-2, ^-10)$ and $(2, 6)$.

rise $= 6 - ^-10 = 16$

run $= 2 - ^-2 = 4$

slope $= \dfrac{\text{rise}}{\text{run}} = \dfrac{16}{4} = 4$

Possible answer: 4

17. rise $= 9 - ^-3 = 12$

run $= ^-1 - 5 = ^-6$

slope $= \dfrac{\text{rise}}{\text{run}} = \dfrac{12}{^-6} = ^-2$

18. rise $= ^-2 - 4 = ^-6$

run $= ^-1 - 3 = ^-4$

slope $= \dfrac{\text{rise}}{\text{run}} = \dfrac{^-6}{^-4} = \dfrac{3}{2}$

19. rise $= 5 - ^-4 = 9$

run $= ^-2 - ^-6 = 4$

slope $= \dfrac{\text{rise}}{\text{run}} = \dfrac{9}{4}$

20. $y = ^-2x + b$

$^-1 = ^-2(^-1) + b$

$^-1 = 2 + b$

$^-3 = b$

$y = ^-2x - 3$

21. rise $= ^-2 - 4 = ^-6$

run $= 8 - 4 = 4$

slope $= \dfrac{\text{rise}}{\text{run}} = \dfrac{^-6}{4} = \dfrac{^-3}{2}$

$y = \dfrac{^-3}{2}x + b$

$4 = \dfrac{^-3}{2}(4) + b$

$4 = ^-6 + b$

$10 = b$

$y = \dfrac{^-3}{2}x + 10$

22a. $y = 3x + 1$

$m = 3$

22b. $y = \dfrac{1}{2}x - 1$

$m = \dfrac{1}{2}$

22c. $\dfrac{1}{2}y = 3 + \dfrac{1}{2}x$

$y = 6 + x$

$y = x + 6$

$m = 1$

22d. $y = ^-x + 2$

$m = ^-1$

22e. $y = 2x(1 - x)$

$y = 2x - 2x^2$

Equation is not linear.

22f. $y = 2x + (1 - x)$

$y = x + 1$

$m = 1$

22g. $3y = 1 - 3x$

$y = (1 - 3x)\dfrac{1}{3}$

$y = \dfrac{1}{3} - x$

$m = ^-1$

22h. $^-4y = 2x$

$y = 2x\left(\dfrac{^-1}{4}\right)$

$y = \dfrac{^-1}{2}x$

22i. $y = \dfrac{1}{2}x - x - 1$

$y = \dfrac{^-1}{2}x - 1$

$m = \dfrac{^-1}{2}$

Equations d and g, c and f, h and i

23. $y - x - 1 = 2x + 1$

$y = 3x + 2$

24. $2(y - 1) = 3x + 1$

$2y - 2 = 3x + 1$

$2y = 3x + 3$

$y = \dfrac{3}{2}x + \dfrac{3}{2}$

25. $1 - y = x + 2(1 - x)$

$1 - y = x + 2 - 2x$

$1 - y = ^-x + 2$

$^-y = ^-x + 1$

$y = x - 1$

Chapter 2 Quadratic and Inverse Relationships

2-1 | Quadratic Relationships

Pages 72–73 Problem Set A

1. The first equation describes the volume in terms of length; the second describes it in terms of width. If x is the length, then $\frac{x}{2}$ is the width, and $V = 9(x)\left(\frac{x}{2}\right) = 4.5x^2$. If y is the width, then $2y$ is the length, and $V = 9(2y)(y) = 18y^2$.

2.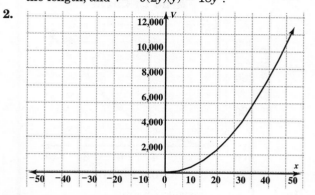

3a–b. Answers will vary.

4.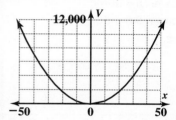

5. the vertical axis

6a. Possible answer: about ⁻45 and 45

6b. Possible answer: about ⁻44.7 and 44.7

Page 73 Share and Summarize

1. Not quadratic; graph is a straight line.

2. Could be quadratic; graph is symmetric and U-shaped.

3. Not quadratic; graph is not U-shaped.

4. Could be quadratic; graph is symmetric and U-shaped.

Pages 74–75 Problem Set B

1. Possible answers: The stages consist of 2 tiles separated by no columns, then separated by 1 column of 3 tiles, then by 2 columns of 4 tiles, then by 3 columns of 5 tiles, and so on. *Or,* in Stage 1 there are 2 tiles that touch at a corner. In Stage 2 these 2 tiles are separated by adding a new column (in this case, 2 tiles) and a new row (in this case, 1 tile) between them. At each subsequent stage, one more row and one more column are added between the original 2 tiles.

2.

Stage, S	1	2	3	4
Tiles, T	2	5	10	17

3. Possible answer: T increases by 3, 5, and 7. It increases by 2 more each time; it appears to be increasing by the next greater odd number as S increases.

4.

Stage, S	1	2	3	4	5	6	7	8
Tiles, T	2	5	10	17	26	37	50	65

5.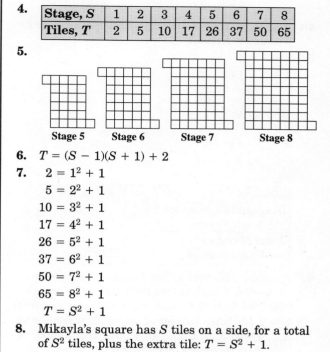

Stage 5   Stage 6   Stage 7   Stage 8

6. $T = (S - 1)(S + 1) + 2$

7.
$$2 = 1^2 + 1$$
$$5 = 2^2 + 1$$
$$10 = 3^2 + 1$$
$$17 = 4^2 + 1$$
$$26 = 5^2 + 1$$
$$37 = 6^2 + 1$$
$$50 = 7^2 + 1$$
$$65 = 8^2 + 1$$
$$T = S^2 + 1$$

8. Mikayla's square has S tiles on a side, for a total of S^2 tiles, plus the extra tile: $T = S^2 + 1$.

9a.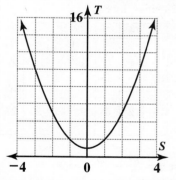

9b. The graph is a parabola that opens upward; its lowest point is at (0, 1).

9c. yes, the vertical axis

9d. 1

Pages 76–77 Problem Set C

1.

2.

Sides, n	3	4	5	6
Diagonals Connected to Each Vertex	0	1	2	3
Total Number of Diagonals, d	0	2	5	9

3a. The number of diagonals at a vertex increases by 1 each time the number of sides increases by 1.

3b. Yes. Possible explanation: The number of diagonals increases by a constant amount, 1, each time the number of sides increases by 1.

4a. The number of diagonals increases by 2, then 3, then 4, and so on.

4b. No; the number of diagonals does not increase by a constant amount.

5a. $3 + 1 = 4$

5b. $9 + 5 = 14$

5c.

Sides, n	3	4	5	6	7
Diagonals Connected to Each Vertex	0	1	2	3	4
Total Number of Diagonals, d	0	2	5	9	14

6. Possible explanation: The number of diagonals connected to each vertex increases by 1 for each side added. As the number of sides increases from 3 to 7, the total number of diagonals increases by 2, 3, 4, and 5. So from 7 to 8 sides, the number of diagonals increases by 6; from 8 to 9 sides, by 7; and from 9 to 10 sides, by 8.

Sides, n	3	4	5	6	7	8	9	10
Diagonals Connected to Each Vertex	0	1	2	3	4	5	6	7
Total Number of Diagonals, d	0	2	5	9	14	20	27	35

7. 170

8. $d = \frac{n(n-3)}{2}$, or $d = \frac{n^2}{2} - \frac{3n}{2}$; Possible explanations: Every vertex is connected by a diagonal to all the other vertices except itself and the two next to it. So, each vertex is connected to $n - 3$ diagonals, for a total of $n(n-3)$. However, since each diagonal joins two vertices, divide $n(n-3)$ by 2 to get the total (otherwise each diagonal would be counted twice). *Or,* each number in the second row is 3 less than the number in the first row. If you multiply the first row by the second row and take half of the result, you get $\frac{n(n-3)}{2}$, or the third row.

9. $d = \frac{100(100-3)}{2} = \frac{100(97)}{2} = \frac{9,700}{2} = 4,850$

10. Predictions will vary; the graph is a parabola.

Page 77 Share and Summarize

1. $y = x^2$, $V = 4.5x^2$, $T = S^2 + 1$, $d = \frac{n(n-3)}{2}$

2. They are all U-shaped curves that open upward. Each has a vertical line of symmetry.

3. Possible answer: The squared variable tells us the equations are not linear. (Note: Students might need to use the distributive property on the last equation to see this.)

Pages 78–82 On Your Own Exercises

1a.

r	0	1	2	3	4	5
A	0	3.14	12.57	28.57	50.27	78.54

r	6	7	8	9	10
A	113.10	153.94	201.06	254.47	314.16

1b.

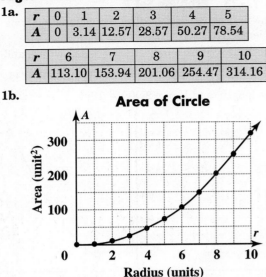

1c. i. Possible answer: 2.8 units

ii. Possible answer: 5.6 units

iii. Possible answer: 9.8 units

1d. Possible answers:

$\pi(2.8)^2 \approx 24.6$

$\pi(5.6)^2 \approx 98.5$

$\pi(9.8)^2 \approx 301.7$

2a.

Number of Rows, n	1	2	3	4	5	6	7	8	9	10
Number of Blocks in Bottom Row, b	1	3	5	7	9	11	13	15	17	19

2b. The number of blocks in the bottom row of the stack is twice the number of rows in the stack minus 1.

25 rows: $25 \cdot 2 - 1 = 49$

n rows: $2n - 1$

2c. linear

2d. 25

2e.

Number of Rows, n	1	2	3	4	5	6	7	8	9	10
Number of Blocks in Bottom Row, b	1	3	5	7	9	11	13	15	17	19
Total Number of Blocks, T	1	4	9	16	25	36	49	64	81	100

2f.

$1 = 1^2$

$4 = 2^2$

$9 = 3^2$

$16 = 4^2$

$25 = 5^2$

$36 = 6^2$

$49 = 7^2$

$64 = 8^2$

$81 = 9^2$

$100 = 10^2$

$T = n^2$

2g. The shape of the recombined blocks is a square, n blocks across and n blocks high with a total of n^2 blocks.

3a. $A = n^2 - 1$

3b. When $n = 1, A = n^2 - 1 = 1 - 1 = 0$.

3c. $5^2 - 1 = 25 - 1 = 24$
$6^2 - 1 = 36 - 1 = 35$
$7^2 - 1 = 49 - 1 = 48$
$8^2 - 1 = 64 - 1 = 63$
$9^2 - 1 = 81 - 1 = 80$
$10^2 - 1 = 100 - 1 = 99$

n	1	2	3	4	5	6	7	8	9	10
A	0	3	8	15	24	35	48	63	80	99

3d.

n	-10	-9	-8	-7	-6	-5	-4	-3	-2	-1	0
A	99	80	63	48	35	24	15	8	3	0	-1

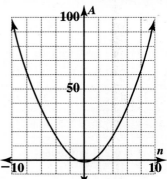

3e. Possible answer: a parabola that opens upward

3f. the vertical axis, $n = 0$

4a. Tables will vary. Possible tables:

$y = x^2$		$y = x^2 + 2$		$y = x^2 - 2$	
x	y	x	y	x	y
0	0	0	2	0	⁻2
1	1	1	3	1	⁻1
⁻2	4	⁻2	6	⁻2	2
⁻4	16	⁻4	18	⁻4	14

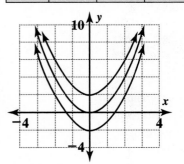

4b. They have the same shape, open upward, and are symmetrical about the y-axis.

4c. They cross the y-axis at different points: $y = x^2 + 2$ passes through (0, 2), $y = x^2$ passes through (0, 0), and $y = x^2 - 2$ through (0, ⁻2).

5a. Tables will vary. Possible tables:

$y = {}^-x^2$		$y = {}^-x^2 + 2$		$y = {}^-x^2 - 2$	
x	y	x	y	x	y
0	0	0	2	0	⁻2
1	⁻1	1	1	1	⁻3
⁻2	⁻4	⁻2	⁻2	⁻2	⁻6
⁻4	⁻16	⁻4	⁻14	⁻4	⁻16

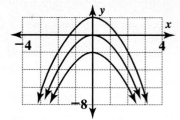

5b. They have the same shape, open downward, and are symmetrical about the y-axis.

5c. They cross the y-axis at different points: $y = {}^-x^2 + 2$ passes through (0, 2), $y = {}^-x^2$ passes through (0, 0), and $y = {}^-x^2 - 2$ through (0, ⁻2).

6a. $R = p(200 - 2p)$

6b. Possible table:

r	0	10	20	30	40	50
A	0	1,800	3,200	4,200	4,800	5,000

r	60	70	80	90	100
A	4,800	4,200	3,200	1,800	0

6c.

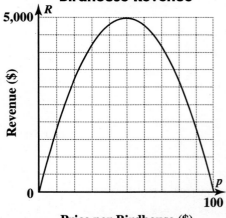

Birdhouse Revenue

Price per Birdhouse ($)

6d. $50; $5,000

7a. Possible answers: The amount added to y increases each time—3, 5, 7, and so on. *Or,* as x increases by 1, y increases by the next odd number.

7b.

x	1	2	3	4	5	6	7	8	9	10
y	0	3	8	15	24	35	48	63	80	99

7c.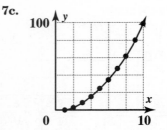

7d. The graph curves upward like the right half of a bowl.

7e. Yes, the graph could be half of a parabola.

8a. The value of y increases at the same rate each time x increases by 1; each value is 3 more than the previous value.

8b.

x	1	2	3	4	5	6	7	8	9	10
y	7	10	13	16	19	22	25	28	31	34

8c.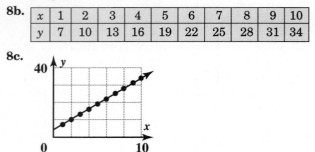

8d. The graph is a line that slopes upward.

8e. No; the graph is a straight line.

9a. reaction distance:

$d = 0.25s$

$d = 0.25(0) = 0$

$d = 0.25(10) = 2.5$

$d = 0.25(20) = 5$

$d = 0.25(30) = 7.5$

$d = 0.25(40) = 10$

$d = 0.25(50) = 12.5$

$d = 0.25(60) = 15$

$d = 0.25(70) = 17.5$

$d = 0.25(80) = 20$

braking distance:

$d = 0.006s^2$

$d = 0.006(0)^2 = 0$

$d = 0.006(10)^2 = 0.6$

$d = 0.006(20)^2 = 2.4$

$d = 0.006(30)^2 = 5.4$

$d = 0.006(40)^2 = 9.6$

$d = 0.006(50)^2 = 15$

$d = 0.006(60)^2 = 21.6$

$d = 0.006(70)^2 = 29.4$

$d = 0.006(80)^2 = 38.4$

Possible table:

Speed (kph)	0	10	20	30	40	50	60	70	80
Reaction Distance (m)	0	2.5	5	7.5	10	12.5	15	17.5	20
Breaking Distance (m)	0	0.6	2.4	5.4	9.6	15	21.6	29.4	38.4

9b.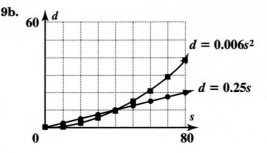

9c. $0 + 0 = 0$

$2.5 + 0.6 = 3.1$

$5 + 2.4 = 7.4$

$7.5 + 5.4 = 12.9$

$10 + 9.6 = 19.6$

$12.5 + 15 = 27.5$

$15 + 21.6 = 36.6$

$17.5 + 29.4 = 46.9$

$20 + 38.4 = 58.4$

Possible table:

Speed (kph)	0	10	20	30	40	50	60	70	80
Reaction Distance (m)	0	2.5	5	7.5	10	12.5	15	17.5	20
Breaking Distance (m)	0	0.6	2.4	5.4	9.6	15	21.6	29.4	38.4
Total Distance (m)	0	3.1	7.4	12.9	19.6	27.5	36.6	46.9	58.4

9d.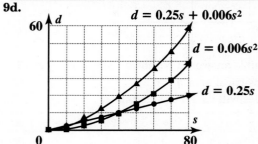

The equation is $d = 0.25s + 0.006s^2$; the relationship is quadratic.

10. $^-2^{-2} = \dfrac{1}{(^-2)^2} = \dfrac{1}{4}$ or 0.25

11. $(^-2)^3 \cdot (^-2)^{-2} = ^-8 \cdot \dfrac{1}{4} = ^-2$

12. $(3 - (^-2))^{-(^-2)} = 5^2 = 25$

13. $(^-2)^{3-(^-2)} = (^-2)^5 = ^-32$

14. $(-2 \cdot 3)^{-(^-2)} = (^-6)^2 = 36$

15. $\dfrac{(^-2)^2}{3^2} = \dfrac{4}{9}$

16. slope $= ^-3$, y-intercept $= 5$

17. slope $= ^-1.6$, y-intercept $= 1$

18. slope $= \dfrac{1}{3}$, y-intercept $= -\dfrac{1}{2}$

19. slope $= 1$, y-intercept $= 0$

20a. $3d$

20b. $\dfrac{1}{10} \cdot 3d = \dfrac{3d}{10}$

20c. $7 + \dfrac{1}{2} \cdot \dfrac{3d}{10} = 7 + \dfrac{3d}{20}$

20d. $s = 7 + \dfrac{3d}{20}$

$13 = 7 + \dfrac{3d}{20}$

$\dfrac{3d}{20} = 6$

$$3d = 120$$
$$d = 40$$
Daniela: 40
$$a = 3d$$
$$a = 3(40)$$
$$a = 120$$
Andrés: 120
$$t = 120 \div 10$$
$$t = 12$$
Tyree: 12

21. $A(4, 1), C(2, {}^-5)$

$$\text{slope} = \frac{\text{rise}}{\text{run}} = \frac{{}^-5 - 1}{2 - 4} = \frac{{}^-6}{{}^-2} = 3$$
$$y = 3x + b$$
$$1 = 3(4) + b$$
$$1 = 12 + b$$
$$b = {}^-11$$
$$y = 3x - 11$$

22. $A(4, 1), B(4, {}^-2)$

$$x = 4$$

23. $D({}^-3, {}^-6), E({}^-4, {}^-2)$

$$\text{slope} = \frac{\text{rise}}{\text{run}} = \frac{{}^-2 + 6}{{}^-4 + 3} = \frac{4}{{}^-1} = {}^-4$$
$$y = {}^-4x + b$$
$${}^-6 = {}^-4({}^-3) + b$$
$${}^-6 = 12 + b$$
$$b = {}^-18$$
$$y = {}^-4x - 18$$

24. $A(4, 1), F({}^-1, {}^-1)$

$$\text{slope} = \frac{\text{rise}}{\text{run}} = \frac{{}^-1 - 1}{{}^-1 - 4} = \frac{{}^-2}{{}^-5} = \frac{2}{5}$$
$$y = \frac{2}{5}x + b$$
$$1 = \frac{2}{5}(4) + b$$
$$1 = \frac{8}{5} + b$$
$$b = -\frac{3}{5}$$
$$y = \frac{2}{5}x - \frac{3}{5}$$

25. $F({}^-1, {}^-1), (0, 0)$

$$\text{slope} = \frac{\text{rise}}{\text{run}} = \frac{0 + 1}{0 + 1} = 1$$
The y-intercept is 0.
$$y = x$$

26. $G(-5, 6), H(-2, 6)$

$$y = 6$$

Page 81   In Your Own Words

Possible answer: The graphs of quadratic relationships are U-shaped, while the graphs of linear relationships are straight lines. In equations of quadratic relationships, the variable is squared. In the equations of linear relationships, however, the variable is not raised to any power.

<table>
<tr><td colspan="7" align="center">**2-2** | **Families of Quadratics**</td></tr>
</table>

2-2   Families of Quadratics

Pages 84–85   Problem Set A

1.

x	A $y=x^2$	B $y=x^2+1$	C $y=x^2-1$	D $y=-x^2$	E $y=(x+1)^2$	F $y=(x-1)^2$
-4	16	17	15	-16	9	25
-3.2	10.24	11.24	9.24	-10.24	4.84	17.64
-2.2	4.84	5.84	3.84	-4.84	1.44	10.24
-1	1	2	0	-1	0	4
-0.5	0.25	1.25	-0.75	-0.25	0.25	2.25
0	0	1	-1	0	1	1
0.5	0.25	1.25	-0.75	-0.25	2.25	0.25
1	1	2	0	-1	4	0
2.2	4.84	5.84	3.84	-4.84	10.24	1.44
3.2	10.24	11.24	9.24	-10.24	17.64	4.84
4	16	17	15	-16	25	9

2. The values in Column B are 1 more than those in Column A, since the equation for Column B is $y = x^2 + 1$ and that of Column A is $y = x^2$. The values in Column C are 1 less than those in Column A, since the equation for Column C is $y = x^2 - 1$. The values in Column D are the negatives of those in Column A, since the equation for Column D is $y = {}^-x^2$. The values in Column E are the squares of 1 more than the numbers that were squared for Column A, since the equation for Column E is $y = (x + 1)^2$. The values in Column F are the squares of 1 less than the numbers that were squared for Column A, since the equation for Column F is $y = (x - 1)^2$.

3a. Column A, $y = x^2$, since the lowest value is at $(0, 0)$.

3b. It is the graph of $y = x^2$.

3c. the y-axis

4a. Column E, $y = (x + 1)^2$, since the lowest y value is 0, when $x = {}^-1$.

4b. It has the same shape as $y = x^2$ but is shifted to the left.

4c. the vertical line passing through $({}^-1, 0)$

5a. Column C, $y = x^2 - 1$, since the lowest y value is ${}^-1$, when $x = 0$.

5b. It has the same shape as $y = x^2$ but is shifted down.

5c. the y-axis

6a. Column B, $y = x^2 + 1$, since the lowest y value is 1, when $x = 0$.

6b. It has the same shape as $y = x^2$ but is shifted up.

6c. the y-axis

7a. Column F, $y = (x - 1)^2$, since the lowest y value is 0, when $x = 1$.

7b. It has the same shape as $y = x^2$ but is shifted to the right.

7c. the vertical line passing through $(1,0)$

8a. Column D, $y = {}^-x^2$, since the greatest y value is 0, when $x = 0$, and all the other y values are negative.

8b. It has the same shape as $y = x^2$ but is flipped upside down.

8c. the y-axis

Page 86   Problem Set B

1. $y = x^2$
2. $y = x^2 + 100$
3. $y = x^2 - 4$
4. $y = x^2 + 4$
5. $y = 10x^2$
6. $y = 10x^2 - 20$
7. $y = 4x^2$
8. $y = 4x^2 + 1$

Pages 86–87   Share and Summarize

1. Graph B: $y = x^2 + 2$; it has the same shape as $y = x^2$ but passes through the y-axis 2 units higher. Graph C: $y = x^2 - 3$; it looks the same as $y = x^2$ but passes through the y-axis 3 units lower.

2. Table B represents $y = {}^-3x^2$ since each y value is ${}^-3$ times the square of the x value. Table C represents $y = (x - 2)^2$ since each y value is the square of 2 less than the x value.

Page 88   Problem Set C

1a.

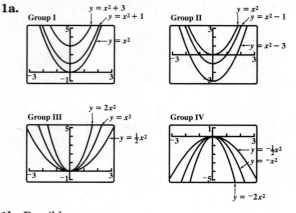

1b. Possible answer:

Group I: The graphs are parabolas that open upward, but they cross the y-axis at different points: (0, 0), (0, 1), and (0, 3), respectively.

Group II: The graphs are parabolas that open upward, but they cross the y-axis at different points: (0, 0), (0, ${}^-1$), and (0, ${}^-3$), respectively.

Group III: The graphs are parabolas that open upward and have their lowest point at (0, 0), but they have different widths. The narrowest is $y = 2x^2$ and the widest is $y = \frac{1}{2}x^2$.

Group IV: The graphs are parabolas that open downward and have their highest point at (0, 0), but they have different widths. The narrowest is $y = {}^-2x^2$ and the widest is $y = \frac{-1}{2}x^2$.

1c. Possible answer:

Group I: $y = x^2 + 4$

Group II: $y = x^2 - 4$

Group III: $y = 7x^2$

Group IV: $y = {}^-7x^2$

2. Graphs in both groups are parabolas that open upward. The graphs in Group I cross the y-axis at or above (0, 0), while the graphs in Group II cross the y-axis at or below (0, 0).

3. Possible answer: The graphs in Group III open upward while the graphs in Group IV open downward. The graph of each equation in Group IV is the mirror image of the graph in Group III with the opposite coefficient.

4a–d.

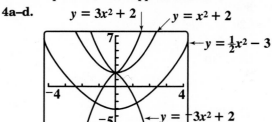

5. If a is positive, the graph opens upward. If a is negative, the graph opens downward. The greater the absolute value of a, the narrower the graph. The value of c determines where the graph crosses the y-axis.

Page 89   Problem Set D

1. The graphs in each group will open in the same direction and have the same width; they will also have the same y-intercept.

2a.

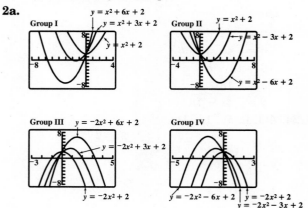

2b. Answers will vary.

2c. Group I: The graphs are parabolas that open upward, seem to be about the same width, and have the same y-intercept.

Group II: The graphs are parabolas that open upward, seem to be about the same width, and have the same y-intercept.

Group III: The graphs are parabolas that open downward, seem to be about the same width, and have the same y-intercept.

Group IV: The graphs are parabolas that open downward, seem to be about the same width, and have the same y-intercept.

3. Possible answer: The parabolas move farther from the origin. In Group I, The graphs have different vertices, moving left and down as b increases. In Group II, the graphs have different vertices, moving right and down as b decreases. In Group III, the graphs have different vertices, moving right and up as b increases. In Group IV, the graphs have different vertices, moving left and up as b decreases.

Page 89   Share and Summarize

1. $y = {}^-2x^2 + 5$
2. It is a parabola opening downward with its vertex at $(0, {}^-2)$; it will be wider than the graph of $y = x^2$.
3a. yes
3b. no
3c. yes
3d. no
3e. yes
3f. no

use graph to solve word probs.

Pages 90–91   Problem Set E

1a. 24 m; This is the height on the graph corresponding to a time of 0 s.
1b. 4.2 s; This is the time value corresponding to the other 24-m height value on the graph.
2. 5.1 s; Find the time at the point where the height is 0 (the ground).
3. about 0.9 s; Find the first point of the graph where the height is 1.5 m. This corresponds to a time value of $^-0.9$ s, which is 0.9 s before filming began.
4. approximately 6 s; Possible explanation: Add the answers to Problems 2 and 3.
5a. 46 m; Find the height value at the highest point on the graph.
5b. about 2.9 s; Add the time it was in the air before the camera started shooting (0.9 s) to the time it took to reach its maximum height (2.0 s).

Pages 91–92   Problem Set F

1. Downward; the coefficient of x^2 is negative.
2.
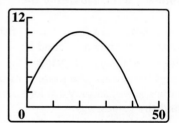
3. 2 yd; this is the y value when $x = 0$.
4. 10 yd; this is the greatest y value on the graph, when $x = 20$.
5. 40 yd; At $x = 0$, the height was 2 yd. The height is 2 yd again at $x = 40$.

Page 92   Share and Summarize

1. Find the highest point on the graph, and estimate the first coordinate, which gives the time.
2. Possible explanation: Draw or imagine a horizontal line through Point P. Find the other intersection of this line and the parabola; estimate its coordinate, which is the time when the ball had the same height it had at $t = 1$.

Page 93   Problem Set G

1. quadratic
2. quadratic
3. quadratic
4. not quadratic; no squared variable
5. not quadratic; the constant is divided, rather than multiplied, by x^2
6. quadratic
7. not quadratic; no squared variable
8. not quadratic; contains a cubed variable
9. quadratic
10. quadratic
11. not quadratic; no squared variable
12. not quadratic; if expanded, would include a cubed variable

Page 94   Problem Set H

1a.
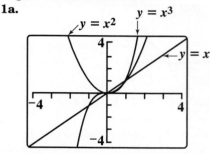

1b. All three pass through $(0, 0)$. The first graph is a line; the others are curves. The second graph has a low point at $(0, 0)$. The third graph changes the direction it curves at $(0, 0)$. The second graph is symmetric about the y-axis; the others aren't. In the first and third graphs, the y values increase from left to right. In the second graph, the y values decrease until $(0, 0)$, and then increase.

1c. $(0, 0)$ and $(1, 1)$

2a.
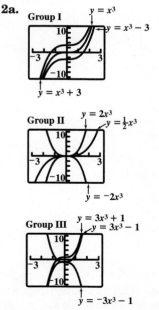

2b. Group I: They have the same shape but different y-intercepts.

Group II: All three go through the origin, but the one with the $\frac{1}{2}$ coefficient is wider. The one with the $^-2$ coefficient goes down from left to right; the other two go up from left to right.

Group III: They're all the same width and shape. The third equation has a graph that goes down from left to right. The second and third go through $(0, ^-1)$; the first goes through $(0, 1)$.

2c. how wide the graph is, and whether it goes up or down from left to right

2d. the y-intercept, or whether the graph is moved up or down from the origin

Page 95   Problem Set I

1.

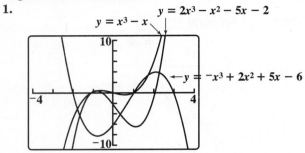

2. The graphs are all curves that change direction twice. Looking from left to right, the graphs with positive x^3 terms go up, then down, then up again. The graph with a negative x^3 term goes down, then up, then down again.

3. $y = x^3 - x$: x-axis $(^-1, 0)$ $(0, 0)$ $(1, 0)$, y-axis $(0, 0)$
$y = ^-x^3 + 2x^2 + 5x - 6$: x-axis $(^-2, 0)$ $(1, 0)$ $(3, 0)$, y-axis $(0, ^-6)$
$y = 2x^3 - x^2 - 5x - 2$: x-axis $(^-1, 0)$ $\left(-\frac{1}{2}, 0\right)$ $(2, 0)$ y-axis $(0, ^-2)$

4a. $y = x^3 - x + 1$

4b.

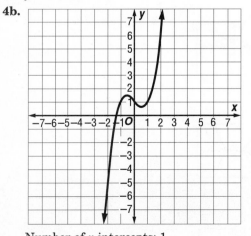

Number of x-intercepts: 1

Page 95   Share and Summarize

Possible answer: Graphs of linear relationships are lines. Graphs of quadratic relationships are symmetrical curves that look like bowls opening upward or downward. Graphs of cubic relationships have one half that opens upward and one that

opens downward. Graphs of linear equations don't turn; those of quadratic equations turn once; those of cubic equations curve but don't turn if there is no x^2 or x term, and turn twice if there is an x^2 or x term.

Pages 96–97   Lab

1.

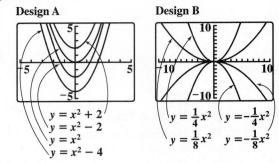

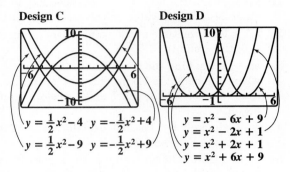

2. Answers will vary.

3. See the answers for Problem 1.

4a–b. Designs will vary.

5a–c. Reports will vary.

Pages 98–107   On Your Own Exercises

1a. $y = x^2$; The y values are the squares of the x values.

1b. $y = (x - 2)^2$; The y values are the squares of the x values two rows up, so they are found by subtracting 2 from x and then squaring.

1c. $y = (x + 3)^2$; The y values are the squares of the x values three rows down, so they are found by adding 3 to x and then squaring.

1d. $y = ^-2x^2$; The y values are $^-2$ times the y values from Table a.

1e. $y = 2x$; The y values are 2 times the corresponding x values.

1f. $y = ^-2x^2 + 10$; The y values are 10 more than the y values from Table d.

2. Graph D; its line of symmetry is the y-axis, and it opens upward.

3. Graph C; its line of symmetry is to the right of the origin, and its lowest point is to the right of the origin.

4. Graph A; its line of symmetry is to the left of the origin, and its lowest point is to the left of the origin.

5. Graph B; its line of symmetry is the y-axis, and it opens downward.

6. Graph B; the number multiplied by x^2 is negative, so the graph must open downward.

7. Graph A; the number multiplied by x^2 is positive, so the graph must open upward.

8. No; in the equation for this graph, the number multiplied by x^2 must be positive since the graph opens upward.

9. No; the equation for this graph must have a positive constant since the graph crosses the y-axis above 0.

10. No; the equation for this graph does not have a constant of 1 since the graph crosses the y-axis at 0.

11a. $y = \frac{x^2}{2}$; Since Graph B is wider than Graph A, the number multiplied by x^2 must be less than 1.

11b. $y = 3x^2$; Since Graph C is narrower than Graph A, the number multiplied by x^2 must be greater than 1.

12a. No; Graph X is symmetrical about a vertical line left of the y-axis. The graph of $y = x^2 + 1$ would be symmetrical about the y-axis.

12b. No; Graph Y is symmetrical about the y-axis. The graph $y = (x + 1)^2$ would be symmetrical about the line $x = {}^-1$.

12c. No; Graph Z has its vertex to the left of (0, 1). The graph of $y = {}^-x^2 + 1$ would have its vertex at (0, 1).

13a.

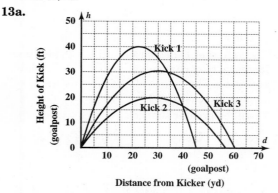

13b. Kick 1: about 40 ft; Kick 2: about 20 ft; Kick 3: about 30 ft

13c. Kick 1: 45 yd; Kick 2: 57 yd; Kick 3: 61 yd

13d. Kick 1 did not reach the goalpost because the ball hit the ground after about 45 yd. Kick 2 reached the goalpost, but passed under the crossbar at a height of about 9 ft when d was 50. Kick 3 could have scored a field goal because it passed over the crossbar at a height of about 18 ft when d was 50.

14. no, no squared variable

15. yes

16. no, no squared variable

17. yes

18. no, no squared variable

19. no, the constant is divided, rather than multiplied, by x^2

20. yes

21. no, contains a cubed variable

22. no, no squared variable

23. no, no squared variable

24a.

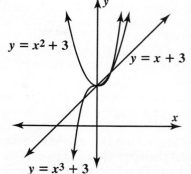

24b. All three graphs pass through (0, 3). The first graph is a line; the others are curves. The second graph has a low point at (0, 3). The third graph changes direction at (0, 3). The second graph is symmetric about the y-axis; the others are not. In the first and third graphs, the y values increase from left to right. In the second graph, the y values decrease until (0, 3), and then increase.

25a. $y = \frac{x^3}{2}$; the graph is wider than the graph of $y = x^3$.

25b. $y = 3x^3$; the graph is narrower than the graph of $y = x^3$.

26a. Tables will vary.

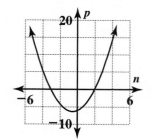

26b. Tables will vary.

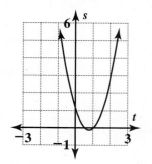

26c. Possible answer: All are parabolas that curve upward, and all have a vertical axis of symmetry near the y-axis.

26d. Possible answer: $y = 3m^2 + 2m + 7$: Lowest point is above and to the left of the origin; line of symmetry is a vertical line to the left of the vertical axis. $p = n^2 + n - 6$: Lowest point is below and slightly to the left of the origin; line of symmetry is a vertical line to the left of the vertical axis. $S = 2t^2 - 3t + 1$: Lowest point is to the right of and slightly below the origin; line of symmetry is a vertical line to the right of the vertical axis.

27a. Graphs A and B represent $y = x^2 + 1$; Graphs C and D represent $y = 2x^2 + 1$. The scales for the horizontal axes are the same for Graphs A and D, showing that Graph D is narrower than Graph A and therefore Graph D represents $y = 2x^2 + 1$ and Graph A represents $y = x^2 + 1$. Similar reasoning shows that Graph C represents $y = 2x^2 + 1$ while Graph B represents $y = x^2 + 1$.

27b. The horizontal scales are different. When plotting the same equation on the different axes, one will be narrower than the other, even though they represent the same equation.

28a. $a = 1, b = {}^-4, c = 0$

28b. $(0, 0)$; The value of c is the y-coordinate of the point where the graph crosses the y-axis.

28c. Tables will vary.

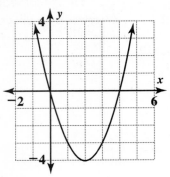

28d. $(0, 0)$; $(4, 0)$

28e. $x(x - 4)$

28f. For $x = 0, y = 0(0 - 4) = 0({}^-4) = 0.$
For $x = 4, y = 4(4 - 4) = 4(0) = 0.$
The x-coordinate of each point makes one of the factors equal to 0.

29a. The third graph; d increases by smaller amounts as h increases.

29b.

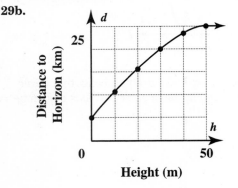

29c. Possible answer: Yes; the graph looks like it could be half of a parabola.

30a.

Stage, n	1	2	3	4
Cubes, C	0	4	18	48

30b. $5 \times 5 \times 4 = 100$

30c. $C = n(n)(n - 1)$, or $C = n^2(n - 1)$, or $C = n^3 - n^2$
Possible explanations: Multiply length × width × height of each design: $n \cdot n \cdot (n - 1)$, which is equivalent to $n^3 - n^2$. Or, if you build a large cube with n^3 unit cubes, and remove one layer (containing n^2 unit cubes), you get a volume of $n^3 - n^2$.

31a.

$2^2 = 4$	$2^2 = 4$
$3^2 = 9$	$2^3 = 8$
$4^2 = 16$	$2^4 = 16$
$5^2 = 25$	$2^5 = 32$
$6^2 = 36$	$2^6 = 64$

x	$^-4$	$^-3$	$^-2$	$^-1$	0	1	2	3	4	5	6
$y = x^2$	16	9	4	1	0	1	4	9	16	25	36
$y = 2^x$	$\frac{1}{16}$	$\frac{1}{8}$	$\frac{1}{4}$	$\frac{1}{2}$	1	2	4	8	16	32	64

31b. 2, 4

31c. $^-4, {}^-3, {}^-2, {}^-1, 3$

31d. 0, 1, 5, 6

31e. The values of x^2 decrease until $x = 0$, and then increase; they change by $^-7, {}^-5, {}^-3, {}^-1, 1, 3,$ and so on. The values of 2^x double each time the x value increases by 1.

31f. 2^x will be greater than x^2.

31g.

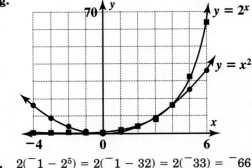

32. $2({}^-1 - 2^5) = 2({}^-1 - 32) = 2({}^-33) = {}^-66$

33. $({}^-3)^2 + ({}^-3)({}^-2) - ({}^-2)^3 = 9 + 6 - ({}^-8)$
$= 9 + 6 + 8 = 23$

34. $({}^-4 - (3 \cdot {}^-4))^3 = ({}^-4 - {}^-12)^3 = 8^3 = 512$

35. $\dfrac{3^3 = 27}{3}$

36. $\dfrac{4^4 = 256}{4}$

37. $\dfrac{({}^-3)^3 = {}^-27}{3}$

38. $\dfrac{8 - 3}{5 + 2} = \dfrac{5}{7}$

39. $\dfrac{0 + 6}{{}^-8 - 0} = \dfrac{6}{{}^-8} = \dfrac{{}^-3}{4}$

40. $\dfrac{2 - 1.5}{0.5 + 3.5} = \dfrac{0.5}{4} = \dfrac{1}{8}$

41. $\dfrac{-2 + 2}{-9 + 7} = \dfrac{0}{-2} = 0$

42a. $9f$

42b. $9f = 108$

42c. $f = 12$

43a. $9 + f + 9 + f$, or $18 + 2f$

43b. $9 + f + 9 + f = 39$, or $18 + 2f = 39$

43c. $2f = 21$
$\quad\ f = 10.5$

44a. $a + 8$

44b. $4(a + 8) - 3$

44c. $4(a + 8) - 3 - 41 = a$ or $4(a + 8) - 3 - a = 41$

44d. $4a + 32 - 3 - a = 41$
$\qquad\quad 3a + 29 = 41$
$\qquad\qquad\ \ 3a = 12$
$\qquad\qquad\quad\ a = 4$

$a + 8 = 4 + 8 = 12$
$4(12) - 3 = 48 - 3 = 45$

She had 4 animal fossils, 12 plant fossils, and 45 insect fossils.

Page 104   In Your Own Words

Possible answer: When the value of a is positive, the graph of $y = ax^2 + c$ is that of a parabola opening upward. If a is negative, the parabola opens downward. The parabola is wider when the absolute value of a is between 0 and 1 and narrower when the absolute value of a is greater than 1. The value of c determines where the graph crosses the y-axis. Positive values of c shift the parabola up and negative values of c shift the parabola down.

2-3 | Inverse Variation

Page 110   Problem Set A

1. Tables will vary.

   The product of x and y must be 2,000 for every pair of values.

   $2{,}000 \div 25 = 80$
   $2{,}000 \div 100 = 20$

x	50	25	100				
y	40	80	20				
Area, xy	2,000	2,000	2,000				

2. Possible answers: $xy = 2{,}000$; $y = \dfrac{2{,}000}{x}$; or $x = \dfrac{2{,}000}{y}$

3.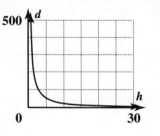

4a.

$2{,}000 \div 40 = 50$	$66.7 - 50 = 16.7$
$2{,}000 \div 50 = 40$	$50 - 40 = 10$
$2{,}000 \div 60 \approx 33.3$	$40 - 33.3 = 6.7$
$2{,}000 \div 70 \approx 28.6$	$33.3 - 28.6 = 4.7$
$2{,}000 \div 80 = 25$	$28.6 - 25 = 3.6$
$2{,}000 \div 90 \approx 22.2$	$25 - 22.2 = 2.8$
$2{,}000 \div 100 = 20$	$22.2 - 20 = 2.2$

x	20	30	40	50	60	70	80	90	100
y	100	66.7	50	40	33.3	28.6	25	22.2	20
Decrease in y	—	33.3	16.7	10	6.7	4.7	3.6	2.8	2.2

4b. a decreasing amount

4c. y is divided in half; y is divided by 3; y is divided by N.

4d. y gets very large; y gets very small.

Page 111   Problem Set B

1. $240 \div \dfrac{1}{2} = 480$
   $240 \div 240 = 1$
   $240 \div 2 = 120$
   $240 \div 48 = 5$
   $240 \div 10 = 24$
   $240 \div 20 = 12$
   $240 \div 8 = 30$

Hours of Work	$\frac{1}{2}$	1	2	5	10	20	30
Hourly Pay Rate	\$480	\$240	\$120	\$48	\$24	\$12	\$8

2. Possible equations: $dh = 240$, $h = \dfrac{240}{d}$, or $d = \dfrac{240}{h}$

3.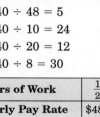

Pages 111–112   Problem Set C

1. $y = \dfrac{3}{x}$

2. Possible table:

x	-6	-0.1	0.01	0.5	-1	2	4	5	7	7.5	10
$y = \dfrac{3}{x}$	-0.5	-30	300	6	-3	1.5	0.75	0.6	0.43	0.4	0.3

3. There is no value of y when $x = 0$ (it is undefined); I get an error message.

4. The graph can't cross the y-axis since x can't be 0.

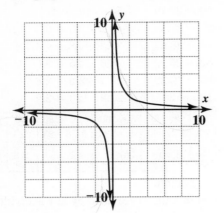

5. Possible answer: In both, the product of two variables is constant. As the value of one variable decreases, the value of the other increases. The shape of the part of this graph in Quadrant I is similar to the shape of the yardwork graph. However, in this situation, we considered both positive and negative values, so the graph has two parts: one in Quadrant I and one in Quadrant III.

Page 112   Share and Summarize

1. Possible answer: The equations are all of the form $xy = \text{constant}$ $\left(\text{or } y = \dfrac{\text{constant}}{x}, \text{ or } x = \dfrac{\text{constant}}{y}\right)$; they differ in the value of the constant.

2. All are curves that approach the x- and y-axes without ever touching them. They differ in the scales used on the x- and y-axes, and in the points they pass through. The graphs for Problem Sets A and B are only in Quadrant I because the situations don't make sense for negative values. The graph for Problem Set C consists of a curve in Quadrant I and a curve in Quadrant III.

Pages 113–114   Problem Set D

1a. $\dfrac{1}{2}$

1b. $\dfrac{1}{5}$

1c. $^{-}1$

1d. 3

1e. $\dfrac{4}{3}$

1f. $\dfrac{^{-}7}{9}$

1g. $\dfrac{3}{7}$

1h. $\dfrac{^{-}1}{10}$

2a. $2, 5, ^{-}1, \dfrac{1}{3}, \dfrac{3}{4}, \dfrac{^{-}9}{7}, \dfrac{7}{3}, ^{-}10$

2b. The reciprocals of the answers are the original numbers.

3. $\dfrac{1}{x}$

4. $\dfrac{1}{\frac{1}{x}} = x$

5. $\dfrac{1}{\frac{1}{x}} = x$

6a. $\dfrac{1}{8} = 0.125$

6b. $\dfrac{1}{100} = 0.01$

6c. $\dfrac{1}{0.2} = 5$

6d. $\dfrac{1}{^{-}0.25} = ^{-}4$

6e. $\dfrac{1}{12} \approx 0.0833$

6f. $\dfrac{1}{7.5} \approx 0.1333$

6g. $\dfrac{1}{^{-}1} = ^{-}1$

6h. $\dfrac{1}{0.0004} = 2{,}500$

7a. $8, 100, 0.2, ^{-}0.25, 12, 7.5, ^{-}1, 0.0004$

7b. The reciprocals of the answers are the original numbers.

8a. y is halved; y is divided by 3; y is divided by 4; y is doubled.

8b. Yes; the product of xy is a constant, 1.

8c.

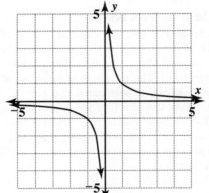

Page 114   Problem Set E

1. y is halved; y is divided by 3; y is divided by 4; y is doubled.

2. Yes; the product of xy is a constant, 5.

3. There is no value of y when $x = 0$, because you can't divide by 0. The calculator gives an error message.

4.

x	-5	-4	-3	-2	-1	$-\dfrac{1}{2}$	$-\dfrac{1}{4}$	0
$y = \dfrac{1}{x}$	$-\dfrac{1}{5}$	$-\dfrac{1}{4}$	$-\dfrac{1}{3}$	$-\dfrac{1}{2}$	-1	-2	-4	—
$y = \dfrac{5}{x}$	-1	$-\dfrac{5}{4}$	$-\dfrac{5}{3}$	$-\dfrac{5}{2}$	-5	-10	-20	—

x	$\dfrac{1}{4}$	$\dfrac{1}{2}$	1	2	3	4	5
$y = \dfrac{1}{x}$	4	2	1	$\dfrac{1}{2}$	$\dfrac{1}{3}$	$\dfrac{1}{4}$	$\dfrac{1}{5}$
$y = \dfrac{5}{x}$	20	10	5	$\dfrac{5}{2}$	$\dfrac{5}{3}$	$\dfrac{5}{4}$	1

5.

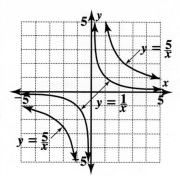

Page 115   Problem Set F
1. yes
2. no, quadratic
3. no, linear
4. no, linear
5. yes
6. yes
7a. linear, because as x increases by 1, y changes by a constant amount, $^-5$
7b. $y = {}^-5x$
8a. quadratic, because q is 1 added to x^2
8b. $q = p^2 + 1$
9a. reciprocal, because the product of each pair of t and r is the same, 1.5
9b. $rt = 1.5$

Page 115   Share and Summarize
1. If the product is the same for every pair of values, the variables are inversely proportional.
2. Possible answer: If the equation can be written in the form $xy = a$, the variables are inversely proportional.

Pages 118–119   Problem Set G
1. *Family A:* For positive a, the graph is in Quadrants I and III; for negative a, in Quadrants II and IV. The greater the absolute value of a, the farther the graph is from the origin and the more slowly the graph approaches the axes.

   Family B: Each graph approaches but does not touch the x-axis and the vertical line $x = {}^-b$.

   Family C: Each graph approaches but does not touch the y-axis and the horizontal line $y = c$.
2. *Family A:* It changes the quadrants the graph is in (I and III for positive a, II and IV for negative a).

   Family B: The vertical line the graph approaches is to the left of the y-axis for positive b values and to the right of the y-axis for negative b values.

   Family C: The horizontal line the graph approaches is above the x-axis for positive c values and below the x-axis for negative c values.
3. *Family A:* 0, for any value of a

   Family B: ^-b

   Family C: 0, for any value of c

4. *Family A:* 0, for any value of a

   Family B: 0, for any value of b

   Family C: c, for any value of c
5. *Family A:* $x = 0$, for any value of a

   Family B: $x = {}^-b$

   Family C: $x = 0$, for any value of c
6. Possible answer: They are all hyperbolas. They have the same general shape as the graph of $y = \frac{1}{x}$. They are farther up or down or left or right. In Family A, with negative values of a, the graph is in Quadrants II and IV instead of I and III.

Page 119   Share and Summarize
1. In both cases, the value of a affects the width of the graph.
2. In both cases, positive values of b move the graph to the left; negative values move it to the right.
3. In both cases, the value of c moves the graph up (for positive values) or down (for negative values).

Pages 120–126   On Your Own Exercises
1a. Tables will vary. All pairs should have a product of $3.00.
1b.
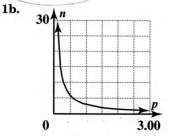
1c. n is halved; n is divided by 3; n is divided by 4.
1d. n is doubled; n is multiplied by 4.
1e. $pn = 3.00$
2a.

n	1	2	3	4	5	6	7	8	9	10	11	12
f	1	$\frac{1}{2}$	$\frac{1}{3}$	$\frac{1}{4}$	$\frac{1}{5}$	$\frac{1}{6}$	$\frac{1}{7}$	$\frac{1}{8}$	$\frac{1}{9}$	$\frac{1}{10}$	$\frac{1}{11}$	$\frac{1}{12}$

2b.
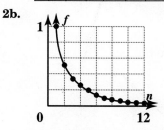
2c. Possible equations: $nf = 1$, $n = \frac{1}{f}$, or $f = \frac{1}{n}$
3a. $y = \frac{10}{x}$
3b. Tables will vary, but all (x, y) pairs should have a product of 10.
3c. There is no y value corresponding to $x = 0$. There is no number you can multiply 0 by to get 10.

3d.

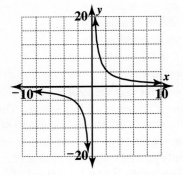

4. yes

5. no, linear

6. no, quadratic

7. no, linear

8. yes

9. yes

10a. $0.5 \cdot 60 = 30$

$1 \cdot 30 = 30$

$2 \cdot 15 = 30$

$3 \cdot 10 = 30$

$4 \cdot 7.5 = 30$

$5 \cdot 6 = 30$

$10 \cdot 3 = 30$

Yes; the product of m and n is constant.

10b.

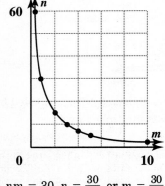

10c. $nm = 30$, $n = \frac{30}{m}$, or $m = \frac{30}{n}$

11a. $0.5 \cdot 0.25 = 0.125$

$1 \cdot 0.5 = 0.5$

No; xy is not constant.

11b.

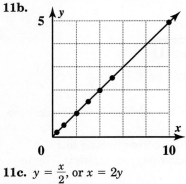

11c. $y = \frac{x}{2}$, or $x = 2y$

12a. $0.25 \cdot 0.5 = 0.125$

$0.5 \cdot 0.25 = 0.125$

$0.75 \cdot 0.25 \approx 0.125$

$1 \cdot 0.125 = 0.125$

$1.25 \cdot 0.1 = 0.125$

$1.5 \cdot 0.0833 \approx 0.125$

$2 \cdot 0.0625 = 0.125$

Yes; the product of t and r is constant.

12b.

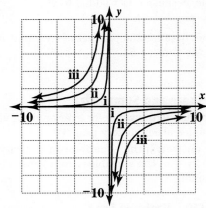

12c. $rt = 0.125$, $r = \frac{0.125}{t}$, or $t = \frac{0.125}{r}$

13a. Yes; the product of p and n (where n is an integer) is constant, $4.

13b. $pn = 4$

14a. No; the product of p and n is not constant.

14b. $p = 4n$

15a. No, the product of m and n is not constant.

15b. $0.40m + 0.80n = 8.00$

16a.

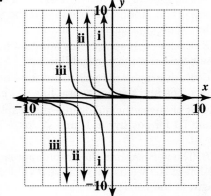

16b. Possible answer: The two parts of the graph move away from the origin.

17a.

17b. The graphs move to the left. The value that x approaches—but never reaches—is equal to ^-b.

18a.

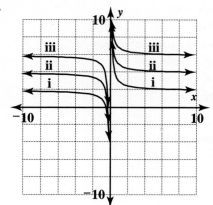

18b. The graphs move upward . The value that y approaches—but never reaches—is equal to c.

19a. Answers will vary. Realistic estimates are light plane: 120 mph; horseback: 10 mph; bicycle: 15 mph; but any values will do.

19b. Tables will vary, but the product of speed and time must be 500 in each case.

$500 \div 30 \approx 16.7$

$500 \div 50 = 10$

$500 \div 85 \approx 5.9$

$500 \div 1,100 \approx 0.45$

Speed (mph)	30	50	85	1,100
Travel Time (h)	16.7	10	5.9	0.45

19c. Possible equations: $ST = 500$, $T = \dfrac{500}{S}$, or $S = \dfrac{500}{T}$

19d.

Speed vs. Travel Time

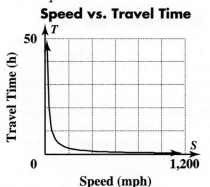

19e. They decrease.

19f. no, because there is no number you can multiply 0 by to get 500

19g. $186,000 \cdot 60 \cdot 60 = 11,160,000$

The speed of light is 669,600,000 miles per hour.

$S = \dfrac{500}{T} = \dfrac{500}{669,600,000} \approx 0.00000075$

$0.00000075 \cdot 60 \approx 0.000045$

$0.000045 \cdot 60 \approx 0.0027$

0.0027 s, or 0.000045 min, or 0.00000075 h; It is highly unlikely that the speed axis on a student's graph will extend this far.

19h. $S = \dfrac{500}{T}$

20a.

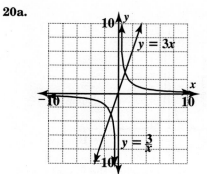

20b. For $y = 3x$, y increases at a steady rate; for $y = \dfrac{3}{x}$, y decreases; the decrease is less and less as x increases.

20c. $y = 3x$ grows closer to $(0, 0)$; $y = \dfrac{3}{x}$ increases, but the graph never actually crosses the y-axis.

20d. $y = 3x$ passes through the origin, but $y = \dfrac{3}{x}$ is not defined (has no y value).

21a.

Organ Pipes

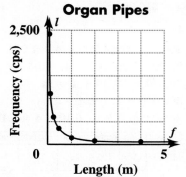

21b. about 0.4 m

21c. about 50 cps

21d. It appears to be a hyperbola, suggesting an inverse variation.

21e. Possible answer: $l = \dfrac{156}{f}$; the last four points don't fit this equation exactly, but that could be due to inaccuracies in measuring lengths or frequencies.

22a. $x - 1 = 0$

$\quad x = 1$

The equation is undefined when $x = 1$.

22b. $1 - 2x = 0$

$\quad {}^{-}2x = {}^{-}1$

$\quad x = \dfrac{1}{2}$

The equation is undefined when $x = \dfrac{1}{2}$.

22c. $x + 2 = 0$

$\quad x = {}^{-}2$

The equation is undefined when $x = {}^{-}2$.

22d. $x = 0$

The equation is undefined when $x = 0$.

22e. defined for all x values

22f. $3x - 12 = 0$

$\quad 3x = 12$

$\quad x = 4$

The equation is undefined when $x = 4$.

23a. Tables will vary.

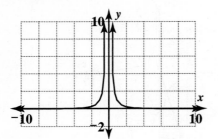

23b. It is a curve that approaches the x- and y-axes without ever reaching them.

23c. Possible answers: It is symmetrical about the y-axis. It has no negative values of y. It gets close to the x-axis more quickly than the graph of $y = \dfrac{1}{x}$. It gets close to the x-axis faster than to the y-axis, while the graph of $y = \dfrac{1}{x}$ approaches both axes at the same rate.

24a. $200{,}000 \div 20 = \$10{,}000$

24b. $10{,}000 + \$4 = \$10{,}004$

24c. $\dfrac{200{,}000}{n} + 4$

24d. $200{,}000 \div 200 = 1{,}000;\ 1{,}000 + 4 = 1{,}004$
$200{,}000 \div 2{,}000 = 100;\ 100 + 4 = 104$
$200{,}000 \div 20{,}000 = 10;\ 10 + 4 = 14$
$200{,}000 \div 200{,}000 = 1;\ 1 + 4 = 5$
$200{,}000 \div 2{,}000{,}000 = 0.10;\ 0.10 + 4 = 4.10$

Units	20	200	2,000	20,000	200,000	2,000,000
Average Total Cost per unit ($)	10,004	1,004	104	14	5	4.10

24e. $4

24f. over 200,000; over 20,000,000

25. $\dfrac{2}{3}x - \dfrac{5}{8} = 2y$
$2y = \dfrac{2}{3}x - \dfrac{5}{8}$
$y = \dfrac{1}{3}x - \dfrac{5}{16}$

26. $3y - 4x - 1 = 8x - 2y$
$5y = 12x + 1$
$y = \dfrac{12}{5}x + \dfrac{1}{5}$

27. $4(x + y) - 6(5 - x) = 6$
$4x + 4y - 30 + 6x = 6$
$4y = {}^{-}10x + 36$
$y = \dfrac{{}^{-}5}{2}x + 9$

28. $\dfrac{7(y + 5)}{x + 2} = 10$
$7(y + 5) = 10(x + 2)$
$7y + 35 = 10x + 20$
$7y = 10x - 15$
$y = \dfrac{10}{7}x - \dfrac{15}{7}$

29. $a + 4a - 8 = 5a - 8$

30. $2b - 8 - 2b = {}^{-}8$

31. $90 - 5c + 1 = 91 - 5c$

32. $8d + 4de - 6 - 4d = 4d + 4de - 6$

33. ${}^{-}7 + 7f + 14f + 4 - 9f - 18 = 12f - 21$

34. Possible equation: $y = 2x$

35. $2n = 4m$
$n = 2m$
Possible equation: $n = 2m + 3$

36. $2(y - 3) = 7x + 1$
$2y - 6 = 7x + 1$
$2y = 7x + 7$
$y = \dfrac{7}{2}x + \dfrac{7}{2}$
Possible equation: $y = \dfrac{7}{2}x$

37. Possible equation: $x = 1$

38a. $3s + 5c$

38b. $3s + 5c = 60$

38c.

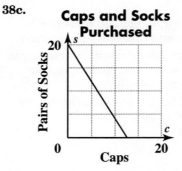

Caps and Socks Purchased

38d. $(0, 20)$; $(3, 15)$; $(6, 10)$; $(9, 5)$; $(12, 0)$

39. The sample space is BY, BG, BG, YB, YG, YG, GB, GY, GG, GB, GY, GG. Two green (G) marbles occurs twice out of 12 possible outcomes. $\dfrac{2}{12}$, or $\dfrac{1}{6}$

40. $6 \cdot 3 + 5 \cdot 7 = 18 + 35 = 53\text{ ft}^2$

Page 125 In Your Own Words

Possible answer: An inverse variation is a relationship in which the product of the two variables is fixed. Given a table of values for two variables, you can tell that the relationship between the two variables could be an inverse variation if the product for every pair of values is the same. The relationship between the two variables, x and y, is an inverse variation if the equation can be written in the form $xy = a$, where a is a constant. A written description of an inverse variation suggests that as one variable increases by a fixed amount, the other variable decreases by a decreasing amount.

2-4 Conjectures

Pages 128–129 Problem Set A

1. ${}^{-}5 - ({}^{-}3) = {}^{-}5 + 3 = {}^{-}2$
${}^{-}7 - ({}^{-}5) = {}^{-}7 + 5 = {}^{-}2$
${}^{-}9 - ({}^{-}7) = {}^{-}9 + 7 = {}^{-}2$
${}^{-}11 - ({}^{-}9) = {}^{-}11 + 9 = {}^{-}2$
All the missing differences are ${}^{-}2$.

2. They're constant.

3. Possible answer: For quadratic equations, second differences are constant.

Pages 129–130   Problem Set B

1. $D = (4 + 1)^2 - 4^2 = 5^2 - 4^2 = 25 - 16 = 9$

    $D = (5 + 1)^2 - 5^2 = 6^2 - 5^2 = 36 - 25 = 11$

    $D = (6 + 1)^2 - 6^2 = 7^2 - 6^2 = 49 - 36 = 13$

    $D = (7 + 1)^2 - 7^2 = 8^2 - 7^2 = 64 - 49 = 15$

    $D = (8 + 1)^2 - 8^2 = 9^2 - 8^2 = 81 - 64 = 17$

n	1	2	3	4	5	6	7	8
D	3	5	7	9	11	13	15	17

2. The first differences are constant, so the relationship is linear.

3. $D = 2n + 1$

4a.

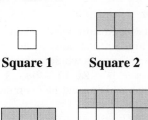

Square 1   Square 2

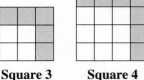

Square 3   Square 4

4b. 3, 5, 7

4c. $2n + 1$; Possible explanation: n are added along the side, n along the top, and 1 in the corner.

4d. Possible explanation: $D = (n + 1)^2 - n^2$ is the number of tiles added to get from Square n to Square $n + 1$. In Part c, I found that $2n + 1$ tiles are added, so $D = 2n + 1$.

Page 130   Share and Summarize

1. Constant first differences indicate a linear relationship; constant second differences indicate a quadratic relationship.

2. Possible answer: Because first differences were constant, I knew the relationship was linear. I then used what I knew about linear equations to determine the equation.

3. Possible answer: I know that squares of whole numbers can be represented by squares made from tiles. By looking at how the number of tiles changes as the side length increases by 1 tile, I found an equation for the difference of consecutive square numbers.

Page 131   Problem Set C

1. $1^2 - 1 + 41 = 41$

    $2^2 - 2 + 41 = 43$

    $3^2 - 3 + 41 = 47$

    $4^2 - 4 + 41 = 53$

    These are all prime numbers.

2. Answers will vary. For $n = 1, 2, \ldots, 40$, the result is prime. Other numbers will give prime results as well.

3. Answers will vary.

4. $41^2 - 41 + 41 = 1{,}681$

    $1{,}681 \div 41 = 41$

    41 is a factor of 1,681.

    no

5. Possible answers: The expression $41^2 - 41 + 41$ is equal to 41^2, which isn't prime because a square number cannot be prime. *Or,* since each term has 41 as a factor, 41 must be a factor of the expression.

Pages 132–133   Problem Set D

1. Answers will vary.

2a. Dante is right. Kai's proof assumes that the two odd numbers being added are equal.

2b. Write the first odd number as $2k + 1$ and the second as $2m + 1$. Their sum is $2k + 2m + 2$. Using the distributive property, this is equal to $2(k + m + 1)$. Since this is a multiple of 2, it is even.

3. Possible answer: The sum of an odd number and an even number is odd. Proof: The odd number can be written $2n + 1$, where n is a whole number. The even number can be written $2m$, where m is a whole number. Their sum is $2(n + m) + 1$. The part $2(n + m)$ is even because it is a multiple of 2, so $2(n + m) + 1$ must be odd.

Page 133   Problem Set E

1. $yx = a$, where a is some constant

    $zx = b$, where b is some constant

    $x = \dfrac{b}{z}$

    $yx = a$

    $y\left(\dfrac{b}{z}\right) = a$

    $by = az$

    $y = \dfrac{a}{b}z$, where $\dfrac{a}{b}$ is some constant

    Answers will vary. The relationship between y and z is linear.

2a. $y = \dfrac{a}{x}$, $xy = a$, or $x = \dfrac{a}{y}$

2b. $z = \dfrac{b}{x}$, $xz = b$, or $x = \dfrac{b}{z}$

3. $x = \dfrac{a}{y}$ and $x = \dfrac{b}{z}$

4. The two expressions for x must be equal; $\dfrac{a}{y} = \dfrac{b}{z}$.

5. Possible answer: $y = \dfrac{az}{b}$ or $y = \left(\dfrac{a}{b}\right)z$, so the relationship is linear. This proves my conjecture.

Page 133   Share and Summarize

1. Possible answer: A formula might work for a great number of cases but not be true in general. Before you can be sure it always works, you have to find a way to prove it.

2. Possible answer: You might have overlooked something or made a mistake in your proof. Someone who is not immediately inclined to agree would be more likely to find an error if there is one.

Pages 134–138   On Your Own Exercises

1.

x	1	2	3	4	5	6	7
y	⁻1	4	15	32	55	84	119
1st Differences		5	11	17	23	29	35
2nd Differences			6	6	6	6	6

Quadratic; second differences are constant.

2.

x	1	2	3	4	5	6	7
y	4	16	64	256	1,024	4,096	16,384
1st Differences		12	48	192	768	3,072	12,288
2nd Differences			36	144	576	2,304	9,216

Neither; neither first nor second differences are constant.

3.

x	1	2	3	4	5	6	7
y	6	8	10	12	14	16	18
1st Differences		2	2	2	2	2	2

Linear; first differences are constant.

4.

x	1	2	3	4	5	6	7
y	4	12	24	40	60	84	112
1st Differences		8	12	16	20	24	28
2nd Differences			4	4	4	4	4

Quadratic; second differences are constant.

5. $y = 2x + 4$

6a. $d = (4 + 2)^2 - 4^2 = 6^2 - 4^2 = 36 - 16 = 20$
$d = (5 + 2)^2 - 5^2 = 7^2 - 5^2 = 49 - 25 = 24$
$d = (6 + 2)^2 - 6^2 = 8^2 - 6^2 = 64 - 36 = 28$

m	1	2	3	4	5	6
d	8	12	16	20	24	28

6b. First differences are constant, so the relationship is linear.

6c. $d = 4m + 4$

6d.

Square 1   Square 3

6e.

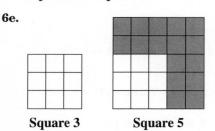

Square 3   Square 5

6f. Two rows of n tiles are added on top, two rows of n tiles are added on the side, and a 2×2 square is added in the corner, for a total of $2n + 2n + 4$ tiles, or $4n + 4$ tiles.

6g. yes; Possible explanation: $d = (n + 2)^2 - n^2$ is the number of tiles added to get from the square for n^2 to the square for $(n + 2)^2$. In part f, I found that $4n + 4$ tiles are added.

7a. He used the variable m in the expressions for both the odd number and the even number. If $2m$ is the even number, $2m + 1$ is the next whole number. It does not represent *any* odd number.

7b. Let $2m$ be the even number and $2n + 1$ be the odd number; then odd − even $= 2n + 1 - 2m$ $= 2(n - m) + 1$. Since $2(n - m)$ must be even, $2(n - m) + 1$ must be odd.

8. The difference of two even numbers is even. Proof: Let $2m$ and $2n$ be two even numbers, where m and n are whole numbers. Then, $2n - 2m = 2(n - m)$, which must be even since it has 2 as a factor.

9. The difference of two odd numbers is even. Proof: Let $2k + 1$ and $2m + 1$ be two odd numbers, where k and m are whole numbers. Then, $2k + 1 - (2m + 1) = 2k + 1 - 2m - 1 = 2k - 2m = 2(k - m)$, which must be even since it has 2 as a factor.

10. $(1 + 2)^2 \stackrel{?}{=} 1^2 + 2^2$
$\qquad 3^2 \stackrel{?}{=} 1 + 4$
$\qquad 9 \neq 5$

Possible answer: If $m = 1$ and $n = 2$, then $(m + n)^2 = 9$ but $m^2 + n^2 = 5$.

11a. The reciprocal of x is $\frac{1}{x}$, and the reciprocal of y is $\frac{1}{y}$. Multiplying gives $\left(\frac{1}{x}\right)\left(\frac{1}{y}\right)$, which is $\frac{1}{xy}$. This is the reciprocal of xy.

11b. Possible counterexample: If $x = 1$ and $y = 2$, then $\frac{1}{x} + \frac{1}{y} = \frac{3}{2}$, but $\frac{1}{x + y} = \frac{1}{3}$.

12a. $18 - 12 = 6$
$24 - 18 = 6$
$30 - 24 = 6$
$36 - 30 = 6$

Third differences are constant (6).

12b. Possible answer: For a cubic equation, third differences are constant.

12c. Possible answer: For a quartic equation, fourth differences are constant.

x	1	2	3	4	5	6	7
y	1	16	81	256	625	1,296	2,401
1st Differences		15	65	175	369	671	1,105
2nd Differences			50	110	194	302	434
3rd Differences				60	84	108	132
4th Differences					24	24	24

13a. 1

x	1	2	3	4	5	6	7
y	2.5	6	10.5	16	22.5	30	38.5
1st Differences		3.5	4.5	5.5	6.5	7.5	8.5
2nd Differences			1	1	1	1	1

13b. ⁻2

x	1	2	3	4	5	6	7
y	0	⁻1	⁻4	⁻9	⁻16	⁻25	⁻36
1st Differences		⁻1	⁻3	⁻5	⁻7	⁻9	⁻11
2nd Differences			⁻2	⁻2	⁻2	⁻2	⁻2

13c. 6

x	1	2	3	4	5	6	7
y	−6	3	18	39	66	99	138
1st Differences		9	15	21	27	33	39
2nd Differences			6	6	6	6	6

13d. The constant second difference is twice the coefficient of x^2.

13e. Answers will vary.

14a. Possible answers:

$10 = 5 + 5$

$12 = 5 + 7$

$100 = 47 + 53$

14b. yes

14c. that it works for every even number

15. True; $n^2 - n = n(n - 1)$. If n is even, the product is even. If n is odd, $n - 1$ is even and the product is still even.

16. True; if n is even, it can be written as $2k$, where k is a whole number. Then, $n^2 = 2k \cdot 2k = 4k^2$, so n^2 is a multiple of 4.

17. false; Possible counterexample: $2^2 - 1^2 = 4 - 1 = 3$, which is odd.

18. No; the first two points lie on line $x = 0$. The third point does not lie on that line. Therefore, the points do not lie on a line.

19. Find the equation of the line defined by two of the points.

$(0.3, {}^-2); ({}^-1, 4.5)$

rise $= 4.5 + 2 = 6.5$

run $= {}^-1 - 0.3 = {}^-1.3$

slope $= \dfrac{\text{rise}}{\text{run}} = \dfrac{6.5}{{}^-1.3} = {}^-5$

$y = {}^-5x + b, (0.3, {}^-2)$

${}^-2 = {}^-5(0.3) + b$

${}^-2 = {}^-1.5 + b$

$b = {}^-0.5$

$y = {}^-5x - 0.5$

Substitute the third point into the equation.

$y = {}^-5x - 0.5, (10.1, {}^-51)$

${}^-51 = {}^-5(10.1) - 0.5$

${}^-51 = {}^-50.5 - 0.5$

${}^-51 = {}^-51$ ✓

yes

20. Find the equation of the line defined by two of the points.

$({}^-3, {}^-14.8); (0, {}^-7.3)$

rise $= {}^-7.3 + 14.8 = 7.5$

run $= 0 + 3 = 3$

slope $= \dfrac{\text{rise}}{\text{run}} = \dfrac{7.5}{3} = 2.5$

$y = 2.5x + b, ({}^-3, {}^-14.8)$

${}^-14.8 = 2.5({}^-3) + b$

${}^-14.8 = {}^-7.5 + b$

$b = {}^-7.3$

$y = 2.5x - 7.3$

Substitute the third point into the equation.

$y = 2.5x - 7.3, (1.4, {}^-3.8)$

${}^-3.8 = 2.5(1.4) - 7.3$

${}^-3.8 = 3.5 - 7.3$

${}^-3.8 = {}^-3.8$ ✓

yes

21.

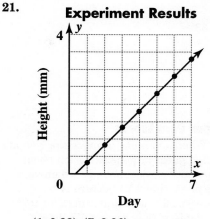

Experiment Results

Height (mm) vs. Day

$(1, 0.38); (7, 3.36)$

rise $= 3.36 - 0.38 = 2.98$

run $= 7 - 1 = 6$

slope $= \dfrac{\text{rise}}{\text{run}} = \dfrac{2.98}{6} \approx 0.5$

$y = 0.5x + b, (1, 0.38)$

$0.38 = 0.5(1) + b$

$0.38 = 0.5 + b$

$b = {}^-0.12$

$y = 0.5x - 0.12$

Possible equation: $y = 0.5x - 0.12$.

22a. $\dfrac{1}{4}$

22b. $\dfrac{{}^-6}{2} = {}^-3$

22c. $\dfrac{3}{10}$

22d. $\dfrac{3}{3} = 1$

22e. $\dfrac{{}^-3}{2} = \dfrac{{}^-3}{2}$

23a. $8 + 3.5r$, where r is the number of rides

23b. $8 + 3.5r = 30$

$3.5r = 22$

$r \approx 6.286$

You can take 6 rides.

24. putting it back; Possible explanation: The probabilities don't change each time, which they would if you kept the drawn marble. Also, Neeraj keeps rolling the die, so the simulation can't represent keeping them out, if it did, it would end after three draws.

25a. $8 \div 4 = 2$

$1.3 < 2 < 2.5$

no

25b. $7 \div 6 \approx 1.17$

$1.17 < 1.3$

yes

25c. $11.4 \div 5 = 2.28$

$1.3 < 2.28 < 2.5$

no

25d. $7 > 6\frac{1}{8}$

$7 \div 7 = 1$

$1 < 1.3$

yes

25e. $10 \div 3 \approx 3.33$

$3.33 > 2.5$

yes

25f. $12 > 11\frac{1}{2}$

yes

Page 136   In Your Own Words

Possible answer: When you *make a conjecture,* you are making an educated guess or generalization about something. A conjecture can be made based on very little evidence. To *prove* that a conjecture is true requires you to present a convincing argument to explain why your conjecture is correct. While a conjecture can suggest that something is true based on a few test cases, proving something true requires an explanation that shows why that conjecture is true for every possible case.

Review and Self-Assessment

Pages 139–143   Strategies and Applications

1. Yes; the graph appears to be a parabola.
2. No; the graph has two separate curves.
3. Yes; the graph appears to be a parabola.
4.

x	$^-3$	$^-2$	$^-1$	0	1	2	3
y	$^-10$	$^-7$	$^-4$	$^-1$	2	5	8
1st Differences		3	3	3	3	3	3

No; first differences are constant, so the relationship is linear.

5.

x	$^-2$	$^-1$	0	1	2	3	4
y	$^-4$	$^-5$	$^-4$	$^-1$	4	11	20
1st Differences		$^-1$	1	3	5	7	9
2nd Differences			2	2	2	2	2

Yes; second differences are constant.

6.

x	0	1	2	3	4	5	6
y	1	2	4	8	16	32	64
1st Differences		1	2	4	8	16	32
2nd Differences			1	2	4	8	16

No; second differences are not constant.

7. No; there is no cubed variable.
8. Yes; using the distributive property gives $y = x^2 + 2$.
9. No; the variable is the exponent.

10. Graph b, because its vertex is at the origin and it opens upward
11. Graph c, because its vertex is at the origin and it opens downward
12. Graph a, because its vertex is shifted to the right 2 units; The equation is factored form is $y = (x - 2)^2$.
13. Graph d, because its vertex is shifted up 4 units
14. No; the graph is linear.
15. Yes; the graph has two separate curves; in each curve, one variable seems to approach a particular value as the other variable increases.
16. No; y drops by a constant amount for each \$5 increase in x, so the relationship is linear.
17. Yes; the product of x and y must be 60, a constant.
18. $1 \cdot 60 = 60$

$2 \cdot 30 = 60$

$4 \cdot 15 = 60$

$5 \cdot 12 = 60$

$6 \cdot 10 = 60$

$9 \cdot 6\frac{2}{3} = 60$

$10 \cdot 6 = 60$

Yes; $xy = 60$ for all pairs.
19. $0.5 \cdot 840 = 420$

$1 \cdot 420 = 420$

$1.5 \cdot 280 = 420$

$2 \cdot 210 = 420$

$2.5 \cdot 168 = 420$

$3 \cdot 140 = 420$

$3.5 \cdot 120 = 420$

Yes; $xy = 420$ for all pairs.
20. $xy = \frac{7}{2}$

Yes; the product xy must be $\frac{7}{2}$, a constant.
21. No; this is a linear relationship.
22. Yes; this can be written $x = \frac{1}{y} - 2$.
23a. 12 s, 90 decibels
23b. $21 - 3 = 18$

about 18 s; The noise level is 70 at about $t = 3$ and $t = 21$.
23c. about 25 s
24a. $t = \frac{120}{n}$
24b. $t = \frac{120}{8} = 15$ min
24c. $10 = \frac{120}{n}$

$n = 12$
25a. $3 \cdot 5 = 15 \qquad 4^2 = 16$

$5 \cdot 7 = 35 \qquad 6^2 = 36$

$0 \cdot 2 = 0 \qquad 1^2 = 1$

$9 \cdot 11 = 99 \qquad 10^2 = 100$

The product of first and last numbers is 1 less than the square of the middle number.
25b. $x - 1$ and $x + 1$

$(x - 1)(x + 1) = x^2 - 1$

25c. Possible proof: If x is an integer, the product of $x - 1$ and $x + 1$ is the area of a rectangle made from square tiles, with dimensions $x - 1$ and $x + 1$.

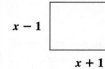

Removing the last column of $x - 1$ tiles leaves a rectangle with dimensions $x - 1$ and x.

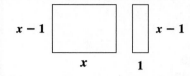

Placing the $x - 1$ tiles across the top gives a figure that is only 1 tile away from being a square with sides x. So, $(x + 1)(x - 1) = x^2 - 1$.

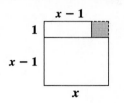

Page 143   Demonstrating Skills

26.

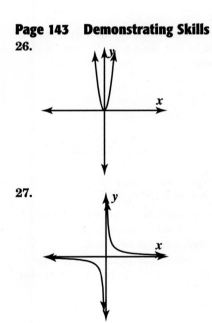

27.

28.

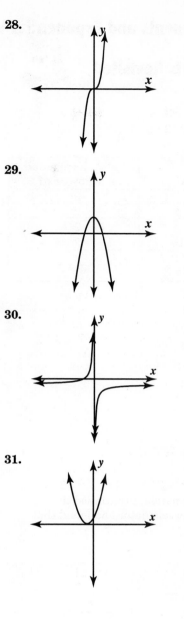

29.

30.

31.

Chapter 3 Exponents and Exponential Variation

3-1 | Exponents Revisited

Page 147   Problem Set A

1a. $128 = 2 \cdot 2 \cdot 2 \cdot 2 \cdot 2 \cdot 2 \cdot 2 = 2^7$

1b.

Position in Sequence	Value	Value Expressed as a Power of 2
1	2	2^1
2	4	2^2
3	8	2^3
4	16	2^4
5	32	2^5
n	?	2^n

2^n

1c. $6,002 \div 2 = 3,001$

$3,001 \div 2 = 1,500.5$

2 is not a factor of 3,001.

No; it is not a power of 2.

prime factor method

1d. $2^8 = 256$

$2^9 = 512$

$2^{10} = 1,024$

$2^{11} = 2,048$

$2^{12} = 4,096$

$2^{13} = 8,192$

$2^{14} = 16,384$

yes; Possible explanation: I continued the sequence using my calculator and found that 16,384 is 2^{14}.

2a. $4^1 = 4$

$4^2 = 16$

$4^3 = 64$

$4^4 = 256$

$4^5 = 1,024$

$4^6 = 4,096$

$4^7 = 16,384$

$4^8 = 65,536$

$4^9 = 262,144$

$4^{10} = 1,048,576$

2b. $2,048,296 \div 4 = 512,074$

$512,074 \div 4 = 128,018.5$

4 is not a factor of 512,074.

No; it is not a power of 4.

prime factor method

2c. yes; Possible explanations: It is a power of 2 and of 4. *Or*, if it's a power of 4, it must also be a power of 2.

2d. $4^6 = 4,096$

4,096 is a power of 4.

$8,192 \div 4 = 2,048$

$2,048 \div 4 = 512$

$512 \div 4 = 128$

$128 \div 4 = 32$

$32 \div 4 = 8$

$8 \div 4 = 2$

$2 \div 4 = 0.5$ ✓

4 is not a factor of 2.

8,192 is not a power of 4.

2e. Possible explanation: 4 is a power of 2, so all powers of 4 are repeated multiplications of 2. That means they're also powers of 2.

Pages 147–148   Problem Set B

1. $2^{11} = 2,048$

sometimes true, $n = 11$

2. $3^9 = 19,683$

$3^{10} = 59,049$

$3^{11} = 177,147$

$3^{12} = 531,441$

$3^{13} = 1,594,323$

sometimes true, $n \leq 12$

3. $4^5 = 1,024$

$4^6 = 4,096$

never true

4. $0.5^1 = 0.5$

$0.5^2 = 0.25$

$0.5^3 = 0.125$

$0.5^4 = 0.0625$

As the powers increase, the result decreases. The answer cannot be less than zero, because the base is positive.

always true

5. 6

6. $6 \cdot 6 = 6^2$

7. $6^2 \cdot 6 = 6^3$

8. $6^3 \cdot 6 = 6^4$

9. $6^4 \cdot 6 = 6^5$

10. 3^{20}; Possible explanation: you can multiply 3^{18} by 3^2, or 9, to get from 3^{18} to 3^{20}.

11. $(^-2)^8$; Possible explanation: a negative number to an even power is positive, but a negative number to an odd power is negative.

12. $^-3^{500}$; Possible explanation: since both answers are negative, the one with the smaller exponent is greater.

13a. $\left(\frac{1}{2}\right)^3 = \frac{1}{2} \cdot \frac{1}{2} \cdot \frac{1}{2} = \frac{1}{8}$

$\left(\frac{1}{2}\right)^4 = \frac{1}{2} \cdot \frac{1}{2} \cdot \frac{1}{2} \cdot \frac{1}{2} = \frac{1}{16}$

$\left(\frac{1}{2}\right)^5 = \frac{1}{2} \cdot \frac{1}{2} \cdot \frac{1}{2} \cdot \frac{1}{2} \cdot \frac{1}{2} = \frac{1}{32}$

$\left(\frac{1}{2}\right)^6 = \frac{1}{2} \cdot \frac{1}{2} \cdot \frac{1}{2} \cdot \frac{1}{2} \cdot \frac{1}{2} \cdot \frac{1}{2} = \frac{1}{64}$

Possible answer: 4, 5, 6

13b. all positive integers greater than 3

13c. Possible answer: When you multiply a number between 0 and 1 by itself, the result is less than the original number, so a higher power gives a smaller number.

14. $\left(\dfrac{-1}{3}\right)^{34}$; Possible explanation: When you multiply a number between 0 and 1 by itself, the result is less than the original number. That means the higher power gives a smaller number. Since the exponents are both even, the result will be positive, so the number with the lower power has the greater value.

Page 148 Problem Set C

1.

Description	Number in Standard Form (approximate)	Number in Scientific Notation
Time since dinosaurs began roaming Earth (years)	225,000,000	2.25×10^8
Projected World population in 2010	6,800,000,000	6.8×10^9
Distance from Earth to Andromeda galaxy (miles)	15,000,000,000,000,000,000	1.5×10^{19}
Mass of the sun (kg)	2,000,000,000,000,000,000,000,000,000,000	2×10^{30}

2. 1.35×10^6

3. 8.1×10^{32}

Page 149 Share and Summarize

1. the product of b a's
2. If $a < 1$, then $a^5 > a^7$. If $a > 1$, then $a^5 < a^7$.

Page 150 Problem Set D

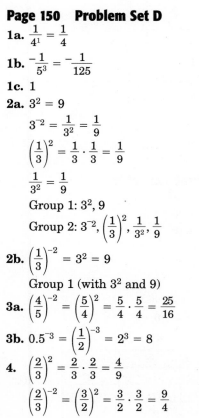

1a. $\dfrac{1}{4^1} = \dfrac{1}{4}$

1b. $\dfrac{-1}{5^3} = \dfrac{-1}{125}$

1c. 1

2a. $3^2 = 9$

$3^{-2} = \dfrac{1}{3^2} = \dfrac{1}{9}$

$\left(\dfrac{1}{3}\right)^2 = \dfrac{1}{3} \cdot \dfrac{1}{3} = \dfrac{1}{9}$

$\dfrac{1}{3^2} = \dfrac{1}{9}$

Group 1: $3^2, 9$

Group 2: $3^{-2}, \left(\dfrac{1}{3}\right)^2, \dfrac{1}{3^2}, \dfrac{1}{9}$

2b. $\left(\dfrac{1}{3}\right)^{-2} = 3^2 = 9$

Group 1 (with 3^2 and 9)

3a. $\left(\dfrac{4}{5}\right)^{-2} = \left(\dfrac{5}{4}\right)^2 = \dfrac{5}{4} \cdot \dfrac{5}{4} = \dfrac{25}{16}$

3b. $0.5^{-3} = \left(\dfrac{1}{2}\right)^{-3} = 2^3 = 8$

4. $\left(\dfrac{2}{3}\right)^2 = \dfrac{2}{3} \cdot \dfrac{2}{3} = \dfrac{4}{9}$

$\left(\dfrac{2}{3}\right)^{-2} = \left(\dfrac{3}{2}\right)^2 = \dfrac{3}{2} \cdot \dfrac{3}{2} = \dfrac{9}{4}$

$\left(\dfrac{3}{2}\right)^2 = \dfrac{3}{2} \cdot \dfrac{3}{2} = \dfrac{9}{4}$

$\left(\dfrac{3}{2}\right)^{-2} = \left(\dfrac{2}{3}\right)^2 = \dfrac{2}{3} \cdot \dfrac{2}{3} = \dfrac{4}{9}$

$\dfrac{3^2}{2^2} = \dfrac{9}{4}$

Group 1: $\left(\dfrac{2}{3}\right)^2, \left(\dfrac{3}{2}\right)^{-2}, \dfrac{4}{9}$

Group 2: $\left(\dfrac{2}{3}\right)^{-2}, \left(\dfrac{3}{2}\right)^2, \dfrac{3^2}{2^2}, \dfrac{9}{4}$

5. $10^3 = 1,000$

$10^{-3} = \dfrac{1}{10^3} = \dfrac{1}{1,000}$

$(^-10)^{-3} = \dfrac{1}{(-10)^3} = {}^-\dfrac{1}{1,000}$

$\dfrac{1}{(^-10)^3} = {}^-\dfrac{1}{1,000}$

$\left(\dfrac{1}{10}\right)^{-3} = 10^3 = 1,000$

$\left(\dfrac{1}{10}\right)^3 = \dfrac{1}{1,000}$

$\left(-\dfrac{1}{10}\right)^{-3} = (^-10)^3 = {}^-1,000$

$\dfrac{1}{10^3} = \dfrac{1}{1,000}$

$\left(-\dfrac{1}{10}\right)^3 = {}^-\dfrac{1}{1,000}$

$(^-10)^3 = {}^-1,000$

Group 1: $10^3, \left(\dfrac{1}{10}\right)^{-3}, 1,000$

Group 2: $^-1,000, \left(-\dfrac{1}{10}\right)^{-3}, (^-10)^3$

Group 3: $\left(-\dfrac{1}{10}\right)^3, (^-10)^{-3}, \dfrac{1}{(-10)^3}, {}^-\dfrac{1}{1,000}$

Group 4: $10^{-3}, \dfrac{1}{1,000}, \left(\dfrac{1}{10}\right)^3, \dfrac{1}{10^3}$

6. $\left(\dfrac{b}{a}\right)^{-3} = \left(\dfrac{a}{b}\right)^3$

$\left(\dfrac{a}{b}\right)^{-3} = \left(\dfrac{b}{a}\right)^3$

$\dfrac{b^3}{a^3} = \left(\dfrac{b}{a}\right)^3$

$b^3 \div a^3 = \dfrac{b^3}{a^3} = \left(\dfrac{b}{a}\right)^3$

$a^3 \div b^3 = \dfrac{a^3}{b^3} = \left(\dfrac{a}{b}\right)^3$

Group 1: $\left(\dfrac{a}{b}\right)^3, \left(\dfrac{b}{a}\right)^{-3}, a^3 \div b^3$

Group 2: $\left(\dfrac{a}{b}\right)^{-3}, \left(\dfrac{b}{a}\right)^3, \dfrac{b^3}{a^3}, b^3 \div a^3$

7. $\dfrac{1}{a^n}, \left(\dfrac{1}{a}\right)^n, 1 \div a^n$

8. $\dfrac{1}{a^{-n}}, a^n$

9. $\left(\dfrac{b}{a}\right)^n, \dfrac{a^{-n}}{b^{-n}}, \dfrac{b^n}{a^n}$

49

Page 151　Problem Set E

1. $2^{11} = 2,048$

 $2^{-11} = \dfrac{1}{2^{11}} = \dfrac{1}{2,048}$

 sometimes true, when $n = {}^{-}11$

2. when $n > 0$, $3^n \geq 3$, for integer values of n

 when $n = 0$, $3^n = 1$

 when $n < 0$, $0 < 3^n \leq \dfrac{1}{3}$, for integer values of n

 sometimes true, when $n < 0$

3. when $n > 0$, $5^n \geq 5$, for integer values of n

 when $n = 0$, $5^n = 1$

 when $n < 0$, $0 < 5^n \leq \dfrac{1}{5}$, for integer values of n

 sometimes true, when $n \leq 0$

4. 7^{-89}; Possible explanation: the more negative exponent gives a fraction with a greater denominator and so a smaller number.

5. 3^{-15}; Possible explanation: the greater base gives a fraction with a greater denominator and so a smaller number.

6. 0.4^{-78}; Possible explanation: 0.4 is $\dfrac{2}{5}$, so you can rewrite these as $\dfrac{5}{2}$ raised to 5 and 78; $\left(\dfrac{5}{2}\right)^{78}$ is much greater because you're multiplying a number greater than 1 by itself many more times than 5.

7. $^{-}9^{-4}$; Possible explanation: 0.5^{-4} is 2^4 and 9^{-4} is $\left(\dfrac{1}{9}\right)^4$; of these 2^4 is obviously greater. Since there's a negative sign in front of both numbers, the greater number is actually less (more negative).

8. $(^{-}2)^{-280}$; Possible explanation: since these are both even powers, the numbers will be positive. These equal $\dfrac{1}{2^{280}}$ and $\dfrac{1}{2^{282}}$; the greater exponent gives a greater denominator and so the number is less.

9. $(^{-}50)^{-51}$; Possible explanation: since both powers are odd, the numbers will be negative. These equal $-\dfrac{1}{50^{45}}$ and $-\dfrac{1}{50^{51}}$; the greater exponent gives a smaller fraction, but since the fractions are negative, it gives a greater number.

10. 0.3^{-50}; Possible explanation: the reciprocal of 0.3 is greater than 1, and the reciprocal of 1.3 is between 0 and 1. Raising them to 50th power makes the first even greater and the second even less.

Page 152　Problem Set F

1.

Description	Number in Standard Form (approximate)	Number in Scientific Notation
Average mass of a hydrogen atom (grams)	0.00000000000000000000000016735	1.6735×10^{-24}
Diameter of the body of a Purkinje cell (meters)	0.00008	8×10^{-5}
Diameter of some fats in the body (meters)	0.0000000005	5×10^{-10}
Average mass of an oxygen atom (grams)	0.000000000000000000000026566	2.6566×10^{-23}

2. 2.34×10^{-5}

3. 3.83312×10^{-31}

Page 152　Share and Summarize

1. Possible answer: 1 divided by the product of b a's. Or, the reciprocal of a^b. Or, the reciprocal of the product of b a's.

2. If $a < 1$, then $a^{-5} < a^{-7}$. If $a > 1$, then $a^{-5} > a^{-7}$.

Page 154　Problem Set G

1a. Possible answer:

 $\dfrac{a^b}{a^c} = \dfrac{\overbrace{a \cdot a \cdot \cdots \cdot a}^{b \text{ times}}}{\underbrace{a \cdot a \cdot \cdots \cdot a}_{c \text{ times}}}$. Dividing the c a's in the denominator into c of the a's in the numerator leaves $b - c$ a's in the numerator, which is a^{b-c}.

1b. Possible answer:

 $\dfrac{a^b}{a^c} = \dfrac{\overbrace{a \cdot a \cdot \cdots \cdot a}^{b \text{ times}}}{\underbrace{a \cdot a \cdot \cdots \cdot a}_{c \text{ times}}}$. Dividing the b of the a's in the denominator into the b a's in the numerator leaves $c - b$ a's in the denominator, $\dfrac{1}{\underbrace{a \cdot a \cdot \cdots \cdot a}_{c-b \text{ times}}}$, which is $\dfrac{1}{a^{c-b}}$. Since $c - b = {}^{-}(b - c)$,

 $\dfrac{1}{a^{c-b}} = \dfrac{1}{a^{-(b-c)}} = a^{b-c}$.

2. Possible answer:

 $a^c \cdot b^c = a^{-x} \cdot b^{-x}$

 $= \dfrac{1}{a^x} \cdot \dfrac{1}{b^x}$

 $= \dfrac{1}{a^x \cdot b^x}$

 $= \dfrac{1}{\underbrace{a \cdot a \cdot \cdots \cdot a}_{x \text{ times}} \cdot \underbrace{b \cdot b \cdot \cdots \cdot b}_{x \text{ times}}}$

 $= \dfrac{1}{\underbrace{ab \cdot ab \cdot \cdots \cdot ab}_{x \text{ times}}}$

 $= \dfrac{1}{(ab)^x}$

 $= (ab)^{-x}$

 $= (ab)^c$

Pages 154–155　Problem Set H

1. $3^4 \times 3^{-2} = 3^{4-2} = 3^2$

 $3^4 \times 3^x = 3^{4+x} = 3^{x+4}$

 $3^4 \times 3^4 = 3^{4+4} = 3^8$

 $3^a \times 3^{-2} = 3^{a-2}$

 $3^a \times 3^x = 3^{a+x}$

 $3^a \times 3^4 = 3^{a+4}$

 $^{-}3^2 \times 3^{-2} = {}^{-}3^{2-2} = {}^{-}3^0$

 $^{-}3^2 \times 3^x = {}^{-}3^{2+x} = {}^{-}3^{x+2}$

 $^{-}3^2 \times 3^4 = {}^{-}3^{2+4} = {}^{-}3^6$

$\times$	3^{-2}	3^x	3^4
3^4	3^2	3^{x+4}	3^8
3^a	3^{a-2}	3^{a+x}	3^{a+4}
$^{-}3^2$	$^{-}3^0$	$^{-}3^{x+2}$	$^{-}3^6$

2. $2a^4 \div a^5 = \dfrac{2a^4}{a^5} = 2a^{4-5} = 2a^{-1}$

$2a^4 \div a^{-2} = \dfrac{2a^4}{a^{-2}} = 2a^{4--2} = 2a^6$

$2a^4 \div (a^3)^2 = 2a^4 \div a^6 = \dfrac{2a^4}{a^6} = 2a^{4-6} = 2a^{-2}$

$a^{-3} \div a^5 = \dfrac{a^{-3}}{a^5} = a^{-3-5} = a^{-8}$

$a^{-3} \div a^{-2} = \dfrac{a^{-3}}{a^{-2}} = a^{-3--2} = a^{-1}$

$a^{-3} \div (a^3)^2 = a^{-3} \div a^6 = \dfrac{a^{-3}}{a^6} = a^{-3-6} = a^{-9}$

$(2a)^5 \div a^5 = 2^5a^5 \div a^5 = \dfrac{2^5a^5}{a^5} = 2^5a^{5-5} = 2^5a^0 = 2^5(1) = 2^5$

$(2a)^5 \div a^{-2} = 2^5a^5 \div a^{-2} = \dfrac{2^5a^5}{a^{-2}} = 2^5a^{5--2} = 2^5a^7$

$(2a)^5 \div (a^3)^2 = 2^5a^5 \div a^6 = \dfrac{2^5a^5}{a^6} = 2^5a^{5-6} = 2^5a^{-1}$

$\div$	a^5	a^{-2}	$(a^3)^2$
$2a^4$	$2a^{-1}$	$2a^6$	$2a^{-2}$
a^{-3}	a^{-8}	a^{-1}	a^{-9}
$(2a)^5$	2^5	2^5a^7	2^5a^{-1}

3. $b^4 \div b^{-4} = \dfrac{b^4}{b^{-4}} = b^{4--4} = b^8$

$b^{-4} \times 2a = 2ab^{-4}$

$a^8 \times b^8 = a^8b^8$

$a^8 \times 2a = 2a^{8+1} = 2a^9$

$a^{10}b^{-4} \div a^8 = \dfrac{a^{10}b^{-4}}{a^8} = a^{10-8}b^{-4} = a^2b^{-4}$

$a^8b^{-8} \div a^8 = \dfrac{a^8b^{-8}}{a^8} = a^{8-8}b^{-8} = a^0b^{-8} = 1 \cdot b^{-8} = b^{-8}$

$b^{-4} \times a^2b^{-4} = a^2b^{-4+-4} = a^2b^{-8}$

$b^{-4} \times b^{-8} = b^{-4+-8} = b^{-12}$

$b \div a^2b^{-4} = \dfrac{b}{a^2b^{-4}} = a^{-2}b^{1--4} = a^{-2}b^5$

$a^{-2}b^5 \times b^8 = a^{-2}b^{5+8} = a^{-2}b^{13}$

$a^{-2}b^5 \times 2a = 2a^{-2+1}b^5 = 2a^{-1}b^5$

$a^{-2}b^5 \times b^{-8} = a^{-2}b^{5+-8} = a^{-2}b^{-3}$

$(2ab)^4 \div 2a = 2^4a^4b^4 \div 2a = \dfrac{2^4a^4b^4}{2a} = 2^{4-1}a^{4-1}b^4 = 2^3a^3b^4 = (2a)^3b^4$

$(2a)^3b^4 \times b^8 = (2a)^3b^{4+8} = (2a)^3b^{12}$

$(2a)^3b^4 \times a^2b^{-4} = 2^3a^3b^4 \times a^2b^{-4} = 2^3a^{3+2}b^{4+-4} = 2^3a^5$

$(2a)^3b^4 \times b^{-8} = (2a)^3b^{4+-8} = (2a)^3b^{-4}$

$\times$	b^8	$2a$	a^2b^{-4}	b^{-8}
b^{-4}	b^4	$2ab^{-4}$	a^2b^{-8}	b^{-12}
a^8	a^8b^8	$2a^9$	$a^{10}b^{-4}$	a^8b^{-8}
$a^{-2}b^5$	$a^{-2}b^{13}$	$2a^{-1}b^5$	b	$a^{-2}b^{-3}$
$(2a)^3b^4$	$(2a)^3b^{12}$	$(2ab)^4$	2^3a^5	$(2a)^3b^{-4}$

1a. $(a^{-m})^0 = a^{-m \cdot 0}$

$\quad\quad = a^0 = 1$

a^0 or 1

1b. $[(^-d)^3]^4 = (^-d)^{3 \cdot 4}$

$\quad\quad = (^-d)^{12}$

$\quad\quad = (^-1 \cdot d)^{12}$

$\quad\quad = (^-1)^{12} \cdot d^{12}$

$\quad\quad = 1 \cdot d^{12}$

$\quad\quad = d^{12}$

$(^-d)^{12}$ or d^{12}

1c. $(^-10^{-4})^{-5} = (^-1 \cdot 10^{-4})^{-5}$

$\quad\quad = (^-1)^{-5} \cdot 10^{-4 \cdot -5}$

$\quad\quad = ^-1 \cdot 10^{20}$

$\quad\quad = ^-10^{20}$

$^-10^{20}$

2a. $(2^3 \cdot 2)^2 = (2^{3+1})^2$

$\quad\quad = (2^4)^2$

$\quad\quad = 2^{4 \cdot 2}$

$\quad\quad = 2^8$

Possible answer: 2^8

2b. $(a^m)^n \div (a^{-m})^n = a^{m \cdot n} \div a^{-m \cdot n}$

$\quad\quad = a^{mn} \div a^{-mn}$

$\quad\quad = \dfrac{a^{mn}}{a^{-mn}}$

$\quad\quad = a^{mn--mn}$

$\quad\quad = a^{2mn}$

a^{2mn}

2c. $4^3 \cdot n^3 \div (^-16n)^3 = 4^3n^3 \div (^-4^2n)^3$

$\quad\quad = 4^3n^3 \div ^-4^{2 \cdot 3}n^3$

$\quad\quad = 4^3n^3 \div ^-4^6n^3$

$\quad\quad = \dfrac{4^3n^3}{^-4^6n^3}$

$\quad\quad = ^-4^{3-6}$

$\quad\quad = ^-4^{-3} = -\dfrac{1}{4^3} = -\dfrac{1}{64}$

Possible answers: $^-4^{-3}, -\dfrac{1}{4^3}, -\dfrac{1}{64}$

3a. $32n^{10} = 8 \cdot 4 \cdot n^3 \cdot n^7$

$\quad\quad = 8n^3 \cdot 4n^7$

$32n^{10} = 2 \cdot 16 \cdot n^4 \cdot n^6$

$\quad\quad = 2n^4 \cdot 16n^6$

Possible answer: $8n^3 \cdot 4n^7, 2n^4 \cdot 16n^6$

3b. $m^7b^{-7} = m^6 \cdot m^1 \cdot b^{-1} \cdot b^{-6}$

$\quad\quad = m^6b^{-1} \cdot mb^{-6}$

$m^7b^{-7} = m^3 \cdot m^4 \cdot b^{-4} \cdot b^{-3}$

$\quad\quad = m^3b^{-4} \cdot m^4b^{-3}$

Possible answer: $m^6b^{-1} \cdot mb^{-6}$ or $m^3b^{-4} \cdot m^4b^{-3}$

Page 155   Share and Summarize

Possible answer:

$\dfrac{2^6n^3}{(16n^2)^3} = \dfrac{2^6n^3}{(2^4n^2)^3}$

$\quad\quad = \dfrac{2^6n^3}{2^{12}n^6} \quad$ product law
$(a^c \cdot b^c = (ab)^c)$ and
power of a power law

$\quad\quad = \dfrac{1}{2^6n^3}$ or $\dfrac{1}{64n^3} \quad$ quotient law $\left(\dfrac{a^b}{a^c} = a^{b-c}\right)$

1a. $4 \times 10^{11} \cdot 10^{11} = 4 \times 10^{11+11}$
$$= 4 \times 10^{22}$$

about 4×10^{22} stars

1b. $1,000 = 10^3$
$$\frac{4 \times 10^{22}}{10^3} = 4 \times 10^{22-3}$$
$$= 4 \times 10^{19}$$

about 4×10^{19} systems

1c. $1,000 = 10^3$
$$\frac{4 \times 10^{19}}{10^3} = 4 \times 10^{19-3}$$
$$= 4 \times 10^{16}$$

about 4×10^{16} systems

1d. 6 billion $= 6 \times 10^9$
$$\frac{4 \times 10^{16}}{6 \times 10^9} \approx 0.667 \times 10^7 = 6.67 \times 10^6$$

Possible answer: If the given assumptions are true, there are about 6,670,000 times as many inhabitable planets as there are people on Earth.

2a. $2 \times 10^{-12} \cdot 4.8 \times 10^8 = 9.6 \times 10^{-12+8}$
$$= 9.6 \times 10^{-4}$$

9.6×10^{-4} g

2b. $\dfrac{1}{9.6 \times 10^{-4}} \approx 10^3$; the paperclip has about 1,000 times the mass of the bacteria population.

3a. $500 = 5 \times 10^2$
$$2 \times 10^5 \cdot 5 \times 10^2 = 10 \times 10^{5+2}$$
$$= 10 \times 10^7$$
$$= 10^{1+7}$$
$$= 10^8$$

about 1×10^8 miles

3b. $\dfrac{2.5 \times 10^{13}}{2 \times 10^5} \approx 1.3 \times 10^{13-5}$
$$= 1.3 \times 10^8$$

about 1.3×10^8 s

3c. 60 s = 1 min
60 min = 1 h
24 h = 1 day
365 day = 1 yr
31,536,000 s $\approx 3.15 \times 10^7$ = 1 yr

$$\frac{1.3 \times 10^8}{3.1536 \times 10^7} \approx 0.41 \times 10^{8-7}$$
$$= 0.41 \times 10^1$$
$$= 4.1$$

about 4.1 yr

4a. $\dfrac{3 \times 10^{19}}{6 \times 10^{18}} = 0.5 \times 10^{19-18}$
$$= 0.5 \times 10^1$$
$$= 5$$

about 5

4b. $\dfrac{8 \times 10^{19}}{6 \times 10^{18}} \approx 1.3 \times 10^{19-18}$
$$= 1.3 \times 10^1$$
$$= 13$$

about 13

5a. $2 \times 10^{12} \cdot 2 = 4 \times 10^{12}$

5b. $2 \times 10^{12} - 2 \times 10^9 = 2,000 \times 10^9 - 2 \times 10^9$
$$= (2,000 - 2) \times 10^9$$
$$= 1,998 \times 10^9$$
$$= 1.998 \times 10^{12}$$

$(^-2 \times 10^{12}) \cdot (4 \times 10^{28}) = {}^-8 \times 10^{12+28} = {}^-8 \times 10^{40}$

$(4 \times 10^5) \div (^-2 \times 10^{12}) = {}^-2 \times 10^{5-12} = {}^-2 \times 10^{-7}$

$(6 \times 10^{-20}) \cdot (4 \times 10^{28}) = 24 \times 10^{-20+28} =$
$24 \times 10^8 = 2.4 \times 10^9$

$(6 \times 10^{-20}) \cdot (^-2 \times 10^{-7}) = {}^-12 \times 10^{-20+{}^-7} =$
$^-12 \times 10^{-27} = {}^-1.2 \times 10^{-26}$

$(8 \times 10^a) \cdot (4 \times 10^{28}) = 32 \times 10^{a+28} =$
$3.2 \times 10^{a+29}$

$(8 \times 10^a) \cdot (^-2 \times 10^{-7}) = {}^-16 \times 10^{a+{}^-7} =$
$^-1.6 \times 10^{a-6}$

$\times$	4×10^{28}	-2×10^{-7}
-2×10^{12}	-8×10^{40}	4×10^5
6×10^{-20}	2.4×10^9	-1.2×10^{-26}
8×10^a	$3.2 \times 10^{29+a}$	$-1.6 \times 10^{a-6}$

$(^-4 \times 10^{12}) \div (2 \times 10^6) = {}^-2 \times 10^{12-6} = {}^-2 \times 10^6$

$(^-4 \times 10^{12}) \div (2 \times 10^5) = {}^-2 \times 10^{12-5} = {}^-2 \times 10^7$

$(8 \times 10^{-10}) \div (2 \times 10^6) = 4 \times 10^{-10-6} = 4 \times 10^{-16}$

$(8 \times 10^{-10}) \div (^-2 \times 10^7) = 4 \times 10^{-10-7} = 4 \times 10^{-17}$

$(8 \times 10^a) \div (2 \times 10^6) = 4 \times 10^{a-6}$

$(8 \times 10^a) \div (^-2 \times 10^7) = {}^-4 \times 10^{a-7}$

$\div$	2×10^6	-2×10^7
-4×10^{12}	-2×10^6	2×10^5
8×10^{-10}	4×10^{-16}	-4×10^{-17}
8×10^a	$4 \times 10^{a-6}$	$-4 \times 10^{a-7}$

Page 158   Share and Summarize

1. correct

2. Incorrect; the product is equal to 12×10^{-12}, or in scientific notation, 1.2×10^{-11}.

3. Incorrect; when subtracting two powers, you can't just subtract the exponents. We don't have a rule about subtracting two powers, but we can use the distributive property to factor out 3×10^{10}, giving $(3 \times 10^{10})(100 - 1)$, which is 297×10^{10} or 2.97×10^{12}.

Pages 159–161   Lab

1. Sketches will vary.

2. Answers will vary.

3. 3.7×10^9 mi

4. Using 100 ft for the model length, multiply by 3.7×10^7.

5. Using 100 ft for the model length, divide the distance from the sun in miles by 3.7×10^7 to get the distance from the sun in the scale version (in feet).

6. Using 100 ft for the model length, gives the distances below:

$(3.6 \times 10^7) \div (3.7 \times 10^7) \approx 1.0$

$(6.7 \times 10^7) \div (3.7 \times 10^7) \approx 1.8$

$(9.3 \times 10^7) \div (3.7 \times 10^7) \approx 2.5$

$(1.4 \times 10^8) \div (3.7 \times 10^7) \approx 3.8$

$(4.8 \times 10^8) \div (3.7 \times 10^7) \approx 13.0$

$(8.9 \times 10^8) \div (3.7 \times 10^7) \approx 24.1$

$(1.8 \times 10^9) \div (3.7 \times 10^7) \approx 48.6$
$(2.8 \times 10^9) \div (3.7 \times 10^7) \approx 75.7$
$(3.7 \times 10^9) \div (3.7 \times 10^7) \approx 100.0$

Planet	Average Distance from Sun (miles)	Average Distance from Sun in Scale Model (feet)
Mercury	3.6×10^7	1.0
Venus	6.7×10^7	1.8
Earth	9.3×10^7	2.5
Mars	1.4×10^8	3.8
Jupiter	4.8×10^8	13.0
Saturn	8.9×10^8	24.1
Uranus	1.8×10^9	48.6
Neptune	2.8×10^9	75.7
Pluto	3.7×10^9	100.0

7. $2.5 - 1.8 = 0.7$ ft
    Venus and Earth
    $9.3 \times 10^7 - 6.7 \times 10^7$
    $= (9.3 - 6.7) \times 10^7$
    $= 2.6 \times 10^7$ mi

8. $75.7 - 48.6 = 27.1$ ft
    Uranus and Neptune
    $2.8 \times 10^9 - 1.8 \times 10^9$
    $= (2.8 - 1.8) \times 10^9$
    $= 1 \times 10^9$ mi

9. $(1 \times 10^9) \div (2.6 \times 10^7)$
    $\approx 0.38 \times 10^{9-7}$
    $= 0.38 \times 10^2$
    $= 38$
    about 38 times

10. Answers will vary.

11. Answers will vary.

12. Answers will vary.

13a. Answers will vary.

13b. $2.4 \times 10^5 \div 3.7 \times 10^7$
    $= 0.6 \times 10^{5-7}$
    $= 0.6 \times 10^{-2}$
    $= 0.006$ ft
    $= 0.08$ in.
    Using 100 ft for the model length gives about 0.006 ft, or 0.08 in.

13c. Answers will vary.

14. Possible answer:

15. Possible explanation for a: $1 \times 10^1 = 10$; $1 \times 10^2 = 100$.
    The distance between 0 and 1×10^1 should not be the same as the distance between 1×10^1 and 1×10^2, so a is not correct.
    Possible explanation for b: $1 \times 10^6 = 1,000,000$; $1 \times 10^7 = 10,000,000$; $2 \times 10^7 = 20,000,000$.
    With the exception of 1×10^6, each number is the same distance from adjacent numbers, so b is correct.
    Possible explanation for c: $8 \times 10^7 = 80,000,000$; $9 \times 10^7 = 90,000,000$; $1 \times 10^8 = 100,000,000$.
    The distance between 8×10^7 and 9×10^7 should be the same as the distance between 9×10^7 and 1×10^8, so c is not correct.

Pages 162–168   On Your Own Exercises

1. 1750: 725,000,000; 1950: 2.56×10^9
    Possible explanation: 725,000,000 is 7.25×10^8, which is less than 2.56×10^9. The world population has increased during this time.

2. If $n < 0$, then $n^2 > 0$, because the square of a negative number is positive.
    If $n > 0$, then $n^2 > 0$, because the square of a positive number is positive.
    If $n = 0$, then $n^2 = 0$, because the square of 0 is 0.
    So n will be equal to or less than 0 when n is 0.

3. If $n < 0$, then $n^3 < 0$, because the cube of a negative number is negative.
    If $n > 0$, then $n^3 > 0$, because the cube of a positive number is positive.
    If $n = 0$, then $n^3 = 0$, because the cube of 0 is 0.
    So n will be equal to or less than 0 when n is 0 or negative.

4. $4^8 = 65,536$. If $n = 8$, then $4^n = 65,536$. If $n \neq 8$, then $4^n \neq 65,536$; sometimes true, $n = 8$.

5. $4^9 = 262,144$; $4^{10} = 1,048,576$. If $n \leq 9$, then $4^n < 1,000,000$. If $n \geq 10$, then $4^n > 1,000,000$; sometimes true, $n \leq 9$.

6. $1^2 = 1$; $2^2 = 4$; $3^2 = 9$
    Since n represents a positive integer, n^2 is always greater than 0; never true

7. $0.9^1 = 0.9$; $0.9^2 = 0.81$; $0.9^3 = 0.729$
    Since n represents a positive integer, 0.9 is always between 0 and 1; always true

8.
$$x^{20} > x^{18}$$
$$\frac{x^{20}}{x^{18}} > \frac{x^{18}}{x^{18}}$$
$$x^{20-18} > x^{18-18}$$
$$x^2 > x^0$$
$$x^2 > 1$$
If $0 < x < 1$, then $x^2 < 1$.
If $x = 1$, then $x^2 = 1$.
If $x > 1$, then $x^2 > 1$.
So x^{20} is greater than x^{18} when $x > 1$.

9.
$$x^{18} > x^{20}$$
$$\frac{x^{18}}{x^{18}} > \frac{x^{20}}{x^{18}}$$
$$x^{18-18} > x^{20-18}$$
$$x^0 > x^2$$
$$1 > x^2$$
$$x^2 < 1$$
If $0 < x < 1$, then $x^2 < 1$.
If $x = 1$, then $x^2 = 1$.
If $x > 1$, then $x^2 > 1$.
So x^{18} is greater than x^{20} when $0 < x < 1$.

10.
$$x^{18} = x^{20}$$
$$\frac{x^{18}}{x^{18}} = \frac{x^{20}}{x^{18}}$$
$$x^{18-18} = x^{20-18}$$
$$x^0 = x^2$$
$$1 = x^2$$
$$x^2 = 1$$
If $0 < x < 1$, then $x^2 < 1$.
If $x = 1$, then $x^2 = 1$.
If $x > 1$, then $x^2 > 1$.
So x^{18} is equal to x^{20} when $x = 1$.

11.
$$x^{20} > x^{18}$$
$$\frac{x^{20}}{x^{18}} > \frac{x^{18}}{x^{18}}$$
$$x^{20-18} > x^{18-18}$$
$$x^2 > x^0$$
$$x^2 > 1$$
If $x < {}^-1$, then $x^2 > 1$.
If $x = {}^-1$, then $x^2 = 1$.
If ${}^-1 < x < 0$, then $x^2 < 1$.
So x^{20} is greater than x^{18} when $x < {}^-1$.

12.
$$x^{18} > x^{20}$$
$$\frac{x^{18}}{x^{18}} > \frac{x^{20}}{x^{18}}$$
$$x^{18-18} > x^{20-18}$$
$$x^0 > x^2$$
$$1 > x^2$$
$$x^2 < 1$$
If $x < {}^-1$, then $x^2 > 1$.
If $x = {}^-1$, then $x^2 = 1$.
If ${}^-1 < x < 0$, then $x^2 < 1$.
So x^{18} is greater than x^{20} when ${}^-1 < x < 0$.

13.
$$x^{18} = x^{20}$$
$$\frac{x^{18}}{x^{18}} = \frac{x^{20}}{x^{18}}$$
$$x^{18-18} = x^{20-18}$$
$$x^0 = x^2$$
$$1 = x^2$$
$$x^2 = 1$$
If $x < {}^-1$, then $x^2 > 1$.
If $x = {}^-1$, then $x^2 = 1$.
If ${}^-1 < x < 0$, then $x^2 < 1$.
So x^{18} is equal to x^{20} when $x = {}^-1$.

14a. $8^1 = 8$
$8^2 = 64$
$8^3 = 512$
$8^4 = 4{,}096$
$8^5 = 32{,}768$

14b. Answers will vary. All answers should be equal to 8 raised to an even power, such as 64 (8^2), 4,096 (8^4), and 262,144 (8^6).

14c. Answers will vary. All answers should be equal to 2 raised to a power that is not divisible by 3, such as 32 (2^5), 128 (2^7), and 256 (2^8).

14d. Answers will vary. All answers should be equal to 4 raised to a power that is not divisible by 3, such as 256 (4^4), 1,024 (4^5), and 16,384 (4^7).
Possible answers: 256; 1,024; 16,384

14e. $2^3 = 8 = 8^1$
$2^6 = 64 = 8^2$
$2^9 = 512 = 8^3$
powers of 2 for which the exponent is divisible by 3

14f. $4^3 = 64 = 8^2$
$4^6 = 4{,}096 = 8^4$
$4^9 = 262{,}144 = 8^6$
powers of 4 for which the exponent is divisible by 3

15.
$$x^{-20} > x^{-18}$$
$$\frac{x^{-20}}{x^{-18}} > \frac{x^{-18}}{x^{-18}}$$
$$x^{-20-{}^-18} > x^{-18-{}^-18}$$
$$x^{-2} > x^0$$
$$x^{-2} > 1$$
$$x^2(x^{-2}) > x^2(1)$$
$$x^{2+{}^-2} > x^2$$
$$x^0 > x^2$$
$$1 > x^2$$
$$x^2 < 1$$
If $0 < x < 1$, then $x^2 < 1$.
If $x = 1$, then $x^2 = 1$.
If $x > 1$, then $x^2 > 1$.
So x^{20} is greater than x^{18} when $0 < x < 1$.

16.
$$x^{-18} > x^{-20}$$
$$\frac{x^{-18}}{x^{-18}} > \frac{x^{-20}}{x^{-18}}$$
$$x^{-18 - {}^-18} > x^{-20 - {}^-18}$$
$$x^0 > x^{-2}$$
$$1 > x^{-2}$$
$$x^2(1) > x^2(x^{-2})$$
$$x^2 > x^{2 + {}^-2}$$
$$x^2 > x^0$$
$$x^2 > 1$$

If $0 < x < 1$, then $x^2 < 1$.
If $x = 1$, then $x^2 = 1$.
If $x > 1$, then $x^2 > 1$.
So x^{18} is greater than x^{20} when $x > 1$.

17.
$$x^{-18} = x^{-20}$$
$$\frac{x^{-18}}{x^{-18}} = \frac{x^{-20}}{x^{-18}}$$
$$x^{-18 - {}^-18} = x^{-20 - {}^-18}$$
$$x^0 = x^{-2}$$
$$1 = x^{-2}$$
$$x^2(1) = x^2(x^{-2})$$
$$x^2 = x^{2 + {}^-2}$$
$$x^2 = x^0$$
$$x^2 = 1$$

If $x < {}^-1$, then $x^2 > 1$.
If $x = {}^-1$, then $x^2 = 1$.
If ${}^-1 < x < 0$, then $x^2 < 1$.
If $0 < x < 1$, then $x^2 < 1$.
If $x = 1$, then $x^2 = 1$.
If $x > 1$, then $x^2 > 1$.
So x^{18} is equal to x^{20} when $x = {}^-1$ and $x = 1$.

18a. $\left(\frac{1}{2}\right)^{-6} = 2^6 = 64$

$(0.5)^{-6} = \frac{1}{0.5^6} = \frac{1}{0.015625} = 64$

$\frac{1}{2^{-6}} = 2^6 = 64$

$8^2 = 64$

$4^3 = 64$

$\left(\frac{1}{8}\right)^{-2} = 8^2 = 64$

$\left(\frac{1}{4}\right)^{-3} = 4^3 = 64$

Possible answer: $\left(\frac{1}{2}\right)^{-6}, (0.5)^{-6}, \frac{1}{2^{-6}}, 8^2, 4^3, \left(\frac{1}{8}\right)^{-2}, \left(\frac{1}{4}\right)^{-3}$

18b. 6.4×10^1

19. $\left(\frac{1}{m}\right)^2 = \frac{1}{m^2}$

$m^{-2} = \frac{1}{m^2}$

$\left(\frac{1}{m}\right)^{-2} = m^2$

$1 \div m^2 = \frac{1}{m^2}$

Group 1: $m^2, \left(\frac{1}{m}\right)^{-2}$

Group 2: $\left(\frac{1}{m}\right)^2, m^{-2}, \frac{1}{m^2}, 1 \div m^2$

20. $\left(\frac{1}{3}\right)^x = \frac{1}{3^x}$

$\left(\frac{1}{3}\right)^{-x} = 3^x$

$3^{-x} = \frac{1}{3^x}$

$1 \div 3^x = \frac{1}{3^x}$

Group 1: $3^x, \left(\frac{1}{3}\right)^{-x}$

Group 2: $\left(\frac{1}{3}\right)^x, \frac{1}{3^x}, 3^{-x}, 1 \div 3^x$

21. Possible answer:
$$\frac{a^c}{b^c} = \frac{\overbrace{a \cdot a \cdot \cdots \cdot a}^{c \text{ times}}}{\underbrace{b \cdot b \cdot \cdots \cdot b}_{c \text{ times}}}$$
$$= \overbrace{\frac{a}{b} \cdot \frac{a}{b} \cdot \cdots \cdot \frac{a}{b}}^{c \text{ times}}$$
$$= \left(\frac{a}{b}\right)^c$$

22. Possible answer:
$(a^b)^c$
$$= \overbrace{a^b \cdot a^b \cdot \cdots \cdot a^b}^{c \text{ times}}$$
$$= \overbrace{\underbrace{a \cdot a \cdot \cdots \cdot a}_{b \text{ times}} \cdot \underbrace{a \cdot a \cdot \cdots \cdot a}_{b \text{ times}} \cdot \cdots \cdot \underbrace{a \cdot a \cdot \cdots \cdot a}_{b \text{ times}}}^{c \text{ times}}$$
$$= \underbrace{a \cdot a \cdot \cdots \cdot a}_{bc \text{ times}}$$
$$= a^{bc}$$

23. $2^7 \cdot 2^{-4} \cdot 2^x = 2^{7 + {}^-4 + x}$
$$= 2^{3 + x}$$

24. $({}^-4^m)^6 = ({}^-4)^{m \cdot 6}$
$$= ({}^-4)^{6m} = ({}^-1 \cdot 4)^{6m} = 4^{6m}$$
4^{6m} or $({}^-4)^{6m}$

25. $m^7 \cdot 28^7 = (m \cdot 28)^7$
$$= (28m)^7$$

26. $({}^-3)^{81} \cdot ({}^-3)^{141} = ({}^-3)^{81 + 141}$
$$= ({}^-3)^{222} = ({}^-1 \cdot 3)^{222} = 3^{222}$$
$({}^-3)^{222}$ or 3^{222}

27. $\frac{55^{-8}}{9^{-8}} = \left(\frac{55}{9}\right)^{-8} = \left(\frac{9}{55}\right)^8$

$\left(\frac{55}{9}\right)^{-8}$ or $\left(\frac{9}{55}\right)^8$

28. $\left(\frac{m^{84}}{m^{12}}\right)^x = (m^{84 - 12})^x$
$$= (m^{72})^x$$
$$= m^{72 \cdot x}$$
$$= m^{72x}$$

29. $3^{-5} \cdot 8^5 = \left(\frac{1}{3}\right)^5 \cdot 8^5$
$$= \left(\frac{1}{3} \cdot 8\right)^5$$
$$= \left(\frac{8}{3}\right)^5 = \left(\frac{3}{8}\right)^{-5}$$
$\left(\frac{8}{3}\right)^5$ or $\left(\frac{3}{8}\right)^{-5}$

30. $n^a \div n^{\frac{a}{3}} = \dfrac{n^a}{n^{\frac{a}{3}}}$

$\qquad\qquad = n^{a - \frac{a}{3}}$

$\qquad\qquad = n^{\frac{2a}{3}}$

31. $(22^2 \cdot 22^5)^0 = (22^{2+7})^0$

$\qquad\qquad = (22^9)^0$

$\qquad\qquad = 22^{9 \cdot 0}$

$\qquad\qquad = 22^0$

$\qquad\qquad = 1$

32. $4a^4 \cdot 3a^3 = 12a^{4+3}$

$\qquad\qquad = 12a^7$

33. $m^{-3} \cdot m^4 \cdot b^7 = m^{-3+4}b^7$

$\qquad\qquad\qquad = mb^7$

34. $\dfrac{10n^{-15}}{5n^5} = 2n^{-15-5}$

$\qquad\qquad = 2n^{-20} = \dfrac{2}{n^{20}}$

$2n^{-20}$ or $\dfrac{2}{n^{20}}$

35. $(4x^{-2})^6 = 4^6 x^{-2 \cdot 6}$

$\qquad\qquad = 4^6 x^{-12} = 4{,}096x^{-12}$

$4^6 x^{-12}$ or $4{,}096x^{-12}$

36. $(^-m^2 n^3)^4 = (^-1)^4 m^{2 \cdot 4} n^{3 \cdot 4}$

$\qquad\qquad = 1m^8 n^{12}$

$\qquad\qquad = m^8 n^{12}$

37. $(a^m)^n \cdot (b^3)^2 = a^{m \cdot n} \cdot b^{3 \cdot 2}$

$\qquad\qquad\qquad = a^{mn} b^6$

38. $(x^{-2})^3 \cdot x^5 = x^{-2 \cdot 3} x^5$

$\qquad\qquad = x^{-6} x^5$

$\qquad\qquad = x^{-6+5}$

$\qquad\qquad = x^{-1} = \dfrac{1}{x}$

x^{-1} or $\dfrac{1}{x}$

39. $\dfrac{12b^5}{4b^{-2}} = 3b^{5 - ^-2}$

$\qquad\qquad = 3b^7$

40. $\dfrac{(x^4 y^{-5})^{-3}}{(xy)^2} = \dfrac{x^{4 \cdot ^-3} y^{-5 \cdot ^-3}}{x^2 y^2}$

$\qquad\qquad = \dfrac{x^{-12} y^{15}}{x^2 y^2}$

$\qquad\qquad = x^{-12-2} y^{15-2}$

$\qquad\qquad = x^{-14} y^{13} = \dfrac{y^{13}}{x^{14}}$

$x^{-14} y^{13}$ or $\dfrac{y^{13}}{x^{14}}$

41. $^-2^{-3} \times 2^{10} = ^-2^{-3+10} = ^-2^7$

$^-2^{-3} \times 2^{-x} = ^-2^{-3 + ^-x} = ^-2^{-3-x}$

$^-2^{-3} \times ^-2^x = 2^{-3+x} = 2^{x-3}$

$2^{a-x} \div 2^{-x} = 2^{a-x- ^-x} = 2^{a-x+x} = 2^a$ ✓

$2^a \times 2^{10} = 2^{a+10}$

$2^a \times ^-2^x = ^-2^{a+x}$

$(2n)^a \div 2^a = \dfrac{(2n)^a}{2^a} = \left(\dfrac{2n}{2}\right)^a = n^a$

$^-2^{-3} \times n^a = ^-2^{-3} n^a$

$2^{2a} \times 2^{10} = 2^{2a+10}$

$2^{2a} \times 2^{-x} = 2^{2a + ^-x} = 2^{2a-x}$

$2^{2a} \times ^-2^x = ^-2^{2a+x}$

$2^{2a} \times n^a = (2^2)^a \times n^a = (2^2 n)^a$

$\times$	2^{10}	2^{-x}	$^-2^x$	n^a
$^-2^{-3}$	$^-2^7$	$^-2^{-3-x}$	2^{x-3}	$^-2^{-3}n^a$
2^a	2^{a+10}	2^{a-x}	$^-2^{a+x}$	$(2n)^a$
2^{2a}	2^{2a+10}	2^{2a-x}	$^-2^{2a+x}$	$(2^2n)^a$

42. $^-4^7 \div 4^{-2} = ^-4^{7- ^-2} = ^-4^9$

$^-4^7 \div 4^x = ^-4^{7-x}$

$^-4^7 \div ^-4^x = 4^{7-x}$

$^-4^7 \div n^7 = \dfrac{^-4^7}{n^7} = -\left(\dfrac{4}{n}\right)^7$

$4^a \div 4^{-2} = 4^{a- ^-2}$

$4^a \div 4^x = 4^{a-x}$

$4^a \div ^-4^x = ^-4^{a-x}$

$4^a \div n^7 = \dfrac{4^a}{n^7} = 4an^{-7}$

$4^7 \div 4^{-2} = 4^{7- ^-2} = 4^9$ ✓

$4^7 \div 4^x = 4^{7-x} = 4^{7-x}$ ✓

$4^7 \div ^-4^x = ^-4^{7-x} = ^-4^{7-x}$ ✓

$4^7 \div n^7 = \dfrac{4^7}{n^7} = \left(\dfrac{4}{n}\right)^7$

$\div$	4^{-2}	4^x	-4^x	n^7
$^-4^7$	$^-4^9$	$^-4^{7-x}$	4^{7-x}	$-\left(\dfrac{4}{n}\right)^{-7}$
4^a	4^{a+2}	4^{a-x}	$^-4^{a-x}$	$4^a n^{-7}$
4^7	4^9	4^{7-x}	$^-4^{7-x}$	$\left(\dfrac{4}{n}\right)^7$

43. $(5 \times 10^{13}) \div (2 \times 10^5) = 2.5 \times 10^{13-5}$

$\qquad\qquad\qquad\qquad = 2.5 \times 10^8$

It takes about 2.5×10^8 seconds for light to travel between Sirius and Earth.

$60 \times 60 \times 24 \times 365 = 31{,}536{,}000$ seconds per year

$31{,}536{,}000 = 3.1536 \times 10^7$

There are 3.1536×10^7 seconds in one year.

$(2.5 \times 10^8) \div (3.1536 \times 10^7) \approx 0.79 \times 10^1$

$\qquad\qquad\qquad\qquad \approx 7.9$

about 7.9 yr

44a. $200{,}000{,}000 = 2 \times 10^8$

1 billion $= 1 \times 10^9$

$(1 \times 10^9) \div (2 \times 10^8) = 0.5 \times 10^{9-8}$

$\qquad\qquad\qquad\qquad = 0.5 \times 10^1$

$\qquad\qquad\qquad\qquad = 5$

about 5

44b. $(6 \times 10^9) \div (1 \times 10^9) = 6 \times 10^{9-9}$

$\qquad\qquad\qquad\qquad = 6 \times 10^0$

$\qquad\qquad\qquad\qquad = 6 \times 1$

$\qquad\qquad\qquad\qquad = 6$

about 6

44c. It grew 6 times from 1850 to 2000 and only 5 times from 1 A.D. to 1850 from 1850 to 2000

45. $(3 \times 10^{-20}) \div (6 \times 10^{-29}) = 0.5 \times 10^{-20- ^-29} =$

$\qquad 0.5 \times 10^9 = 5 \times 10^8$

$(6 \times 10^{14}) \div (5 \times 10^8) = 1.2 \times 10^{14-8} =$

$\qquad 1.2 \times 10^6$

$(6 \times 10^{14}) \div (3 \times 10^{134}) = 2 \times 10^{14-134} =$

$\qquad 2 \times 10^{-120}$

$(3 \times 10^{-20}) \div (2 \times 10^{-120}) = 1.5 \times 10^{-20 - {}^-120} =$
1.5×10^{100}

$(3 \times 10^{-20}) \div (3 \times 10^x) = 1 \times 10^{-20 - x}$

$(6 \times 10^{14}) \div (3 \times 10^x) = 2 \times 10^{14 - x}$

$(3 \times 10^x) \times (5 \times 10^{a-x-1}) = 15 \times 10^{x + a - x - 1} =$
$15 \times 10^{a-1} = 1.5 \times 10^a$

$(1.5 \times 10^a) \div (5 \times 10^8) = 0.3 \times 10^{a-8} = 3 \times 10^{a-9}$

$(1.5 \times 10^a) \div (2 \times 10^{-120}) = 0.75 \times 10^{a - {}^-120} =$
$7.5 \times 10^{a + 119}$

$\div$	5×10^8	2×10^{-120}	3×10^x
3×10^{-20}	6×10^{-29}	1.5×10^{100}	$1 \times 10^{-20-x}$
6×10^{14}	1.2×10^6	3×10^{134}	$2 \times 10^{14-x}$
1.5×10^a	$3 \times 10^{a-9}$	$7.5 \times 10^{a+119}$	$5 \times 10^{a-x-1}$

46. $3^{13} = 1,594,323$

$3^{14} = 4,782,969$

3^{14} is closest.

$4^{10} = 1,048,576$

$4^{11} = 4,194,304$

4^{11} is closest.

$5^9 = 1,953,125$

$5^{10} = 9,765,625$

5^9 is closest.

47. a. $6 = 3 \cdot 2$

b. 7 is prime

c. $16 = 2^4$

only c; Possible explanation: the other numbers all have factors that are not 2.

48. 1st C: x

2nd C: $2x$

3rd C: 2^2x

4th C: 2^3x

nth C: $2^{n-1}x$

8th C: $2^{8-1}x = 2^7x$

2^7x

49a.

Day	Amount Received Each Day	Total Amount
1	$0.01	$0.01
2	$0.02	$0.01 + $0.02 = $0.03
3	$0.04	$0.03 + $0.04 = $0.07
4	$0.08	$0.07 + $0.08 = $0.15
5	$0.16	$0.15 + $0.16 = $0.31
6	$0.32	$0.31 + $0.32 = $0.63
7	$0.64	$0.63 + $0.64 = $1.27
8	$1.28	$1.27 + $1.28 = $2.55
9	$2.56	$2.55 + $2.56 = $5.11
10	$5.12	$5.11 + $5.12 = $10.23
11	$10.24	$10.23 + $10.24 = $20.47
12	$20.48	$20.47 + $20.48 = $40.95
13	$40.96	$40.95 + $40.96 = $81.91

He will have a great deal more than $50 based on his plan; by the 13th day he will have already received more than $50 altogether.

49b. $40.96 \cdot 2 = \$81.92$

On the 14th day he will receive $81.92.

49c. Look for a pattern as you compute the number pennies received each day.

Day	Pennies Received Each Day	Power of 2
1	1	2^0
2	$1 \cdot 2 = 2$	2^1
3	$2 \cdot 2 = 4$	2^2
4	$4 \cdot 2 = 8$	2^3
5	$8 \cdot 2 = 16$	2^4
6	$16 \cdot 2 = 32$	2^5
7	$32 \cdot 2 = 64$	2^6
n	—	2^{n-1}
30	—	2^{29}

The number of pennies received on day n is 2^{n-1}.

$2^{29} = 536,870,912$ pennies $= \$5,368,709.12$

He would receive $5,368,709.12 on the last day of June.

49d. Look for a pattern as you compute the cumulative amount of money received after each day.

Day	Amount Received Each Day	Total Amount
1	$0.01	$0.01
2	$0.02	$0.01 + $0.02 = $0.03
3	$0.04	$0.03 + $0.04 = $0.07
4	$0.08	$0.07 + $0.08 = $0.15
5	$0.16	$0.15 + $0.16 = $0.31
6	$0.32	$0.31 + $0.32 = $0.63
7	$0.64	$0.63 + $0.64 = $1.27
n	x	$2x - \$0.01$
30	$5,368,709.12	$2 \cdot \$5,368,709.12 - \$0.01 = \$10,737,418.23$

The total amount of money received after n days is 1 penny less than twice the amount of money received on day n.

He would receive $10,737,418.23 in the month of June.

50. Look for a pattern as you compute the number of players that remain after each round.

Round, r	Players Remaining, p
1	$32 = \dfrac{64}{2} = \dfrac{64}{2^1}$
2	$16 = \dfrac{64}{4} = \dfrac{64}{2^2}$
3	$8 = \dfrac{64}{8} = \dfrac{64}{2^3}$
4	$4 = \dfrac{64}{16} = \dfrac{64}{2^4}$
5	$2 = \dfrac{64}{32} = \dfrac{64}{2^5}$
6	$1 = \dfrac{64}{64} = \dfrac{64}{2^6}$
r	$p = \dfrac{64}{2^r}$

Any rule that is equivalent to $p = \dfrac{64}{2^r}$ is correct.

Mi-Yung: $p = 64 \cdot 2^{-r} = 64 \cdot \dfrac{1}{2^r} = \dfrac{64}{2^r}$

Antonia: $p = 64 \cdot \dfrac{1}{2^r} = \dfrac{64}{2^r}$

Peter: $p = 64 \cdot \left(\dfrac{1}{2}\right)^r = 64 \cdot \dfrac{1}{2^r} = \dfrac{64}{2^r}$

Damon: $p = 64 \cdot 0.5^r = 64 \cdot \left(\dfrac{1}{2}\right)^r = 64 \cdot \dfrac{1}{2^r} = \dfrac{64}{2^r}$

Tamika: $p = 64 \cdot (^-2)^r$

Terrill, Mi-Yung, Antonia, Peter, and Damon are correct. Tamika is not correct. Possible explanation: p will be negative for odd values of r.

51a. $\dfrac{1}{5} = 5^{-1}$
$1 = 5^0$
$5 = 5^1$
$25 = 5^2$
$125 = 5^3$
$625 = 5^4$
5^n

51b. $625 = 5^4; n = 4$
$1 = 5^0; n = 0$
$\dfrac{1}{5} = 5^{-1}, n = {}^-1$

52. 4^{42} is greater; $4^{42} = (2^2)^{42} = 2^{2 \cdot 42} = 2^{84}$, which is greater than 2^{80}.

53. 27^{-500} is greater; $27^{-500} = (3^3)^{-500} = 3^{3 \cdot {}^-500} = 3^{-1,500}$, which is greater than $3^{-1,600}$.

54. 4^{45}; Possible explanation: If the first number were 16^{20}, it would be equal to $(4^2)^{20}$ or $4^{2 \cdot 20} = 4^{40}$. Since 12 is less than 16, 12^{20} is less than 16^{20} or 4^{40}, which is less than 4^{45}.

55. The baker seems to have used the product law $a^c b^c = (ab)^c$ for an addition expression. The actual difference is $(45 + 2)^2 - 45^2 = 2,209 - 2,025 = 184 \text{ cm}^2$.

56. $60 \times 60 \times 24 \times 365 = 31{,}536{,}000$ seconds per year
$31{,}536{,}000 = 3.1536 \times 10^7$
There are 3.1536×10^7 seconds in one year.
$(6 \times 10^8) \div (3.1536 \times 10^7) \approx 1.9 \times 10^{8-7}$
$\approx 1.9 \times 10^1$
about 1.9×10^1 miles per second

57a. $1{,}000 = 10^3$
$8 \times 10^{-5} \cdot 10^3 = 8 \times 10^{-5+3}$
$= 8 \times 10^{-2}$
8×10^{-2} m

57b. $100 \text{ cm} = 1 \text{ m}$
$100 = 10^2$
$8 \times 10^{-2} \cdot 10^2 = 8 \times 10^{-2+2}$
$= 8 \times 10^0$
$= 8 \times 1$
$= 8$
8 cm

58. no; Possible explanation: The b values don't change by a constant amount as the a values increase by 1.

59. yes; Possible explanation: The d values increase by a constant amount as the c values increase by 1.

60. b-intercept: 0
slope $= \dfrac{^-6.6 + 8.8}{^-3 + 4} = \dfrac{2.2}{1} = 2.2$
Possible equation: $b = 2.2a$

61. f-intercept: $^-10$
slope $= \dfrac{^-13.75 + 15}{^-3 + 4} = \dfrac{1.25}{1} = 1.25$
Possible equation: $f = 1.25e - 10$

62. $4x - 4y = {}^-3$
$^-4y = {}^-4x - 3$
$y = x + \dfrac{3}{4}$
$y = x + 0.75$
increasing, since the slope is positive

63. $2y = 4 - 3x$
$y = 2 - \dfrac{3}{2}x$
$y = {}^-1.5x + 2$
decreasing, since the slope is negative

64. $^-x = {}^-12 - 2y$
$2y = x - 12$
$y = \dfrac{1}{2}x - 6$
increasing, since the slope is positive

65. $y = 4x + 6$
increasing, since the slope is positive

66a. Possible equations:
Site 1: $C = 0.75s + 4$
Site 2: $C = 0.6s + 5.5$
Site 3: $C = 1.25s$

66b.

Sticker Cost

[Graph showing three lines labeled Site 1, Site 2, Site 3, with vertical axis C from 0 to 20 and horizontal axis s from 0 to 20.]

66c. Site 2
66d. Site 1 or 2
67a. $(0, 2)$
67b. the y-axis

Page 166   In Your Own Words

Possible answer:

Dear Classmate,

I hear you are confused about multiplying numbers written as exponents. Let's look at three cases.

Case 1 If the numbers have the same exponent, as in $3^2 \cdot 4^2$, you can express this product as the product of the two bases raised to their common power, $(3 \cdot 4)^2$ or 12^2, which is 144. Here you are using one of the Product Laws, which states that $a^c \cdot b^c = (ab)^c$.

Case 2 If the numbers have the same base, as in $2^3 \cdot 2^4$, you can express this product as the common base raised to the sum of the two powers, 2^{3+4} or 2^7, which is 128. Here you are using the other Product Law, which states that $a^b \cdot a^c = a^{b+c}$.

Case 3 If the numbers have different exponents and different bases, as in $2^5 \cdot 3^4$, you <u>cannot</u> multiply the bases or add the exponents, $2^5 \cdot 3^4 \neq (2 \cdot 3)^{5+4}$. To multiply these numbers, you must evaluate each power, then multiply. $2^5 \cdot 3^4 = 32 \cdot 81$ or 2,592.

Sincerely,

A Fellow Classmate

3-2 | Exponential Relationships

Page 171 Problem Set A

1. Each year is 1.02 times more than the previous year.

   1.02

2. $102{,}000(1.02) = 104{,}040$; the answers are the same.

3.

Years After 1994	Estimated Population of Tonga	
	Written as a Product	**Using Exponential Notation**
0	100,000	$100{,}000 \cdot 1.02^0$
1	$100{,}000 \cdot 1.02$	$100{,}000 \cdot 1.02^1$
2	$100{,}000 \cdot 1.02 \cdot 1.02$	$100{,}000 \cdot 1.02^2$
3	$100{,}000 \cdot 1.02 \cdot 1.02 \cdot 1.02$	$100{,}000 \cdot 1.02^3$
4	$100{,}000 \cdot 1.02 \cdot 1.02 \cdot 1.02 \cdot 1.02$	$100{,}000 \cdot 1.02^4$
5	$100{,}000 \cdot 1.02 \cdot 1.02 \cdot 1.02 \cdot 1.02 \cdot 1.02$	$100{,}000 \cdot 1.02^5$

4. $100{,}000 \cdot 1.02^{25} \approx 164{,}061$

5. 1.02

6. $p = 100{,}000 \cdot 1.02^n$

7. 1.05; Possible explanation: $100{,}000 \cdot 0.05 + 100{,}000 = 100{,}000(1.05)$

8. $100{,}000 \cdot 0.2 + 100{,}000 = 100{,}000 \cdot 1.2$

   $1.2; p = 100{,}000 \cdot 1.2^n$

Page 172 Problem Set B

1a. growth factor 1.1 → weight increase of 10%

   kitten

1b. kitten grows 10% per week; there are 4 weeks in a month

   4

2a. growth factor 1.2 → weight increase of 20%

   orangutan

2b. orangutan grows 20% per month

   1

3a. growth factor 1.5 → weight increase of 50%

   duckweed

3b. duckweed grows 50% per week; there are 4 weeks in a month

   4

4a. growth factor 1.05 → weight increase of 5%

   wheat plant

4b. wheat plant grows 5% per day; there are 30 days in a month

   30

Page 172 Share and Summarize

1. Table a:

   x values increase by 1.

   y values: $3 \cdot 4 = 12$

   $\phantom{y \text{ values: }}12 \cdot 4 = 48$

   $\phantom{y \text{ values: }}48 \cdot 4 = 192$

   Table b:

   x values increase by 1.

   y values: $4 \cdot 2 = 8$

   $\phantom{y \text{ values: }}8 \cdot 2 = 16$

   $\phantom{y \text{ va}}16 \cdot 1.75 = 28$

   Table c:

   x values increase by 1.

   y values: $2 \cdot 2 = 4$

   $\phantom{y \text{ values: }}4 \cdot 1.5 = 6$

   $\phantom{y \text{ values: }}6 \cdot \dfrac{4}{3} = 8$

   Table d:

   x values increase by 1.

   y values: $^-60 \cdot 0.5 = {}^-30$

   $\phantom{y \text{ values: }}^-30 \cdot \dfrac{2}{3} = {}^-20$

   $\phantom{y \text{ val}}^-20 \cdot 0.75 = {}^-15$

   Only Table a; it's the only one in which the first y value is repeatedly multiplied by the same number.

2. Possible answer: convert R to a decimal and add 1. Take that result to the t power, and multiply by c.

Page 173 Problem Set C

1. $50 \cdot 2 = 100$

   $100 \cdot 2 = 200$

   $200 \cdot 2 = 400$

   $400 \cdot 2 = 800$

   $800 \cdot 2 = 1{,}600$

   1,600

2. $50 \cdot 2^0 = 50$

   $50 \cdot 2^1 = 100$

   $50 \cdot 2^2 = 200$

   $50 \cdot 2^3 = 400$

   $50 \cdot 2^4 = 800$

   $p = 50 \cdot 2^n$

3. 2; it's the base you take powers of.

4a. Evan's; although the population does begin at 50, it increases by 50 only the first hour.

4b. Since it doesn't define a starting point, Tamika's description could define other populations as well, such as 20, 40, 80, ... Jesse's description can produce only this output.

5. The power of 2 is multiplied by the starting population.

6a.

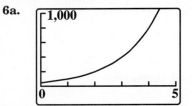

6b. yes; Possible explanation: The bacteria still exist in the 60 min between the times given, and you wouldn't expect the population to double in an instant.

7. $50 \cdot 2^5 = 1,600$
$50 \cdot 2^6 = 3,200$
$50 \cdot 2^7 = 6,400$
$50 \cdot 2^8 = 12,800$
$50 \cdot 2^9 = 25,600$
$50 \cdot 2^{10} = 51,200$
$50 \cdot 2^{11} = 102,400$

At Hour 11, the population is 102,400. Explanations will vary. Possible explanation: I let n be greater and greater until the population was over 100,000.

Page 174   Problem Set D

1. $25,000 \cdot 5 = 125,000$
$125,000 \cdot 5 = 625,000$
5

2. Hour 4: $25,000 \div 5 = 5,000$
Hour 3: $5,000 \div 5 = 1,000$
Hour 2: $1,000 \div 5 = 200$
Hour 1: $200 \div 5 = 40$
Hour 0: $40 \div 5 = 8$

8; If you start at Hour 7 and go backward, you divide by 5, so divide 25,000 by 5 for each hour until Hour 0.

3. $p = 8 \cdot 5^n$; Multiply the starting population by the growth factor to a power.

4a.

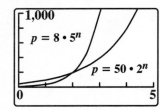

4b. They have the same general shape, but the graph of $p = 8 \cdot 5^n$ starts lower and increases more quickly than the graph of $p = 50 \cdot 2^n$.

Page 174   Share and Summarize

1. Find the growth factor (the constant multiplier), and then look for the starting point. The equation is the starting point times the growth factor raised to a power.

2. $c \cdot x^t$

Pages 175–176   Problem Set E

1. $2,000 \cdot \dfrac{3}{5} = 1,200$

$1,200 \cdot \dfrac{3}{5} = 720$

$720 \cdot \dfrac{3}{5} = 432$

Mirror Number	Reflected Light (lumens)
0	2,000
1	1,200
2	720
3	432

2. $2,000 = 2,000\left(\dfrac{3}{5}\right)^0$

$1,200 = 2,000\left(\dfrac{3}{5}\right)^1$

$720 = 2,000\left(\dfrac{3}{5}\right)^2$

$432 = 2,000\left(\dfrac{3}{5}\right)^3$

$2,000\left(\dfrac{3}{5}\right)^n$ lumens or $2,000(0.6)^n$ lumens

3.

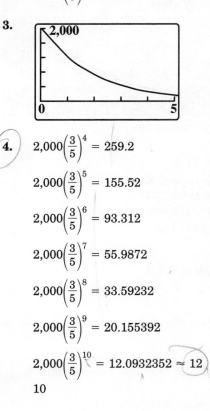

4. $2,000\left(\dfrac{3}{5}\right)^4 = 259.2$

$2,000\left(\dfrac{3}{5}\right)^5 = 155.52$

$2,000\left(\dfrac{3}{5}\right)^6 = 93.312$

$2,000\left(\dfrac{3}{5}\right)^7 = 55.9872$

$2,000\left(\dfrac{3}{5}\right)^8 = 33.59232$

$2,000\left(\dfrac{3}{5}\right)^9 = 20.155392$

$2,000\left(\dfrac{3}{5}\right)^{10} = 12.0932352 \approx 12$

10

5. $2{,}000\left(\dfrac{3}{5}\right)^{11} \approx 7.26$

$2{,}000\left(\dfrac{3}{5}\right)^{12} \approx 4.35$

$2{,}000\left(\dfrac{3}{5}\right)^{13} \approx 2.61$

$2{,}000\left(\dfrac{3}{5}\right)^{14} \approx 1.57$

$2{,}000\left(\dfrac{3}{5}\right)^{15} \approx 0.94$

$2{,}000\left(\dfrac{3}{5}\right)^{16} \approx 0.56$

$2{,}000\left(\dfrac{3}{5}\right)^{17} \approx 0.34$

$2{,}000\left(\dfrac{3}{5}\right)^{18} \approx 0.20$

$2{,}000\left(\dfrac{3}{5}\right)^{19} \approx 0.12$

19

6a. 1,000 lumens

6b. 700 lumens

6c. $700 \div 1{,}000 = 0.7$

0.7

Pages 177–178 Problem Set F

1. end of second year: $\$1{,}200 \cdot 0.80 = \$960$

end of third year: $\$960 \cdot 0.80 = \$768$

2.

Year	Value at the End of the Year
0	$1,500
1	$1,200
2	$960
3	$768
4	$614.40
5	$491.52
6	$393.22
7	$314.57
8	$251.66
9	$201.33
10	$161.06
11	$128.85
12	$103.08
13	$82.46
14	$65.97
15	$52.78
16	$42.22
17	$33.78
18	$27.02
19	$21.62
20	$17.29
21	$13.84
22	$11.07
23	$8.85
24	$7.08
25	$5.67

about \$5.67; Possible explanation: I multiplied 1,500 by 0.8, 25 times.

3. $1{,}500 = 1{,}500 \cdot 0.8^0$

$1{,}200 = 1{,}500 \cdot 0.8^1$

$960 = 1{,}500 \cdot 0.8^2$

$768 = 1{,}500 \cdot 0.8^3$

$V = 1{,}500 \cdot 0.8^n$

4. yes, 0.8

5a.

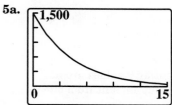

5b. in a little over 3 years

5c. in a little over 6 years

6. 0.83; Possible explanation: 17% is the amount of change (loss) each year. To find the value, not the amount of loss, multiply by $1 - 0.17 = 0.83$

7. $1 - 0.40 = 0.60$

8a. $n = 0$

$v = 219(0.75)^0$

$\quad = 219(1)$

$\quad = 219$

$219

8b. $n = 1$

$v = 219(0.75)^1$

$\quad = 219(0.75)$

$\quad = 164.25$

$164.25

8c. 0.75

8d. The telephone was originally worth \$219, and it was worth 25% less each year, or 75% of the previous year's value. The decay factor is 0.75.

Page 178 Share and Summarize

1. the starting value or amount

2. the decay factor; Possible explanation: For every increase of 1 in x, the starting value is multiplied by that number of b's.

Pages 178–180 Problem Set G

1a. The growth factor is 3, and $3 > 1$.

exponential growth

1b. The growth factor is 0.3, and $0.3 < 1$.

exponential decay

1c. The relationship does not involve a variable exponent.

not exponential

1d. The growth factor is $\frac{1}{4}$, and $\frac{1}{4} < 1$.

exponential decay

1e. The growth factor is 1.5, and $1.5 > 1$.

exponential growth

1f. The relationship does not involve a variable exponent.

not exponential

2a. Graphs ii and iii; Possible explanation: Exponential relationships don't change directions (increasing/decreasing, or up/down) like these do.

2b. Graph i: growth; Graph iv: decay

3a. Answers will vary.

3b. no

4a. $6 \cdot 1.5 = 9$

$9 \cdot 1.3 \approx 12$

$12 \cdot 1.25 = 15$

Could not be exponential; y values are not multiplied by a constant amount from one to the next.

4b. $6 \cdot 1.5 = 9$

$9 \cdot 1.5 = 13.5$

$13.5 \cdot 1.5 = 20.25$

Could be exponential growth; multiply each y value by 1.5 to get the next.

4c. $56 \cdot 0.5 = 28$

$28 \cdot 0.5 = 14$

$14 \cdot 0.5 = 7$

Could be exponential decay; multiply each y value by 0.5 to get the next.

5.

Day, x	Amoebas at the End of the Day, y
1	4
2	16
3	64
4	256

$4 \cdot 4 = 16 = 4^2$

$16 \cdot 4 = 64 = 4^3$

$64 \cdot 4 = 256 = 4^4$

The y value is repeatedly multiplied by the same number, 4, to get the next y value.

$y = 4^x$

Yes; the growth factor is 4.

6.

Day, x	Miles Hiked by the End of the Day, y
1	15
2	30
3	45
4	60

$15 \cdot 2 = 30$

$30 \cdot 1.5 = 45$

$45 \cdot 1.\overline{3} = 60$

The y value is not repeatedly multiplied by the same number to get the next y value.

$y = 15x$

No; she adds 15 mi every day, which makes this a linear relationship.

Pages 180–181   Problem Set H

1.   Culture 1:

$300 \div 100 = 3$

The growth factor is 3.

$300 \cdot 3 = 900$

$900 \cdot 3 = 2{,}700$

$2{,}700 \cdot 3 = 8{,}100$

Culture 2:

$25 \div 100 = 0.25$

$\sqrt{0.25} = 0.5$

The decay factor is 0.5.

$100 \cdot 0.5 = 50$

$25 \cdot 0.5 = 12.5 \approx 12$

$12 \cdot 0.5 = 6$

Culture 3:

$70 \div 100 = 0.7$

The decay factor is 0.7.

$70 \cdot 0.7 = 49$

$49 \cdot 0.7 = 34.3 \approx 34$

$34 \cdot 0.7 = 23.8 \approx 24$

Culture 4:

$12{,}500 \div 100 = 125$

$\sqrt[3]{125} = 5$

The growth factor is 5.

$100 \cdot 5 = 500$

$500 \cdot 5 = 2{,}500$

$12{,}500 \cdot 5 = 62{,}500$

Days	Culture 1	Culture 2	Culture 3	Culture 4
0	100	100	100	100
1	300	50	70	500
2	900	25	49	2,500
3	2,700	12	34	12,500
4	8,100	6	24	62,500

2.   Culture 1, growth factor 3

Culture 4, growth factor 5

3.   Culture 2, decay factor 0.5

Culture 3, decay factor 0.7

4a. Culture 1: starting population 100, growth factor 3

$p = 100(3^d)$

Culture 2: starting population 100, decay factor 0.5

$p = 100(0.5^d)$

Culture 3: starting population 100, decay factor 0.7

$p = 100(0.7^d)$

Culture 4: starting population 100, growth factor 5

$p = 100(5^d)$

4b. They have 100 for the multiplier.

4c. They have different growth or decay factors.

5a.

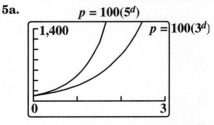

5b.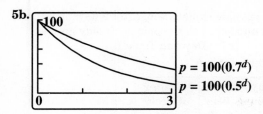

$p = 100(0.7^d)$
$p = 100(0.5^d)$

5c. The exponential growth graphs begin close to the horizontal axis and increase from left to right. The exponential decay graphs decrease from left to right and end close to the horizontal axis.

5d. Each graph is a curve that starts at (0, 100).

5e. Graphs that increase more rapidly (steeper growth) have greater growth factors. Graphs that decrease less rapidly (less steep decay) have greater decay factors; for example, the graph with decay factor of 0.7 is less steep than the graph with decay factor 0.5.

Page 181　Share and Summarize

1. For the relationship to be exponential, the other quantity must be multiplied by a constant factor.

2. Possible answer: The graph must be a smooth curve that increases or decreases without changing direction as a parabola does; there will be a horizontal line that the graph doesn't cross.

3. For exponential growth, the graphs increase, getting steeper from left to right. For exponential decay, the graphs decrease, getting less steep from left to right. In growth equations, the base for the exponent is greater than 1; in decay equations, it is less than 1.

Pages 182–189　On Your Own Exercises

1a. $24\% = 0.24$
$1 + 0.24 = 1.24$
1.24

1b. $1,000 \cdot 1.24 = 1,240$

1c. $6.9\% = 0.069$
$1 + 0.69 = 1.069$
1.069

1d. $1,000 \cdot 1.069 = 1,069$

2a.

Years after 1995	Written as a Product	Using Exponential Notation
0	10,000,000	$10,000,000 \cdot 1.04^0$
1	10,400,000	$10,000,000 \cdot 1.04^1$
2	10,816,000	$10,000,000 \cdot 1.04^2$
3	11,248,640	$10,000,000 \cdot 1.04^3$
4	11,698,586	$10,000,000 \cdot 1.04^4$
5	12,166,529	$10,000,000 \cdot 1.04^5$

2b. $10,000,000 \cdot 1.04^{25} \approx 26,658,363$

2c. $p = 10,000,000 \cdot 1.04^n$

2d. 1.04

3. $2 \cdot 5 = 10$
$10 \cdot 5 = 50$
5

4. $15,000,000 \cdot 4 = 60,000,000$
$60,000,000 \cdot 4 = 240,000,000$
4

5. $3 \times 10^8 \cdot 2 = 6 \cdot 10^8$
$6 \cdot 10^8 \cdot 2 = 12 \times 10^8 = 1.2 \cdot 10^9$
2

6. $2 \cdot 5^1 = 10$
$2 \cdot 5^2 = 50$
The starting population is 2 and the growth factor is 5.
$2 \cdot 5^n$

7a. $1 - 0.24 = 0.76$
0.76

7b. $1 - 0.069 = 0.931$
0.931

8. Tamika; the depreciation is how much value the car loses each year. When the car depreciates 40%, the decay factor—the base for the exponent is—$1 - 0.4 = 0.6$.

9. There is no exponential variable.
no

10. yes, growth factor 4

...actor

16a. When $x = 0, y = 2$. It is an exponential growth equation since $1.1 > 1$, so the graph curves upward.
Graph iv

16b. When $x = 0, y = 2$. It is an exponential decay equation since $0.2 < 1$, so the graph curves downward. $0.2 < 0.9$, so the graph shows more rapid decay in the neighborhood of (0, 2) than Graph i.
Graph v

16c. When $x = 0$, $y = 0.1$. It is an exponential growth equation since $1.3 > 1$, so the graph curves upward. $1.3 < 1.5$, so the graph shows less rapid growth in the interval following $(0, 0.1)$ than Graph iii.

Graph ii

16d. When $x = 0$, $y = 0.1$. It is an exponential growth equation since $1.5 > 1$, so the graph curves upward. $1.5 > 1.3$, so the graph shows more rapid growth in the interval following $(0, 0.1)$ than Graph ii.

Graph iii

16e. When $x = 0$, $y = 2$. It is an exponential decay equation since $0.9 < 1$, so the graph curves downward. $0.9 > 0.2$, so the graph shows less rapid decay in the neighborhood of $(0, 2)$ than Graph v.

Graph i

17a. $200 \cdot 0.05 = 10$

$10

17b. $200 + 10 = 210$

$210

17c. I added the original investment to the interest.

17d. $210 \cdot 0.05 = 10.50$

$10.50

17e. $200 \cdot 1.05 = 210$

$210 \cdot 1.05 = 220.5$

$220.5 \cdot 1.05 = 231.525$

$231.525 \cdot 1.05 = 243.10125$

$243.10125 \cdot 1.05 = 255.2563125$

Answers may vary due to rounding.

Years	Account Value
0	$200
1	$210
2	$220.50
3	$231.53
4	$243.10
5	$255.26

17f. $200 \cdot 1.05^{50} = \$2,293.48$

$200 \cdot 1.05^{n}$

17g. Ella: $n = 60 - 20 = 40$

$600 \cdot 1.05^{40} = \$4,223.99$

Jan: $n = 60 - 45 = 15$

$600 \cdot 1.05^{15} = \$4,157.86$

18a. $192 \div 128 = 1.5$

$128 \cdot 1.5 = 192$

$192 \cdot 1.5 = 288$

$200 \cdot 1.5 = 300$

$300 \cdot 1.5 = 450$

$648 \cdot 1.5 = 972$

$972 \cdot 1.5 = 1,458$

1.5

18b. no; Possible explanation: After 2 days in Table A, the number of sick people is already greater than it is for Day 5 in Table B.

18c. Extend Table A

Days Since Illness Was Identified	Number of Sick People
3	432
4	648

Yes; if you extend Table A, you find that you have a population of 648 in Day 4, as is indicated in Table C.

19a. $21,600 \div 600 = 36$

There are 2 hours between 600 and 21,600.

$\sqrt{36} = 6$

The growth factor is 6.

$600 \div 6 = 100$

$600 \cdot 6 = 3,600$

$21,600 \cdot 6 = 129,600$

Hour	Population
0	100
1	600
2	3,600
3	21,600
4	129,600

19b. 6

19c. The starting population is 100 and the growth factor is 6.

$100 \cdot 6^{n}$

20a. $x = 0$

$y = 1,000(0.7)^{0}$

$\quad = 1,000(1)$

$\quad = 1,000$

20b. $y = 1,000(0.7)^{20}$

$\quad \approx 0.8$

Yes; although y never reaches 0, it does get below 1. You can't have part of a bird, so that means the population will eventually drop to 0.

21a. **i.** The amount of compound is 0.5 of the previous value since $100 \cdot 0.5 = 50$.

Sample 4

ii. The amount of compound is 0.8 of the previous value since $51.2 \cdot 0.8 = 41.0$.

Sample 1

iii. The amount of compound is 0.6 of the previous value since $36.0 \cdot 0.6 = 21.6$

Sample 3

iv. The amount of compound is 0.7 of the previous value since $8.2 \cdot 0.7 \approx 5.8$.

Sample 2

21b. For i: the starting value is given at 100 g

For ii:

   Time = 2: $51.2 \div 0.8 = 64$

   Time = 1: $64 \div 0.8 = 80$

   Time = 0: $80 \div 0.8 = 100$

   100 g

For iii:

   Time = 1: $36.0 \div 0.6 = 60$

   Time = 0: $60 \div 0.6 = 100$

   100 g

For iv:

   Time = 6: $8.2 \div 0.7 \approx 11.7$

   Time = 5: $11.7 \div 0.7 \approx 16.7$

   Time = 4: $16.7 \div 0.7 \approx 23.9$

   Time = 3: $23.9 \div 0.7 \approx 34.2$

   Time = 2: $34.2 \div 0.7 \approx 48.8$

   Time = 1: $48.8 \div 0.7 \approx 69.7$

   Time = 1: $69.7 \div 0.7 \approx 100$

   100 g

21c. Sample 1: 0.8; Sample 2: 0.7; Sample 3: 0.6; Sample 4: 0.5

21d. 1: Graph W; 2: Graph X; 3: Graph Y; 4: Graph Z

21e. Check to see how long it takes for each sample to reach 50 g.

Sample 1: a little over 3 centuries

Sample 2: about 2 centuries

Sample 3: a little over 1 century

Sample 4: 1 century

22a. The starting point of the data is 10 and the growth factor is 2.

yes

22b. 1 hour = $\dfrac{1}{24}$

2 hours = $\dfrac{2}{24} = \dfrac{1}{12}$

3 hours = $\dfrac{3}{24} = \dfrac{1}{8}$

24 hours = $\dfrac{24}{24} = 1$

22c. 1 hour: $p = 10 \cdot 16{,}777{,}216^{\frac{1}{24}} = 20$

2 hours: $p = 10 \cdot 16{,}777{,}216^{\frac{1}{12}} = 40$

3 hours: $p = 10 \cdot 16{,}777{,}216^{\frac{1}{8}} = 80$

24 hours: $p = 10 \cdot 16{,}777{,}216^{1} = 167{,}772{,}160$

yes

22d. Both are correct. Possible explanation: Dion's equation uses time in hours. If time is given in days, d, you need to multiply by 24 to get the time in hours. So Dion's equation is also $p = 10 \cdot 2^{24d} = 10 \cdot (2^{24})^{d} = 10 \cdot 16{,}777{,}216^{d}$, which is Lucita's equation.

23a.

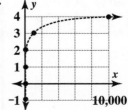

23b. The x values are multiplied by 10.

10

24. $3 \cdot 3 = 9 \text{ m}^2$

25. $22 \cdot 22 = 484 \text{ cm}^2$

26. $m = \text{slope} = \dfrac{\text{rise}}{\text{run}} = \dfrac{^-6 - 0}{^-6 - ^-2} = \dfrac{^-6}{^-4} = \dfrac{3}{2}$

$y = mx + b$

$y = \dfrac{3}{2}x + b,\ (^-2, 0)$

$0 = \dfrac{3}{2}(^-2) + b$

$0 = ^-3 + b$

$b = 3$

$y = \dfrac{3}{2}x + 3$

Possible equation: $y = \dfrac{3}{2}x + 3$

27. $y = ^-2.5x + b,\ (2, ^-4)$

$^-4 = ^-2.5(2) + b$

$^-4 = ^-5 + b$

$b = 1$

$y = ^-2.5x + 1$

28a. The negative sign indicates the graph opens downward. The vertex is at $(0, 2)$.

Graph H

28b. The vertex is at $(2, 0)$.

Graph J

28c. The negative sign indicates the graph opens downward. The vertex is at $(0, 0)$.

Graph F

28d. The negative sign indicates the graph opens downward. The vertex is at $(^-2, 0)$.

Graph G

29a.

x	y
1	0.5
2	1

$1 - 0.5 = 0.5$

29b.

x	y
1	0.5
$^-2$	$^-1$

$^-1 - 0.5 = ^-1.5$

30a.

x	y
1	0
2	2

$2 - 0 = 2$

30b.

x	y
1	0
$^-2$	$^-6$

$^-6 - 0 = ^-6$

31a.

x	y
1	9
2	18

$18 - 9 = 9$

31b.

x	y
1	9
⁻2	⁻18

⁻18 − 9 = ⁻27

32a. $h = 18 - 4.9t^2$

$h = 18 - 4.9(0)^2 = 0$

$h = 18 - 4.9(0.25)^2 = 17.69375$

$h = 18 - 4.9(0.5)^2 = 16.775$

$h = 18 - 4.9(0.75)^2 = 15.24375$

$h = 18 - 4.9(1)^2 = 13.1$

$h = 18 - 4.9(1.25)^2 = 10.34375$

$h = 18 - 4.9(1.5)^2 = 6.975$

$h = 18 - 4.9(1.75)^2 = 2.99375$

$h = 18 - 4.9(2.0)^2 = ⁻1.6$

Possible table:

t	0	0.25	0.5	0.75	1	1.25	1.5	1.75	2.0
h	18	17.7	16.8	15.2	13.1	10.3	7.0	3.0	⁻1.6

32b.

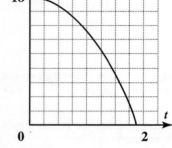

32c. about 1.4 s

23d. about 1.9 s

Page 185   In Your Own Words

Possible answer: Jill has $100 in a savings account. She adds $25 to the account each month from the money she makes at an after-school job. The relationship between the number of months since she started adding money to the account and the total amount of money in the account is linear.

Month	1	2	3	4	5	6	7	8
Balance	125	150	175	200	225	250	275	300

Her account balance grows at a slow but steady rate of $25 each month. If she could increase the amount of money in her account by 20% each month, then her account would experience exponential growth. Her account balance would at first appear to grow slowly, but would soon grow more rapidly than by just adding $25 each month.

Month	1	2	3	4	5	6	7	8
Balance	120	144	172.8	207.36	248.83	298.60	358.32	429.98

3-3 Radicals

Page 191   Problem Set A

1. $49 = 7 \cdot 7$
   $\sqrt{49} = 7$

2. $\sqrt{100} = 10 \cdot 10$
   $\sqrt{100} = 10$
   $100 = ⁻10 \cdot ⁻10$
   $⁻\sqrt{100} = ⁻10$
   10 and ⁻10

3. $225 = 15 \cdot 15$
   $⁻\sqrt{225} = ⁻15$

4. $2.25 = 1.5 \cdot 1.5$
   $\sqrt{2.25} = 1.5$
   $2.25 = ⁻1.5 \cdot ⁻1.5$
   $⁻\sqrt{2.25} = ⁻1.5$
   1.5 and ⁻1.5

5. $0 = 0 \cdot 0$
   $\sqrt{0} = 0$

6. $0.01 = ⁻0.1 \cdot ⁻0.1$
   $⁻\sqrt{0.01} = ⁻0.1$

7. 2

8. 1

9. A positive times a positive is a positive.
   A negative times a negative is a positive.
   A number times itself cannot be negative.
   none

10. False; although ⁻4 is a square root of 16, when you use the radical sign you must use the positive square root.

Page 192   Problem Set B

1. $(\sqrt{49})^2 = 7^2$
   $= 49$

2. $(\sqrt{2.25})^2 = 1.5^2$
   $= 2.25$

3. $(\sqrt{81})^2 = 9^2$
   $= 81$

4. $(⁻\sqrt{100})^2 = (⁻10)^2$
   $= 100$

5. $(⁻\sqrt{4})^2 = (⁻2)^2$
   $= 4$

6. $⁻(\sqrt{0.04})^2 = ⁻(0.2)^2$
   $= ⁻0.04$

7. You get n; the square root of n is another number that you multiply by itself to get n. Since squaring is multiplying by itself, you're multiplying the square root of n by the square root of n, which is n.

8. $\sqrt{100^2} = \sqrt{10,000}$
   $= 100$

9. $\sqrt{(^-4)^2} = \sqrt{16}$
   $= 4$
10. $\sqrt{0.04^2} = \sqrt{0.0016}$
    $= 0.04$
11. $\sqrt{(^-0.04)^2} = \sqrt{0.0016}$
    $= 0.04$

12a. n

12b. ^-n or $|n|$

12c. When n is positive, the answer is n, a positive number.

When n is negative, the answer is ^-n or $|n|$, a positive number.

$|n|$ is a positive number regardless if n is positive or negative.

Page 192   Problem Set C

1. $(\sqrt{x})^2 = 7^2$ Square both sides.
   $x = 49$

2. $\sqrt{x} + 8 = ^-6$
   $\sqrt{x} = ^-14$

   No solution; $\sqrt{x}$ would have to be negative, and the radical sign represents only the nonnegative square root.

3. $0 = 2.3 + \sqrt{x}$
   $^-2.3 = \sqrt{x}$

   No solution; $\sqrt{x}$ would have to be negative, and the radical sign represents only the nonnegative square root.

4. $(\sqrt{x + 2})^2 = 5^2$ Square both sides.
   $x + 2 = 25$
   $x = 23$

5. $x = \sqrt{^-16}$

   No solution; there is no square root of a negative number.

6. $x^2 = 64$
   $8 \cdot 8 = 64$
   $^-8 \cdot ^-8 = 64$
   $x = 8, ^-8$

Page 193   Share and Summarize

1. Possible answer: Finding half produces a number that, when you *add* it to itself, gives the original number. Finding the square root produces a number that, when you *multiply* it by itself, gives the original number.

2. $\sqrt{0} = 0; 0 \div 2 = 0$
   $\sqrt{4} = 2; 4 \div 2 = 2$
   yes, 0 and 4

Pages 193–194   Problem Set D

1. $\sqrt{0} + \sqrt{0} = 0 + 0 = 0$
   $\sqrt{0 + 0} = \sqrt{0} = 0$
   $\sqrt{4} + \sqrt{4} = 2 + 2 = 4$
   $\sqrt{4 + 4} = \sqrt{8} \approx 2.83$
   $\sqrt{36} + \sqrt{16} = 6 + 4 = 10$
   $\sqrt{36 + 16} = \sqrt{52} \approx 7.21$
   $\sqrt{25} + \sqrt{\frac{1}{4}} = 5 + \frac{1}{2} = 5.5$
   $\sqrt{25 + \frac{1}{4}} = \sqrt{25.25} \approx 5.02$

(x, y)	$(0, 0)$	$(4, 4)$	$(36, 16)$	$\left(25, \frac{1}{4}\right)$	$(\_\_, \_\_)$
$\sqrt{x} + \sqrt{y}$	0	4	10	5.5	
$\sqrt{x + y}$	0	$\sqrt{8}$	$\sqrt{52}$	$\sqrt{25.25}$	

The square root of a sum is not equal to the sum of the square roots.

2. $\sqrt{0} \cdot \sqrt{0} = 0 \cdot 0 = 0$
   $\sqrt{0 \cdot 0} = \sqrt{0} = 0$
   $\sqrt{5} \cdot \sqrt{5} = (\sqrt{5})^2 = 5$
   $\sqrt{5 \cdot 5} = \sqrt{25} = 5$
   $\sqrt{9} \cdot \sqrt{25} = 3 \cdot 5 = 15$
   $\sqrt{9 \cdot 25} = \sqrt{225} = 15$
   $\sqrt{0.64} \cdot \sqrt{100} = 0.8 \cdot 10 = 8$
   $\sqrt{0.64 \cdot 100} = \sqrt{64} = 8$

(x, y)	$(0, 0)$	$(5, 5)$	$(9, 25)$	$(0.64, 100)$	$(\_\_, \_\_)$
$\sqrt{x} \cdot \sqrt{y}$	0	5	15	8	
$\sqrt{x \cdot y}$	0	5	15	8	

The square root of a product is equal to the product of the square roots.

3. $\sqrt{0} - \sqrt{0} = 0 - 0 = 0$
   $\sqrt{0 - 0} = \sqrt{0} = 0$
   $\sqrt{4} - \sqrt{4} = 2 - 2 = 0$
   $\sqrt{4 - 4} = \sqrt{0} = 0$
   $\sqrt{81} - \sqrt{49} = 9 - 7 = 2$
   $\sqrt{81 - 49} = \sqrt{32} \approx 5.66$
   $\sqrt{\frac{25}{9}} - \sqrt{\frac{16}{9}} = \frac{5}{3} - \frac{4}{3} = \frac{1}{3}$
   $\sqrt{\frac{25}{9} - \frac{16}{9}} = \sqrt{\frac{9}{9}} = \sqrt{1} = 1$

(x, y)	$(0, 0)$	$(4, 4)$	$(81, 49)$	$\left(\frac{25}{9}, \frac{16}{9}\right)$	$(\_\_, \_\_)$
$\sqrt{x} - \sqrt{y}$	0	0	2	$\frac{1}{3}$	
$\sqrt{x - y}$	0	0	$\sqrt{32}$	1	

The square root of a difference is not equal to the difference of the square roots.

4. $\sqrt{0} \div \sqrt{2} = 0 \div \sqrt{2} = 0$

$\sqrt{0 \div 2} = \sqrt{0} = 0$

$\sqrt{3} \div \sqrt{3} = 1$

$\sqrt{3 \div 3} = \sqrt{1} = 1$

$\sqrt{4} \div \sqrt{16} = 2 \div 4 = \dfrac{1}{2}$

$\sqrt{4 \div 16} = \sqrt{\dfrac{1}{4}} = \dfrac{1}{2}$

$\sqrt{\dfrac{4}{9}} \div \sqrt{2.25} = \dfrac{2}{3} \div \dfrac{3}{2} = \dfrac{2}{3} \cdot \dfrac{2}{3} = \dfrac{4}{9}$

$\sqrt{\dfrac{4}{9} \div 2.25} = \sqrt{\dfrac{4}{9} \div \dfrac{9}{4}} = \sqrt{\dfrac{4}{9} \cdot \dfrac{4}{9}} = \dfrac{4}{9}$

(x, y)	$(0, 2)$	$(3, 3)$	$(4, 16)$	$\left(\dfrac{4}{9}, 2.25\right)$	$(\underline{\ \ }, \underline{\ \ })$
$\sqrt{x} \div \sqrt{y}$	0	1	$\dfrac{1}{2}$	$\dfrac{4}{9}$	
$\sqrt{x \div y}$	0	1	$\dfrac{1}{2}$	$\dfrac{4}{9}$	

The square of a quotient is equal to the quotient of the square roots.

Page 195   Problem Set E

1. $\sqrt{75} = \sqrt{25} \cdot \sqrt{3}$
$\quad = 5\sqrt{3}$

2. $\sqrt{60} = \sqrt{4} \cdot \sqrt{15}$
$\quad = 2\sqrt{15}$

3. already simplified

4. $\sqrt{\dfrac{1}{8}} = \sqrt{\dfrac{1}{4}} \cdot \sqrt{\dfrac{1}{2}}$
$\quad = \dfrac{1}{2}\sqrt{\dfrac{1}{2}}$

5. $\sqrt{50x^3} = \sqrt{25x^2} \cdot \sqrt{2x}$
$\quad = 5x\sqrt{2x}$

6. $\sqrt{72a^4b^5} = \sqrt{36a^4b^4} \cdot \sqrt{2b}$
$\quad = 6a^2b^2\sqrt{2b}$

7. $2\sqrt{3} = \sqrt{4} \cdot \sqrt{3}$
$\quad = \sqrt{12}$
Possible answer: $\sqrt{12}$

8. $6\sqrt{2} = \sqrt{36} \cdot \sqrt{2}$
$\quad = \sqrt{72}$
Possible answer: $\sqrt{72}$

9. $5y\sqrt{3} = \sqrt{25y^2} \cdot \sqrt{3}$
$\quad = \sqrt{75y^2}$
Possible answer: $\sqrt{75y^2}$

10. $\dfrac{1}{4}x^2\sqrt{3x} = \sqrt{\dfrac{1}{16}x^4} \cdot \sqrt{3x}$
$\quad = \sqrt{\dfrac{3}{16}x^5}$
Possible answer: $\sqrt{\dfrac{3}{16}x^5}$

Page 196   Problem Set F

1. no; Possible explanation:
$\sqrt{2} + \sqrt{2} + \sqrt{2} = 3\sqrt{2}$
$\qquad\qquad\qquad\quad = \sqrt{9} \cdot \sqrt{2}$
$\qquad\qquad\qquad\quad = \sqrt{18}$
$\qquad\qquad\qquad\quad \neq \sqrt{6}$

2. no; Possible explanation: Just as you can't combine $3x + y$, you can't combine $3\sqrt{2} + \sqrt{3}$.

3. yes; Possible explanation:
$\sqrt{50} + \sqrt{98} = \sqrt{25 \cdot 2} + \sqrt{49 \cdot 2}$
$\qquad\qquad\qquad = 5\sqrt{2} + 7\sqrt{2}$
$\qquad\qquad\qquad = 12\sqrt{2}$

4. yes; Possible explanation:
$-\dfrac{1}{2}\sqrt{80} = -\dfrac{1}{2}\sqrt{16 \cdot 5}$
$\qquad\qquad = -\dfrac{1}{2}\left(4\sqrt{5}\right)$
$\qquad\qquad = {}^-2\sqrt{5}$

$\sqrt{45} + \sqrt{20} - 7\sqrt{5} = \sqrt{9 \cdot 5} + \sqrt{4 \cdot 5} - 7\sqrt{5}$
$\qquad\qquad\qquad\qquad = 3\sqrt{5} + 2\sqrt{5} - 7\sqrt{5}$
$\qquad\qquad\qquad\qquad = {}^-2\sqrt{5}$

5. $\sqrt{3} + \sqrt{3} = 2\sqrt{3}$
Possible answer: $\sqrt{3} + \sqrt{3}$

6a. i. $\ {}^-3\sqrt{3} + \sqrt{48} = {}^-3\sqrt{3} + \sqrt{16 \cdot 3}$
$\qquad\qquad\qquad = {}^-3\sqrt{3} + 4\sqrt{3}$
$\qquad\qquad\qquad = 1\sqrt{3}$
$\qquad\qquad\qquad = \sqrt{3}$

ii. $2\sqrt{12} - \sqrt{27} = 2\sqrt{4 \cdot 3} - \sqrt{9 \cdot 3}$
$\qquad\qquad\qquad = 2 \cdot 2\sqrt{3} - 3\sqrt{3}$
$\qquad\qquad\qquad = 4\sqrt{3} - 3\sqrt{3}$
$\qquad\qquad\qquad = 1\sqrt{3}$
$\qquad\qquad\qquad = \sqrt{3}$

iii. $12\sqrt{2} - 7\sqrt{2} = 5\sqrt{2}$

iv. $3\sqrt{32} - \sqrt{98} = 3\sqrt{16 \cdot 2} - \sqrt{49 \cdot 2}$
$\qquad\qquad\qquad = 3 \cdot 4\sqrt{2} - 7\sqrt{2}$
$\qquad\qquad\qquad = 12\sqrt{2} - 7\sqrt{2}$
$\qquad\qquad\qquad = 5\sqrt{2}$

6b. Yes; Expressions i and ii are equivalent, and Expressions iii and iv are equivalent.

Page 197   Share and Summarize

1. $\sqrt{60} = \sqrt{4 \cdot 15}$
$\quad = 2\sqrt{15}$

2. Possible answer: Find the prime factorization of the number, and then find pairs of factors. Multiply all the pairs together to get a perfect square factor of the original number. Then multiply any remaining factors together to get a factor that is not a perfect square.

$60 = 2 \cdot 2 \cdot 15$ $\qquad$ Find the prime factorization.
$60 = 4 \cdot 15$ $\qquad\qquad$ Multiply pairs.
$\sqrt{60} = \sqrt{4 \cdot 15}$ $\qquad$ Square both sides.
$\sqrt{60} = 2\sqrt{15}$

Page 198　Problem Set G

1. $2^3 = 8$
   $\sqrt[3]{8} = 2$
2. $(^-5)^3 = {}^-125$
   $\sqrt[3]{^-125} = {}^-5$
3. $0.01^3 = 0.000001$
   $\sqrt[3]{0.000001} = 0.01$
4. $\sqrt[3]{8} = 2$
   $(\sqrt[3]{8})^3 = 2^3$
   $\qquad\quad = 8$
5. $\sqrt[3]{^-125} = {}^-5$
   $(\sqrt[3]{^-125})^3 = (^-5)^3$
   $\qquad\qquad\quad = {}^-125$
6. $(\sqrt[3]{37})^3 = 37$
7. You get the original number. The cube root is a number n, where n^3 is the original number. So when you cube the cube root, you get the original number.
8. $(\sqrt[3]{x})^3 = \left(-\dfrac{1}{8}\right)^3$
   $\qquad x = {}^-\dfrac{1}{512}$
9. $\quad 6^3 = (\sqrt[3]{2n})^3$
   $\quad 216 = 2n$
   $\quad 108 = n$
10. $(\sqrt[3]{z+5})^3 = (^-2)^3$
    $\qquad z + 5 = {}^-8$
    $\qquad\quad z = {}^-13$

Page 199　Problem Set H

1. $2^5 = 32$
   $\sqrt[5]{32} = 2$
2. $4^4 = 256$
   $\sqrt[4]{256} = 4$
   $(^-4)^4 = 256$
   $^-\sqrt[4]{256} = {}^-4$
   $^-4$ and 4
3. $(^-2)^7 = {}^-128$
   $\sqrt[7]{^-128} = {}^-2$
4. $3^6 = 729$
   $\sqrt[6]{729} = 3$
5. $\sqrt{0} = 0; \sqrt{1} = 1$
   $\sqrt[3]{0} = 0; \sqrt[3]{1} = 1$
   $\sqrt[4]{0} = 0; \sqrt[4]{1} = 1$
   $\sqrt[5]{0} = 0; \sqrt[5]{1} = 1$
   $\sqrt[6]{0} = 0; \sqrt[6]{1} = 1$
   yes, 0 and 1
6. Yes; any positive number is an example.
7. no; Possible explanation: If a number has a positive fourth root, the negative of that number is also a fourth root, because a negative multiplied by itself four times is positive.

8. No; when you raise a positive number to the fifth power, it must be positive; when you do the same with a negative number, it must be negative. The sign of the root must be the same as the original number.
9. $\sqrt[6]{7}, \sqrt[5]{7}, \sqrt[4]{7}, \sqrt[3]{7}, \sqrt{7}$
10. $\sqrt{\dfrac{1}{4}}, \sqrt[4]{\dfrac{1}{4}}, \sqrt[80]{\dfrac{1}{4}}, \sqrt[81]{\dfrac{1}{4}}$

Page 199　Share and Summarize

1. Possible answer: To find the nth root, you have to think of a number that, when taken to the nth power, gives the original number. To find the nth power, you just multiply the number by itself n times.
2. no; Possible explanation: Odd powers have the same sign as the original number, so odd roots also have the same sign. You can have a positive or a negative, but not both.

Page 201　Problem Set I

1. Most will display 4.472135955.
2. Answers will vary. Most students will answer 20.
3. Answers will vary. If the rightmost digit of the original number is 5, the rightmost digit of the squared number will also be 5.
4. no; Possible explanations: The calculator rounded. *Or*, there are more digits in the number than can fit on the screen.

Page 202　Problem Set J

1. rational; Possible ratio: $\dfrac{7}{2}$
2. $\sqrt{3} \cdot \sqrt{45} = \sqrt{3} \cdot \sqrt{3 \cdot 15}$
   $\qquad\qquad\quad = \left(\sqrt{3}\right)^2 \cdot \sqrt{15}$
   $\qquad\qquad\quad = 3\sqrt{15}$
   irrational; Possible explanation: $\sqrt{3} \cdot \sqrt{45}$ simplifies to $3\sqrt{15}$, and since 15 isn't a square number, $3\sqrt{15}$ is irrational.
3. rational; Possible ratio: $\dfrac{4,627,803}{1,000,000}$
4. $\sqrt[3]{32} \div \sqrt[3]{4} = \sqrt[3]{\dfrac{32}{4}}$
   $\qquad\qquad\quad = \sqrt[3]{8}$
   $\qquad\qquad\quad = 2$
   $\qquad\qquad\quad = \dfrac{2}{1}$
   rational; Possible ratio: $\dfrac{2}{1}$
5. $\sqrt{40} - \sqrt{10} = \sqrt{4 \cdot 10} - \sqrt{10}$
   $\qquad\qquad\quad = 2\sqrt{10} - \sqrt{10}$
   $\qquad\qquad\quad = \sqrt{10}$
   irrational; Possible explanation: $\sqrt{40} - \sqrt{10}$ simplifies to $\sqrt{10}$, and since 10 isn't a perfect square, $\sqrt{10}$ is irrational.

Chapter 3

6. irrational; Possible explanation: Since 22 isn't a perfect square, $\sqrt{22}$ is irrational.

7. $\sqrt{8} \cdot \sqrt{2} = \sqrt{16}$
$$= 4$$
$$= \frac{4}{1}$$

rational; Possible ratio: $\frac{4}{1}$

8. rational; Possible ratio: $\frac{0}{8}$

9. $1.\overline{6} = 1\frac{2}{3} = \frac{5}{3}$

rational; Possible ratio: $\frac{5}{3}$

10. irrational; Possible explanation: Although this is a fraction, the numerator isn't an integer and it can't be written as a ratio of integers.

Page 202   Share and Summarize

1. always rational; Possible explanation: Every integer can be written as itself over 1, for example, $n = \frac{n}{1}$.

2. sometimes rational; Possible explanation: $\sqrt[3]{21}$ is irrational, but $\sqrt[3]{27}$ is rational.

3. sometimes rational: Possible explanation: $\sqrt{21}$ is irrational, but $\sqrt{25}$ is rational.

4. sometimes rational: Possible explanation: $\sqrt{3} \cdot \sqrt{45}$ is irrational, but $\sqrt{5} \cdot \sqrt{45}$ is rational.

Pages 203–207   On Your Own Exercises

1. $1.21 = 1.1 \cdot 1.1$
$\sqrt{1.21} = 1.1$
$1.21 = {}^-1.1 \cdot {}^-1.1$
${}^-\sqrt{1.21} = {}^-1.1$
1.1 and ${}^-1.1$

2. $\sqrt{1.21} = 1.1$

3. $\frac{4}{49} = \frac{2}{7} \cdot \frac{2}{7}$

$\sqrt{\frac{4}{49}} = \frac{\sqrt{4}}{\sqrt{49}} = \frac{2}{7}$

$\frac{4}{49} = \frac{{}^-2}{7} \cdot \frac{{}^-2}{7}$

$-\sqrt{\frac{4}{49}} = \frac{-\sqrt{4}}{\sqrt{49}} = \frac{{}^-2}{7}$

$\frac{2}{7}$ and $\frac{{}^-2}{7}$

4. $\sqrt{\frac{4}{49}} = \frac{\sqrt{4}}{\sqrt{49}} = \frac{2}{7}$

5. $0.0064 = 0.08 \cdot 0.08$
$\sqrt{0.0064} = 0.08$
$0.0064 = {}^-0.08 \cdot {}^-0.08$
${}^-\sqrt{0.0064} = {}^-0.08$
0.08 and ${}^-0.08$

6. $\sqrt{0.0064} = 0.08$

7. $(\sqrt{26})^2 = 26$

8. $0.09 = 0.3 \cdot 0.3$
$\sqrt{0.09} = 0.3$
$(\sqrt{0.09})^2 = 0.3^2 = 0.09$

9. $\sqrt{\left({}^-3\right)^2} = \sqrt{9} = 3$

10. $|x|$

11. $(\sqrt{x-3})^2 = 9^2$
$x - 3 = 81$
$x = 84$

12. $5\sqrt{x} = 25$
$\sqrt{x} = 5$
$(\sqrt{x})^2 = (5)^2$
$x = 25$

13. $\left(\sqrt{\frac{x}{7}}\right)^2 = 3^2$

$\frac{x}{7} = 9$

$x = 63$

14. $(\sqrt{x})^2 = 36^2$
$x = 1{,}296$

15. $\sqrt{x+2} + 8 = 1$
$\sqrt{x+2} = {}^-7$

A square root cannot equal a negative number.
no solution

16. $\sqrt{x-20} = {}^-18$

A square root cannot equal a negative number.
no solution

17. The product of two roots is equal to the root of the product.
correct

18. The sum of two roots is not equal to the root of the sum.
incorrect

19. correct

20. $\sqrt{20} \div \sqrt{45} = \sqrt{\frac{20}{45}} = \sqrt{\frac{4}{9}} = \frac{2}{3}$
correct

21. $\dfrac{\sqrt{20} + \sqrt{80}}{\sqrt{20}} = \dfrac{\sqrt{20}}{\sqrt{20}} + \dfrac{\sqrt{80}}{\sqrt{20}}$
$$= 1 + \sqrt{4}$$
$$= 1 + 2$$
$$= 3$$

22. already simplified

23. $\sqrt{8} \cdot \sqrt{12} = \sqrt{4 \cdot 2} \cdot \sqrt{4 \cdot 3}$
$$= 2\sqrt{2} \cdot 2\sqrt{3}$$
$$= 4\sqrt{6}$$

24. $\sqrt{x+2} + \sqrt{4x+8} = \sqrt{x+2} + \sqrt{4(x+2)}$
$$= \sqrt{x+2} + \sqrt{2x+2}$$
$$= 3\sqrt{x+2}$$

25a. **i.** $\sqrt{800x^3} = \sqrt{400x^2 \cdot 2x}$
        $= 20x\sqrt{2x}$

   ii. $4x\sqrt{50x} = 4x\sqrt{25 \cdot 2x}$
           $= 4x \cdot 5\sqrt{2x}$
           $= 20x\sqrt{2x}$

  iii. $3\sqrt{32x^3} = 3\sqrt{16x^2 \cdot 2x}$
           $= 3 \cdot 4x\sqrt{2x}$
           $= 12x\sqrt{2x}$

  iv. $5\sqrt{8x^3} + 2x\sqrt{2x} + 2\sqrt{32x^3}$
        $= 5\sqrt{4x^2 \cdot 2x} + 2x\sqrt{2x} + 2\sqrt{16x^2 \cdot 2x}$
        $= 5 \cdot 2x\sqrt{2x} + 2x\sqrt{2x} + 2 \cdot 4x\sqrt{2x}$
        $= 10x\sqrt{2x} + 2x\sqrt{2x} + 8x\sqrt{2x}$
        $= 20x\sqrt{2x}$

25b. Expressions i, ii, and iv

26. yes; combining three $\sqrt{5}$s gives $3\sqrt{5}$.

27. $\sqrt{32} - \sqrt{18} = \sqrt{16 \cdot 2} - \sqrt{9 \cdot 2}$
             $= 4\sqrt{2} - 3\sqrt{2}$
             $= 1\sqrt{2}$
             $= \sqrt{2}$

    no

28. $(^-6)^3 = {}^-216$
    $\sqrt[3]{^-216} = {}^-6$

29. $\sqrt[3]{^-216} = {}^-6$

30. $(^-2)^6 = 64$
    $^-\sqrt[6]{64} = {}^-2$
    $2^6 = 64$
    $\sqrt[6]{64} = 2$
    $^-2$ and 2

31. $\sqrt[6]{64} = 2$

32. $(^-3)^5 = {}^-243$
    $\sqrt[5]{^-243} = {}^-3$

33. $^-\sqrt[5]{^-243} = {}^-3$

34. $(^-x^2)^8 = x^{2 \cdot 8} = x^{16}$
    $\sqrt[8]{x^{16}} = {}^-x^2$
    $(x^2)^8 = x^{2 \cdot 8} = x^{16}$
    $\sqrt[8]{x^{16}} = x^2$
    $^-x^2$ and x^2

35. $\sqrt[8]{x^{16}} = x^2$

36. The nth root of a negative number is negative if n is odd.

    All of the numbers are negative.

    The smallest number will have the smallest value of n.
    $\sqrt[3]{^-41}, \sqrt[5]{^-41}, \sqrt[7]{^-41}, \sqrt[9]{^-41}, \sqrt[11]{^-41}$

37. The nth root of a negative number is negative if n is odd.

    All of the numbers are negative.

    Since the number under the radical is a fraction, the smallest number will have the largest value of n.
    $\sqrt[311]{-\frac{1}{3}}, \sqrt[105]{-\frac{1}{3}}, \sqrt[5]{-\frac{1}{3}}, \sqrt[3]{-\frac{1}{3}}$

38. Possible answer: $\frac{356}{100}$

39. Possible answer: $-\frac{23}{100,000}$

40. Possible answer: $-\frac{5}{3}$

41. Possible answer: $\frac{43}{8}$

42. rational; Possible ratio: $-\frac{10}{3}$

43. rational: Possible ratio: $\frac{13}{3}$

44. $-\sqrt{28} = -\sqrt{4 \cdot 7}$
          $= {}^-2\sqrt{7}$

    Irrational; it simplifies to $^-2\sqrt{7}$ which has a radical sign.

45. rational; Possible ratio: $-\frac{58,237}{10,000}$

46. $\sqrt[4]{32} = \sqrt[4]{16 \cdot 2}$
       $= 2\sqrt[4]{2}$

    Irrational; it simplifies $2\sqrt[4]{2}$, which has a radical sign.

47. $\sqrt{45} - \sqrt{10} \cdot \sqrt{2} = \sqrt{45} - \sqrt{20}$
                 $= \sqrt{9 \cdot 5} - \sqrt{4 \cdot 5}$
                 $= 3\sqrt{5} - 2\sqrt{5}$
                 $= 1\sqrt{5}$
                 $= \sqrt{5}$

    Irrational; it simplifies to $\sqrt{5}$, which is irrational.

48a. $\sqrt{4} = 2; 2 < 4$
     $\sqrt{9} = 3; 3 < 9$
     $\sqrt{25} = 5; 5 < 25$
     Possible answer: 4, 9, 25

48b. $\sqrt{\frac{1}{4}} = \frac{1}{2}; \frac{1}{2} > \frac{1}{4}$

     $\sqrt{\frac{1}{9}} = \frac{1}{3}; \frac{1}{3} > \frac{1}{9}$

     $\sqrt{\frac{1}{25}} = \frac{1}{5}; \frac{1}{5} > \frac{1}{25}$

     Possible answer: $\frac{1}{4}, \frac{1}{9}, \frac{1}{25}$

48c. If $0 < x < 1$, then $\sqrt{x} > x$.

49a. Answers will vary.
     Possible answer:
     If $x^2 = y^2 = 4$, $x = 2$ or $^-2$, $y = 2$ or $^-2$

49b. no; counterexample: $x = 2, y = {}^-2$

50. If $x = 0$, then
    $\sqrt{0} + \sqrt{y} = 0 + \sqrt{y}$
              $= \sqrt{y}$
    $\sqrt{0 + y} = \sqrt{y}$
    If $y = 0$, then
    $\sqrt{x} + \sqrt{0} = \sqrt{x} + 0$
              $= \sqrt{x}$
    $\sqrt{x + 0} = \sqrt{x}$
    $x = 0$ or $y = 0$

51. If $y = 0$, then
$$\sqrt{x} - \sqrt{0} = \sqrt{x} - 0$$
$$= \sqrt{x}$$
$$\sqrt{x - 0} = \sqrt{x}$$
If $x = y$, then
$$\sqrt{x} - \sqrt{y} = 0$$
$$\sqrt{x - y} = \sqrt{0}$$
$$= 0$$
$y = 0$, or $x = y$

52a. $uv = \sqrt{x} \cdot \sqrt{y}$
$\sqrt{x} \cdot \sqrt{y}$

52b. $u^2 = (\sqrt{x})^2 = x$
$v^2 = (\sqrt{y})^2 = y$

52c. $(\sqrt{x} \cdot \sqrt{y})^2 = (\sqrt{x})^2 \cdot (\sqrt{y})^2 = xy$

52d.
$$(uv)^2 = xy$$
$$\sqrt{(uv)^2} = \sqrt{xy}$$
$$uv = \sqrt{xy}$$
$\sqrt{xy}$

52e. yes

52f. $\dfrac{u}{v} = \dfrac{\sqrt{x}}{\sqrt{y}}$ and $\dfrac{u^2}{v^2} = \left(\dfrac{u}{v}\right)^2 = \dfrac{x}{y}$, so $\dfrac{u}{v} = \sqrt{\dfrac{x}{y}}$;

that means $\dfrac{\sqrt{x}}{\sqrt{y}} = \sqrt{\dfrac{x}{y}}$.

53.
$$a^2 + a^2 = c^2$$
$$2a^2 = c^2$$
$$\sqrt{2a^2} = c$$
$$a\sqrt{2} = c$$
$a\sqrt{2}$

54. $\sqrt[51]{-2}$, $^-1$, $\sqrt[51]{-0.2}$, 0, $\sqrt[51]{0.2}$, 1, $\sqrt[51]{2}$

55a. less than

55b. greater than

56a. x is positive; Possible explanation: If n is even, x must be positive for the nth root to exist. If n is odd, x must be positive for the root to be positive.

56b. x is negative and n is odd; Possible explanation: Since the root is negative and there's no negative sign in front, n must be odd; that means the value of x must have the same sign as the root, so x is negative.

57a. $1.44^{\frac{1}{2}} = \sqrt{1.44}$
$= 1.2$

57b. $1.25^{\frac{1}{3}} = \sqrt[3]{1.25}$
$= 5$

57c. $(^-32)^{\frac{1}{5}} = \sqrt[5]{-32}$
$= ^-2$

57d. $^-32^{\frac{1}{5}} = ^-\sqrt[5]{32}$
$= ^-2$

57e. $\left(3^{\frac{1}{3}}\right)^3 = 3^{\frac{1}{3} \cdot 3}$
$= 3^1$
$= 3$

57f. $\left(\dfrac{9}{25}\right)^{\frac{1}{2}} = \sqrt{\dfrac{9}{25}}$
$= \dfrac{3}{5}$

57g. $64^{\frac{-1}{3}} = \dfrac{1}{\sqrt[3]{64}}$
$= \dfrac{1}{4}$

57h. $16^{\frac{3}{4}} = 16^{\frac{1}{4} \cdot 3}$
$= (\sqrt[4]{16})^3$
$= 2^3$
$= 8$

58a. n, $n\sqrt{3}$, $2n$

58b. yes; Possible example: $n = \sqrt{2}$; side lengths $\sqrt{2}$, $\sqrt{2} \cdot \sqrt{3} = \sqrt{6}$, and $2\sqrt{2}$

58c. $A = \dfrac{1}{2}bh$
$= \dfrac{1}{2}(1)(\sqrt{3})$
$= \dfrac{1}{2}\sqrt{3}$
Irrational; the area is $\dfrac{1}{2}(1)(\sqrt{3}) = \dfrac{1}{2}\sqrt{3}$, which is irrational.

58d. If $n = \sqrt[4]{3}$, then
$$2n = 2\sqrt[4]{3}$$
$$n\sqrt{3} = \sqrt[4]{3} \cdot \sqrt{3}$$
$$= \sqrt[4]{3} \cdot \sqrt[4]{3^2}$$
$$= \sqrt[4]{3^3}$$
$$= \sqrt[4]{27}$$
$$A = \dfrac{1}{2}bh$$
$$= \dfrac{1}{2}(\sqrt[4]{3})(\sqrt[4]{3^3})$$
$$= \dfrac{1}{2}(\sqrt[4]{3^4})$$
$$= \dfrac{1}{2} \cdot 3$$
$$= \dfrac{3}{2}, \text{ which is rational}$$
yes; Possible example: $n = \sqrt[4]{3}$; side lengths $\sqrt[4]{3}$, $2\sqrt[4]{3}$, $\sqrt[4]{3^3}$, or $\sqrt[4]{27}$

59a. Irrational; it is simplified, but it includes a radical sign.

59b. Irrational; if it were rational, half of it would also be rational—that is π would be $\dfrac{a}{2b}$. But since π is irrational, you can't do that.

59c. Irrational; if it were rational, then $nm = \dfrac{a}{b}$ for integers a and b. But then $m = \dfrac{a}{bn}$, a ratio of two integers that is impossible since m is irrational.

60.
$$\dfrac{8}{10} = \dfrac{4}{5}$$
$$\dfrac{28}{48} = \dfrac{7}{12}$$
$$\dfrac{20}{25} = \dfrac{4}{5}$$
$$\dfrac{6}{27} = \dfrac{2}{9}$$
$$\dfrac{12}{36} = \dfrac{1}{3}$$
$\dfrac{1}{3}$ and $\dfrac{12}{36}$, $\dfrac{7}{12}$ and $\dfrac{28}{48}$, $\dfrac{2}{9}$ and $\dfrac{6}{27}$, $\dfrac{8}{10}$ and $\dfrac{20}{25}$

61. $\dfrac{48 \div 16}{80 \div 16} = \dfrac{3}{5}$

62. $\dfrac{140 \div 28}{196 \div 28} = \dfrac{5}{7}$

63. $\dfrac{198 \div 33}{231 \div 33} = \dfrac{6}{7}$

64. $\dfrac{140 \div 35}{315 \div 35} = \dfrac{4}{9}$

65a. $p = \dfrac{3}{2}q + \dfrac{5}{2}$

$p = 1.5q + 2.5$

Equations a and c; both are linear with a slope of 1.5.

66. $\dfrac{0 + 1.6}{5 - 1} = \dfrac{1.6}{4} = 0.4$

$\dfrac{0.4 - 0}{6 - 5} = \dfrac{0.4}{1} = 0.4$

yes

67. $\dfrac{^-1 + 4}{3 - 7} = \dfrac{^-3}{4} = {}^-0.75$

$\dfrac{2.75 + 1}{^-2 - 3} = \dfrac{^-3.75}{5} = {}^-0.75$

yes

68. $y = {}^-x^2$

69. $y = x^2 + 50$

70. $y = 2x^2$

71a.

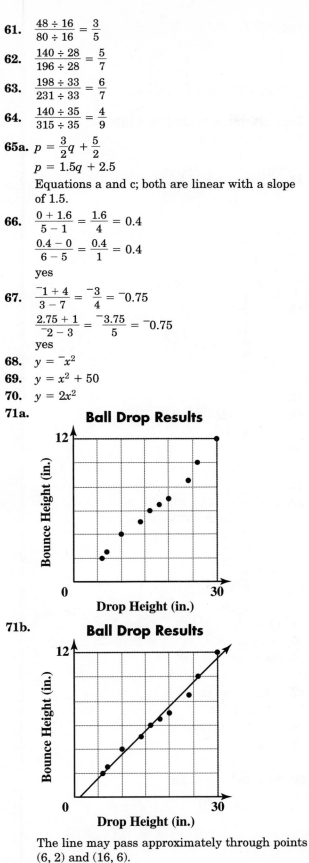

Ball Drop Results

71b.

Ball Drop Results

The line may pass approximately through points (6, 2) and (16, 6).

$\dfrac{6 - 2}{16 - 6} = \dfrac{4}{10} = 0.4$

$y = 0.4x + b$

$2 = 0.4(6) + b$

$2 = 2.4 + b$

$b = 0.4$

Possible equation: $y = 0.4x - 0.4$

71c. $171 \div 10 = 17.1$

$63.5 \div 10 = 6.35$

71d. See students' work; possible equation:

$y = 0.39x - 0.319$.

Page 205　In Your Own Words

Possible answer:

Dear Younger Student,

A rational number is a number that can be written as the ratio, or quotient, of two integers. Integers are a set of numbers that includes all the counting numbers like 1, 2, and 3, their opposites, $^-1$, $^-2$, and $^-3$, and zero. Examples of rational numbers are $\dfrac{2}{3}$, $^-1.8$, 5, $0.\overline{3}$, and $\sqrt{36}$. Numbers that *cannot* be written as the ratio of two integers are called irrational numbers. Examples of irrational numbers are $\sqrt{30}$, π, and 1.12233445566....

Sincerely,

An Older Student

Review and Self-Assessment

Pages 208–210　Strategies and Applications

1a. y x's multiplied together

1b. $x^{-y} = \dfrac{1}{x^y}$

They are reciprocals.

2a. r^{21}; Since r is greater than 1, multiplying a number by r gives a greater product, so multiplying 21 times will give a greater product than multiplying only 11 times.

2b. r^{11}; Since r is between 0 and 1, multiplying a number by r gives a lesser product, so multiplying 21 times will give a lesser product than multiplying only 11 times.

2c. r^{21}; Since r is negative and the exponents are odd, the final products will be negative. If the numbers were positive the result would be the same as in Part b, but since they're negative, the order is switched and r^{21} is greater.

2d. r^{11}; Since r is negative and the exponents are odd, the final products will be negative. If the numbers were positive the result would be the same as in Part a, but since they're negative, the order is switched and r^{11} is greater.

3. 2.3×10^{32}; Possible explanation: The exponent on the 10 in 2.3×10^{32} is 9 greater than the exponent on 3.2×10^{23}, which means the number is about 10^9 as great.

4a. $1.7 \times 10^{-24} = 17{,}000 \times 10^{-28}$

$(17{,}000 \times 10^{-28}) - (9.1 \times 10^{-28}) = 16{,}990.9 \times 10^{-28}$

about $16{,}990.9 \times 10^{-28}$, or about 1.69909×10^{-24}

4b. $1.7 \times 10^{-24} = 17{,}000 \times 10^{-28}$

$(17{,}000 \times 10^{-28}) \div (9.1 \times 10^{-28}) = 1{,}868$

about 1.868×10^3, or about $1{,}868$

5. An exponential relationship will have a variable for an exponent.

The base will be greater than 1 for a growth relationship.

The base will be between 0 and 1 for a decay relationship

$y = 3(4^x)$ growth; $y = \left(\frac{1}{4}\right)^x$ decay

6a. exponential

6b. At each round the number of contestants is multiplied by $\frac{1}{2}$.

6c. The starting value is 2,048.

The decay factor is 0.5.

If c is the number of contestants and r is the round number, $c = 2{,}048(0.5)^{r-1}$.

7a. exponential

7b.

x	0	1	2	3	4
y	$\frac{1}{2}$	1	2	4	8

The y values for integer x values increase by a factor of 2 with each increase in x.

7c. The starting value is $\frac{1}{2}$.

The growth factor is 2.

$y = \left(\frac{1}{2}\right)2^x$

8a. not exponential

8b. $1{,}200 \cdot 2 = 2{,}400$

$2{,}400 \cdot 2 = 4{,}800$

$4{,}800 \cdot 2 = 9{,}600$

$9{,}600 \cdot 1.5 = 14{,}400$

The speeds aren't all multiplied by the same number to get the next speed in the table.

9a. $(a^b)^{-c} = \dfrac{1}{(a^b)^c}$

$= \dfrac{1}{a^{bc}}$

$= a^{-bc}$

9b. $(a^{-b})^c = \left(\dfrac{1}{a^b}\right)^c$

$= \dfrac{1^c}{a^{bc}}$

$= \dfrac{1}{a^{bc}}$

$= a^{-bc}$

10. Both 4 and $^-4$ have 16 as their square, because when you multiply two positive numbers or two negative numbers you get a positive product. For $x = \sqrt{16}$, though, the radical sign indicates you want only the positive root, 4.

11. because $(^-3)^5 = ^-243$

12a. Let $x = 0.\overline{4}$

$\quad 10x = 4.\overline{4}$

$\quad\quad x = 0.\overline{4}$

$10x - x = 4.\overline{4} - 0.\overline{4}$

$\quad\quad 9x = 4$

$\quad\quad x = \dfrac{4}{9}$

Possible ratio: $\frac{4}{9}$, rational

12b. Possible ratio: $\frac{2}{5}$, rational

12c. Not possible; irrational

12d. $\sqrt{0.4} \cdot \sqrt{10} = \sqrt{4}$

$\quad\quad\quad\quad = 2$

$\quad\quad\quad\quad = \dfrac{2}{1}$

Possible ratio: $\frac{2}{1}$, rational

Page 211   Demonstrating Skills

13. $0.4^3 = 0.4 \cdot 0.4 \cdot 0.4$

$\quad\quad = 0.064$

14. $\left(\dfrac{2}{3}\right)^4 = \left(\dfrac{2}{3}\right)\left(\dfrac{2}{3}\right)\left(\dfrac{2}{3}\right)\left(\dfrac{2}{3}\right)$

$\quad\quad = \dfrac{16}{81}$

15. $8^{-3} = \dfrac{1}{8^3}$

$\quad\quad = \dfrac{1}{8 \cdot 8 \cdot 8}$

$\quad\quad = \dfrac{1}{512}$

16. $\left(\dfrac{2}{3}\right)^{-4} = \left(\dfrac{3}{2}\right)^4$

$\quad\quad = \left(\dfrac{3}{2}\right)\left(\dfrac{3}{2}\right)\left(\dfrac{3}{2}\right)\left(\dfrac{3}{2}\right)$

$\quad\quad = \dfrac{81}{16}$

17. 11

18. $\sqrt{32} = \sqrt{16 \cdot 2}$

$\quad\quad = 4\sqrt{2}$

19. $^-10$

20. 0.3

21. 2

22. $2\sqrt[7]{(^-3)^{14}} = 2\sqrt[7]{(^-3)^7(^-3)^7}$

$\quad\quad\quad = 2(^-3)(^-3)$

$\quad\quad\quad = 18$

23. $\dfrac{1}{3}\sqrt{27} = \dfrac{1}{3}\sqrt{9 \cdot 3}$

$\quad\quad\quad = \dfrac{1}{3} \cdot 3\sqrt{3}$

$\quad\quad\quad = \sqrt{3}$

24. 13

25. $a^3 \cdot b^3 = (ab)^3$

26. $(2x)^4 \cdot (2x)^{-7} = (2x)^{4 + ^-7}$

$\quad\quad\quad\quad = (2x)^{-3}$

27. $\sqrt{52} = \sqrt{4 \cdot 13}$

$\quad\quad = 2\sqrt{13}$

28. already simplified

29. $\sqrt{18x^3} = \sqrt{9x^2 \cdot 2x}$

$\quad\quad\quad = 3x\sqrt{2x}$

30. $3m\sqrt{4m^6} = 3m \cdot 2m^3$

$\quad\quad\quad = 6m^4$

Chapter 4 Solving Equations

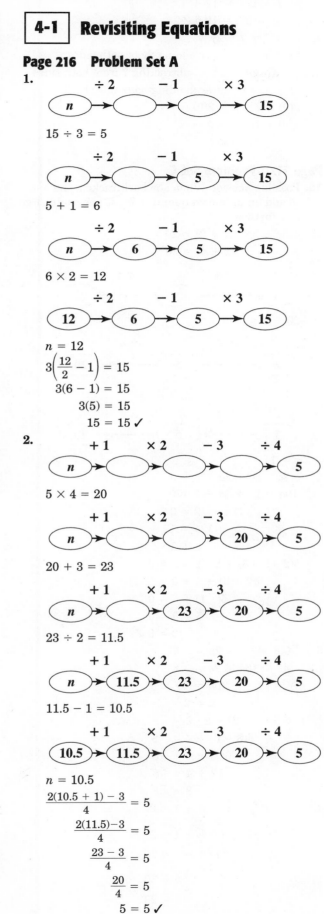

4-1 | Revisiting Equations

Page 216   Problem Set A

1.

$15 \div 3 = 5$

$5 + 1 = 6$

$6 \times 2 = 12$

$n = 12$

$3\left(\dfrac{12}{2} - 1\right) = 15$

$3(6 - 1) = 15$

$3(5) = 15$

$15 = 15 \checkmark$

2.

$5 \times 4 = 20$

$20 + 3 = 23$

$23 \div 2 = 11.5$

$11.5 - 1 = 10.5$

$n = 10.5$

$\dfrac{2(10.5 + 1) - 3}{4} = 5$

$\dfrac{2(11.5) - 3}{4} = 5$

$\dfrac{23 - 3}{4} = 5$

$\dfrac{20}{4} = 5$

$5 = 5 \checkmark$

3.

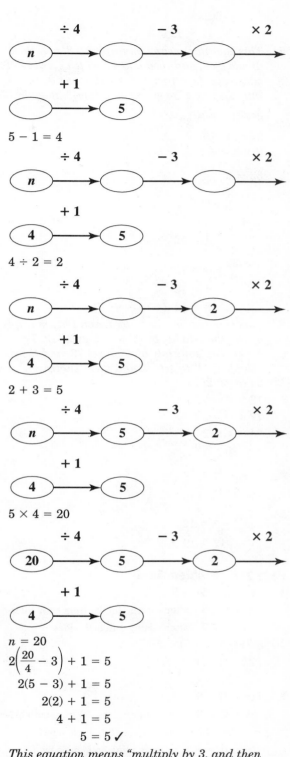

$5 - 1 = 4$

$4 \div 2 = 2$

$2 + 3 = 5$

$5 \times 4 = 20$

$n = 20$

$2\left(\dfrac{20}{4} - 3\right) + 1 = 5$

$2(5 - 3) + 1 = 5$

$2(2) + 1 = 5$

$4 + 1 = 5$

$5 = 5 \checkmark$

4. *This equation means "multiply by 3, and then subtract 4, and then multiply the difference by 6," which gives 12. To backtrack, "divide by 6" to get 2, and then "add 4" to get 6, and then "divide by 3" to get 2.*

$12 \div 6 = 2$

$2 + 4 = 6$

$6 \div 3 = 2$

$m = 2$

$6(3 \cdot 2 - 4) = 12$

$6(6 - 4) = 12$

$6(2) = 12$

$12 = 12 \checkmark$

5. *This equation means "multiply by 3, and then divide by 4, and then add 4," which gives 12. To backtrack, "subtract 4" from 12 to get 8, and then "multiply by 4" to get 32, and then "divide by 3" to get $\frac{32}{3}$, or $10\frac{2}{3}$.*

$12 - 4 = 8$

$8 \times 4 = 32$

$32 \div 3 = \frac{32}{3}$

$m = \frac{32}{3}$, or $10\frac{2}{3}$

$\frac{3\left(\frac{32}{3}\right)}{4} + 4 = 12$

$\frac{32}{4} + 4 = 12$

$8 + 4 = 12$

$12 = 12 \checkmark$

6. *This equation means "add 4, and then multiply by 3, and then divide by 6," which gives 12. To backtrack, "multiply by 6" to get 72, and then "divide by 3" to get 24, and then "subtract 4" from 24 to get 20.*

$12 \times 6 = 72$

$72 \div 3 = 24$

$24 - 4 = 20$

$n = 20$

$\frac{3(20 + 4)}{6} = 12$

$\frac{3(24)}{6} = 12$

$\frac{72}{6} = 12$

$12 = 12 \checkmark$

Page 217   Problem Set B

1. $3a - 4 = 2a + 3$

$a - 4 = 3$ after subtracting $2a$ from both sides

$a = 7$ after adding 4 to both sides

$3(7) - 4 = 2(7) + 3$

$21 - 4 = 14 + 3$

$17 = 17 \checkmark$

2. $11b - 6 = 9 + 6b$

$5b - 6 = 9$ after subtracting $6b$ from both sides

$5b = 15$ after adding 6 to both sides

$b = 3$ after dividing both sides by 5

$11(3) - 6 = 9 + 6(3)$

$33 - 6 = 9 + 18$

$27 = 27 \checkmark$

3. $7 - 5x = 12 - 3x$

$7 = 12 + 2x$ after adding $5x$ to both sides

$^-5 = 2x$ after subtracting 12 from sides

$^-2.5 = x$ after dividing both sides by 2

$7 - 5(^-2.5) = 12 - 3(^-2.5)$

$7 + 12.5 = 12 + 7.5$

$19.5 = 19.5 \checkmark$

4. $3y + 7 = 7 - 2y$

$5y + 7 = 7$ after adding $2y$ to both sides

$5y = 0$ after subtracting 7 from both sides

$y = 0$ after dividing both sides by 5

$3(0) + 7 = 7 - 2(0)$

$0 + 7 = 7 - 0$

$7 = 7 \checkmark$

Page 217   Problem Set C

1a. Possible answer: When she backtracked, she had to add an unknown quantity, $2x$, so she couldn't go any further.

1b. $4(3x + 2 - 2x + 2) = 20$

$4(x + 4) = 20$

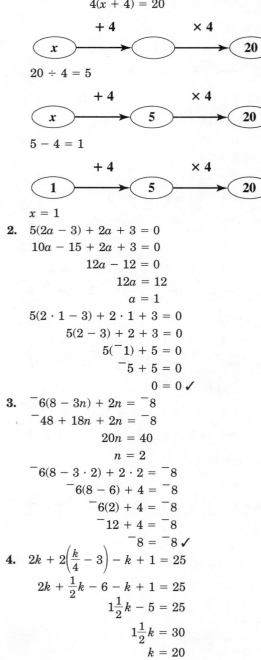

$20 \div 4 = 5$

$5 - 4 = 1$

$x = 1$

2. $5(2a - 3) + 2a + 3 = 0$

$10a - 15 + 2a + 3 = 0$

$12a - 12 = 0$

$12a = 12$

$a = 1$

$5(2 \cdot 1 - 3) + 2 \cdot 1 + 3 = 0$

$5(2 - 3) + 2 + 3 = 0$

$5(^-1) + 5 = 0$

$^-5 + 5 = 0$

$0 = 0 \checkmark$

3. $^-6(8 - 3n) + 2n = ^-8$

$^-48 + 18n + 2n = ^-8$

$20n = 40$

$n = 2$

$^-6(8 - 3 \cdot 2) + 2 \cdot 2 = ^-8$

$^-6(8 - 6) + 4 = ^-8$

$^-6(2) + 4 = ^-8$

$^-12 + 4 = ^-8$

$^-8 = ^-8 \checkmark$

4. $2k + 2\left(\frac{k}{4} - 3\right) - k + 1 = 25$

$2k + \frac{1}{2}k - 6 - k + 1 = 25$

$1\frac{1}{2}k - 5 = 25$

$1\frac{1}{2}k = 30$

$k = 20$

$$2 \cdot 20 + 2\left(\frac{20}{4} - 3\right) - 20 + 1 = 25$$
$$40 + 2(5 - 3) - 19 = 25$$
$$21 + 2(2) = 25$$
$$21 + 4 = 25$$
$$25 = 25 \checkmark$$

Page 218   Problem Set D

1. $\dfrac{8(n - 3)}{3} = 32$

    $8(n - 3) = 96$

    $8n - 24 = 96$

    $8n = 120$

    $n = 15$

2. Neva: n, Owen: $5n$, Owen: $n + 60$

    $5n = n + 60$

    $4n = 60$

    $n = 15$

    $5n = 5(15) = 75$

    Neva: 15, Owen: 75

3a. $x + 1, x + 2, x + 3$

3b. $x + (x + 1) + (x + 2) + (x + 3) = 150$

    $4x + 6 = 150$

    $4x = 144$

    $x = 36$

    $x + 1 = 36 + 1 = 37$

    $x + 2 = 36 + 2 = 38$

    $x + 3 = 36 + 3 = 39$

    The numbers are 36, 37, 38, and 39.

4a. $n + 2, n + 4$

4b. $n + (n + 2) + (n + 4) = 78$

    $3n + 6 = 78$

    $3n = 72$

    $n = 24$

    $n + 2 = 24 + 2 = 26$

    $n + 4 = 24 + 4 = 28$

    The numbers are 24, 26, and 28.

5a. first: x, second: x, third: $3x$, fourth: $x + 20$

    $x + x + 3x + (x + 20) = 800$

    $6x + 20 = 800$

    $6x = 780$

    $x = 130$

    $3x = 3(130) = 390$

    $x + 20 = 130 + 20 = 150$

    first: 130, second: 130, third: 390, fourth: 150

5b. $x + x + 3x + (x + 20) = 700$

    $6x + 20 = 700$

    $6x = 680$

    $x \approx 113.3$

    $3x = 3(113) = 339$

    $x + 120 = 113 + 20 = 133$

    first: 113, second: 113, third: 339, fourth: 133

    Possible answer: 113, 113, 339, and 133 fit the description but leave 2 videos undistributed. Give these to two of the stores.

Page 218   Share and Summarize

1. yes

2. Equations will vary; Possible answer: When you do the same thing to both sides, you are undoing each operation, step by step. This is just what you do when you backtrack.

Pages 219–222   Lab

1a. $4 + 2 = 6$

    $4 + 4 = 8$

    $4 + 7 = 11$

    6:00, 8:00, 11:00

1b. Possible answer: I added the number of hours to 4.

2a. $4 + 10 - 12 = 14 - 12 = 2$

    $4 + 12 - 12 = 16 - 12 = 4$

    $4 + 20 - 12 = 24 - 12 = 12$

    2:00, 4:00, 12:00

2b. Possible answer: I added the number of hours to 4 and subtracted 12.

2c. $4 + 21 - 12 = 13 - 12 = 1$

    $4 + 35 - 12 = 27 - 12 = 15 - 12 = 3$

    1:00, 3:00

3a. Possible explanation: Because every time you subtract 12 from a sum greater than 12, you go all the way around the clock and land on the same number.

3b. Possible answers: Yes; I can subtract the greatest multiple of 12 that's less than $h + 4$. For $50 + 4 = 54$, subtract $4(12)$ or 48 to get 6:00.

4a. The clock only goes to 12 and then starts over again at 1.

4b. 12

5.

1	12	1	2	3	4	5	6	7	8	9	10	11
12	12	1	2	3	4	5	6	7	8	9	10	11
1	1	2	3	4	5	6	7	8	9	10	11	12
2	2	3	4	5	6	7	8	9	10	11	12	1
3	3	4	5	6	7	8	9	10	11	12	1	2
4	4	5	6	7	8	9	10	11	12	1	2	3
5	5	6	7	8	9	10	11	12	1	2	3	4
6	6	7	8	9	10	11	12	1	2	3	4	5
7	7	8	9	10	11	12	1	2	3	4	5	6
8	8	9	10	11	12	1	2	3	4	5	6	7
9	9	10	11	12	1	2	3	4	5	6	7	8
10	10	11	12	1	2	3	4	5	6	7	8	9
11	11	12	1	2	3	4	5	6	7	8	9	10

6a. $4 + 8 = 12 = 0$

6b. $0 + 5 = 5$

6c. $6 + 11 = 17$

    $= 12 + 5$

    $= 0 + 5$

    $= 5$

7. $0 + 0 = 0$
$1 + 11 = 12 = 0$
$2 + 10 = 12 = 0$
$3 + 9 = 12 = 0$
$4 + 8 = 12 = 0$
$5 + 7 = 12 = 0$
$6 + 6 = 12 = 0$
0, 0; 1, 11; 2, 10; 3, 9; 4, 8; 5, 7; 6, 6

8a. $5 + 7 = 12 = 0$
7

8b. $6 + 6 = 12 = 0$
6

9. $x + 4 + 8 = 3 + 8$
$x + 12 = 11$
$x + 0 = 11$
$x = 11$

10. $y + 5 = 5$
$y = 0$

11. $1 + x + 11 = 0 + 11$
$x + 12 = 11$
$x + 0 = 11$
$x = 11$

12. no solution

13.

+	0	1	2	3	4	5
0	0	1	2	3	4	5
1	1	2	3	4	5	0
2	2	3	4	5	0	1
3	3	4	5	0	1	2
4	4	5	0	1	2	3
5	5	0	1	2	3	4

14. $0 + 0 = 0$
$1 + 5 = 6 = 0$
$2 + 4 = 6 = 0$
$3 + 3 = 6 = 0$
0, 0; 1, 5; 2, 4; 3, 3

15. $4 + 5 = 9$
$= 6 + 3$
$= 0 + 3$
$= 3$

16. $2 + 3 = 5$

17. $5 + 1 = 6 = 0$

18. $7 + 1 = 8$
$= 6 + 2$
$= 0 + 2$
$= 2$

19. $4 + 2 = 6 = 0$
2

20. $x + 5 + 1 = 0 + 1$
$x + 6 = 1$
$x + 0 = 1$
$x = 1$

21. $3 + y = 3$
$y = 0$

22. $1 + 5 + j = 0 + 5$
$6 + j = 5$
$0 + j = 5$
$j = 5$

23. $k + 2 + 4 = 1 + 4$
$k + 6 = 5$
$k + 0 = 5$
$k = 5$

24. $m + 3 + 3 = 1 + 3$
$m + 6 = 4$
$m + 0 = 4$
$m = 4$

25a–c. Answers will vary.

26. Equations will vary.

27. Possible answer: Find the additive inverse of the number being added to the variable, and add it to both sides of the equation.

28. Possible answer: In the real number system, there are negative numbers and fractions. In a clock system, there are a limited number of possible answers to addition problems; in the real number system, there are an infinite number of sums. In a clock system, when you add two (positive) numbers, you don't always get a greater number as an answer.

Pages 223–225   On Your Own Exercises

1. $45 \div 5 = 9$
$9 + 2 = 11$
$n = 11$
$5(11 - 2) = 45$
$5(9) = 45$
$45 = 45$ ✓

2. $7 \div 2 = 3.5$
$3.5 + 5 = 8.5$
$n = 8.5$
$2(8.5 - 5) = 7$
$2(3.5) = 7$
$7 = 7$ ✓

3. $7 - 5 = 2$
$2 \cdot 2 = 4$
$n = 4$
$\frac{4}{2} + 5 = 7$
$2 + 5 = 7$
$7 = 7$ ✓

4. $12 \div 3 = 4$
$4 + 6 = 10$
$10 \div 4 = 2.5$
$m = 2.5$
$3(4 \cdot 2.5 - 6) = 12$
$3(10 - 6) = 12$
$3(4) = 12$
$12 = 12$ ✓

5. $12 \cdot 6 = 72$
$72 + 3 = 75$

$75 \div 3 = 25$

$m = 25$

$\dfrac{3 \cdot 25 - 3}{6} = 12$

$\dfrac{75 - 3}{6} = 12$

$\dfrac{72}{6} = 12$

$12 = 12$ ✓

6. $12 \div 3 = 4$

$4 + 4 = 8$

$8 \cdot 6 = 48$

$m = 48$

$3\left(\dfrac{48}{6} - 4\right) = 12$

$3(8 - 4) = 12$

$3(4) = 12$

$12 = 12$ ✓

7. $2x + 3 = x + 5$

$\quad x + 3 = 5$ after subtracting x from both sides

$\quad\quad x = 2$ after subtracting 3 from both sides

8. $7y - 4 = 4y - 13$

$3y - 4 = {}^-13$ after subtracting $4y$ from both sides

$\quad 3y = {}^-9$ after adding 4 to both sides

$\quad\quad y = {}^-3$ after dividing both sides by 3

9. $4 - 2({}^-5a - 10) = 30$

$4 + 10a + 20 = 30$

$10a + 24 = 30$

$10a = 6$

$a = \dfrac{6}{10} = \dfrac{3}{5}$

10. $\dfrac{b - 2}{4} = \dfrac{6}{5}$

$20\left(\dfrac{b - 2}{4}\right) = 20\left(\dfrac{6}{5}\right)$

$5(b - 2) = 4(6)$

$5b - 10 = 24$

$5b = 34$

$b = \dfrac{34}{5}$, or $6\dfrac{4}{5}$

11. Javier: n, Ken: $2n + 3$, Khalid: $n - 5$

$n + (2n + 3) + (n - 5) = 50$

$4n - 2 = 50$

$4n = 52$

$n = 13$

$2n + 3 = 2(13) + 3 = 26 + 3 = 29$

$n - 5 = 13 - 5 = 8$

Javier: 13, Ken: 29, Khalid: 8

12. Austin: n, Da-Chun: $5n$, Da-Chun: $n + 16$

$5n = n + 16$

$4n = 16$

$n = 4$

$5n = 5(4) = 20$

Austin: 4, Da-Chun: 20

13. Ty: n, Kai: $2n - 2$, Kai: $n + 23$

$2n - 2 = n + 23$

$n = 25$

$2n - 2 = 2(25) - 2 = 50 - 2 = 48$

Ty: 25, Kai: 48

14. Jacob: n, Emilio: $2n - 3$, Latisha: $3n + 20$

$n + (2n - 3) + (3n + 20) = 65$

$6n + 17 = 65$

$6n = 48$

$n = 8$

$2n - 3 = 2(8) - 3 = 16 - 3 = 13$

$3n + 20 = 3(8) + 20 = 24 + 20 = 44$

Jacob: 8, Emilio: 13, Latisha: 44

15. $2(5x - 4) = 62$

$10x - 8 = 62$

$10x = 70$

$x = 7$

16. normal number of boxes delivered: x

Sam's Pizzeria: $2x$

Pizza House: $x + 3$

Pizza Pit: $x + 6$

Paul's Pizza Parlor: $0.5x$

Pizza Heaven: x

$2x + (x + 3) + (x + 6) + 0.5x + x = 64$

$5.5x + 9 = 64$

$5.5x = 55$

$x = 10$

17. Equations and explanations will vary.

18a. Possible explanation: Stage n of the pattern can be thought of as n pentagons, with three sides removed from the first pentagon. So, $5n$ is the number of toothpicks in n pentagons. Subtracting 3 takes away the three toothpicks in the first pentagon.

18b. Stage n: $t = 5n - 3$

Stage 10: $t = 5(10) - 3 = 50 - 3 = 47$

Stage 100: $t = 5(100) - 3 = 500 - 3 = 497$

18c. $t = 5n - 3$

$122 = 5n - 3$

$125 = 5n$

$25 = n$

Stage 25

18d. $t = 5n - 3$

$137 = 5n - 3$

$140 = 5n$

$28 = n$

Yes; when $n = 28$, $t = 137$.

18e. $t = 5n - 3$

$163 = 5n - 3$

$166 = 5n$

$33.2 = n$

No; there is no whole number n such that $5n - 3 = 163$.

18f. $t = 5n - 3$

$250 = 5n - 3$

$253 = 5n$

$50.6 = n$

Stage 50; $5(50) - 3 = 247$ toothpicks. Stage 51 requires 252 toothpicks, more than Evan has.

19a. $a = 2.5$
$a = {}^-2.5$
$2.5, {}^-2.5$

19b. $2b + 3 = 8$
$2b = 5$
$b = 2.5$
${}^-(2b + 3) = 8$
${}^-2b - 3 = 8$
${}^-2b = 11$
$b = {}^-5.5$
$2.5, {}^-5.5$

19c. $9 - 3c = 6$
${}^-3c = {}^-3$
$c = 1$
${}^-(9 - 3c) = 6$
${}^-9 + 3c = 6$
$3c = 15$
$c = 5$
$1, 5$

19d. $\frac{5d}{25} = 1$
$5d = 25$
$d = 5$
$\frac{{}^-5d}{25} = 1$
${}^-5d = 25$
$d = {}^-5$
$5, {}^-5$

19e. ${}^-3e = 15$
$e = {}^-5$
${}^-({}^-3e) = 15$
$3e = 15$
$e = 5$
$5, {}^-5$

19f. $|2.5f| = 60$
$2.5f = 60$
$f = 24$
${}^-2.5f = 60$
$f = {}^-24$
$24, {}^-24$

20. length of Tamika's segments: x
length of Tamika's ribbon: $7x + 2$
length of Lydia's segments: $2x$
$4(2x) = (7x + 2) + 1$
$8x = 7x + 3$
$x = 3$
$2x = 2(3) = 6$
Tamika's: 3 ft, Lydia's: 6 ft

21a. $9a^2 = 36$
$a^2 = 4$
$a = 2$
2 ft by 2 ft

21b. Possible layout:

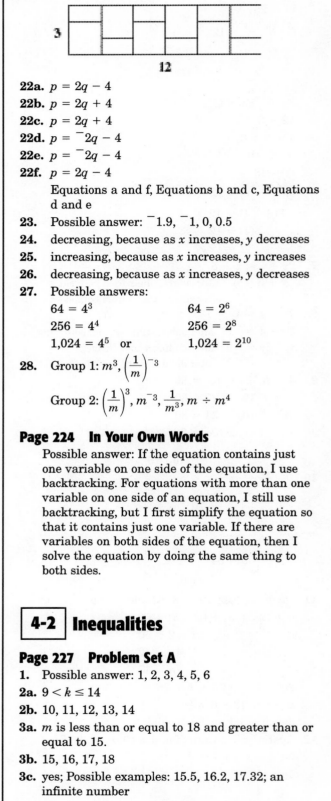

22a. $p = 2q - 4$
22b. $p = 2q + 4$
22c. $p = 2q + 4$
22d. $p = {}^-2q - 4$
22e. $p = {}^-2q - 4$
22f. $p = 2q - 4$
Equations a and f, Equations b and c, Equations d and e

23. Possible answer: ${}^-1.9, {}^-1, 0, 0.5$

24. decreasing, because as x increases, y decreases

25. increasing, because as x increases, y increases

26. decreasing, because as x increases, y decreases

27. Possible answers:

$64 = 4^3$ $64 = 2^6$

$256 = 4^4$ $256 = 2^8$

$1{,}024 = 4^5$ or $1{,}024 = 2^{10}$

28. Group 1: $m^3, \left(\dfrac{1}{m}\right)^{-3}$

Group 2: $\left(\dfrac{1}{m}\right)^3, m^{-3}, \dfrac{1}{m^3}, m \div m^4$

Page 224   In Your Own Words

Possible answer: If the equation contains just one variable on one side of the equation, I use backtracking. For equations with more than one variable on one side of an equation, I still use backtracking, but I first simplify the equation so that it contains just one variable. If there are variables on both sides of the equation, then I solve the equation by doing the same thing to both sides.

4-2 | Inequalities

Page 227   Problem Set A

1. Possible answer: 1, 2, 3, 4, 5, 6

2a. $9 < k \le 14$

2b. 10, 11, 12, 13, 14

3a. m is less than or equal to 18 and greater than or equal to 15.

3b. 15, 16, 17, 18

3c. yes; Possible examples: 15.5, 16.2, 17.32; an infinite number

4. $10 < n < 20 \rightarrow$ 11, 12, 13, 14, 15, 16, 17, 18, 19
$11 \le n \le 19 \rightarrow$ 11, 12, 13, 14, 15, 16, 17, 18, 19
$11 \le n < 20 \rightarrow$ 11, 12, 13, 14, 15, 16, 17, 18, 19
$11 < n < 19 \rightarrow$ 12, 13, 14, 15, 16, 17, 18
$10 < n \le 19 \rightarrow$ 11, 12, 13, 14, 15, 16, 17, 18, 19
$11 < n < 19$

5. Possible answer: 11, 12, 13, 14, 11.5, 13.37

6. Possible answer: 15.4; 16; 17.2; 18; 73; 10,000

7. Possible answer: 17.75, 18, 18.5, $^-$19, $^-$19.123, $^-$20

8. Possible answer: 4.001, 5, 9, 43, 95.4, 989

9. Possible answer: 0.5, 1, 2, 2.3, 3, 4

Pages 228–229   Problem Set B

1. $48 \le n < 55$

2. $100 \cdot \$5 = \$500$
$120 \cdot \$5 = \$600$
$\$500 \le m \le \$600$

3. $155 < F < 165$
$D \ge 165$

4. $2^2 = 4$
$20^2 = 400$
$4 \le a \le 400$

5. $13 \le t \le 17$

6a. $40n + 120$

6b. $4 \text{ m} = 400 \text{ cm}$
$40n + 120 < 400$

7a. $3p + 7p + 200 = 10p + 200$

7b. $10p + 200 \le 500$

8. $\sqrt{4} = 2$
$\sqrt{2.25} = 1.5$
$1.5 \le s \le 2$

Page 229   Share and Summarize

Possible answer: Contestants in the talent contest must be at least 13 years old but younger than 18; $13 \le a < 18$, where a is the age of a contestant.

Page 230   Problem Set C

1a. $3a - 10 = 35$
$\quad 3a = 45$
$\quad\;\; a = 15$

1b. $3a - 10 > 35$
$\quad 3a > 35$
$\quad\;\; a > 15$

1c. $3a - 10 < 35$
$\quad 3a < 35$
$\quad\;\; a < 15$

2a. yes

2b. Possible answer: When $a = 15$, $y = 35$. The graph shows that a values greater than 15 correspond to y values greater than 35, and that a values less than 15 correspond to y values less than 35.

3. Use backtracking to find the solution for
$5a + 7 = 42$.
$42 - 7 = 35$
$35 \div 5 = 7$
$a = 7$
Choose a value less than 7 and test it for a in $5a + 7$.
$5(6) + 7 = 30 + 7 = 37$

For values less than 7, $5a + 7 < 42$.
$a < 7$

4. Use backtracking to find the solution for
$\dfrac{b}{7} + 1 = 6$.
$6 - 1 = 5$
$5 \times 7 = 35$
$b = 35$
Choose a value greater than 35 and test it for b in $\dfrac{b}{7} + 1$.
$\dfrac{70}{7} + 1 = 10 + 1 = 11$
For values greater than 35, $\dfrac{b}{7} + 1 > 6$.
$b \ge 35$

5. Use backtracking to find the solution for
$4c - 3 = 93$.
$93 + 3 = 96$
$96 \div 4 = 24$
$c = 24$
Choose a value greater than 24 and test it for c in $4c - 3$.
$4(30) - 3 = 120 - 3 = 117$
For values greater than 24, $4c - 3 > 93$.
$c > 24$

6. Use backtracking to find the solution for
$^-6(d + 1) = 24$.
$24 \div {}^-6 = {}^-4$
$^-4 - 1 = {}^-5$
$d = {}^-5$
Choose a value less than $^-5$ and test it for d in $^-6(d + 1)$.
$^-6({}^-8 + 1) = {}^-6({}^-7) = 42$
For values less than $^-5$, $^-6(d + 1) > 24$.
$d \le {}^-5$

Page 231   Problem Set D

1. Ben's:
$7x + 2 \ge 100$
$\quad 7x \ge 98$ after subtracting 2 from both sides
$\quad\;\; x \ge 14$ after both sides are divided by 7

Tamika's:
Use backtracking to find the solution for
$7x + 2 = 100$.
$100 - 2 = 98$
$98 \div 7 = 14$
$x = 14$
Choose a value greater than 14 and test it for x in $7x + 2$.
$7(15) + 2 = 105 + 2 = 107$
For values greater than 14, $7x + 2 > 100$.
$x \ge 14$
both methods: $x \ge 14$

2. Ben's:

$$^-7x + 2 \le 100$$
$$^-7x \le 98 \qquad \text{after subtracting 2 from both sides}$$
$$x \le {}^-14 \qquad \text{after both sides are divided by } {}^-7$$

Tamika's:

Use backtracking to find the solution for
$^-7x + 2 = 100$.

$$100 - 2 = 98$$
$$98 \div {}^-7 = {}^-14$$
$$x = {}^-14$$

Choose a value greater than $^-14$ and test it for x in $^-7x + 2$.

$$^-7({}^-13) + 2 = 91 + 2 = 93$$

For values greater than $^-14$, $^-7x + 2 < 100$.

$$x \ge {}^-14$$

Tamika's is correct.

3a. The resulting inequality is not true. If you reverse the inequality symbol (that is, change $<$ to $>$ and change $>$ to $<$), the inequalities will be true.

3b. The resulting inequality is not true. If you reverse the inequality symbol (that is, change $<$ to $>$ and change $>$ to $<$), the inequalities will be true.

3c. When you multiply or divide both sides of an inequality by a negative number, the direction of the inequality symbol must be reversed. Ben's method does not account for this. Since Tamika's method involves testing a point, it does not lead to the same mistake.

3d. If you multiply or divide both sides by a negative number, reverse the inequality symbol.

4. $2b > 15$

$b > 7.5$

5. $^-2c > 15$

$c < {}^-7.5$

6. $12 + 6d \le 54$

$6d \le 42$

$d \le 7$

7. $12 - 6e \le 54$

$^-6e \le 42$

$e \ge {}^-7$

8. $^-3(f - 12) < {}^-93$

$^-3f + 36 < {}^-93$

$^-3f < {}^-129$

$f > 43$

9. $\dfrac{5g}{-7} + 1 \ge -\dfrac{23}{7}$

$$^-7\left(\dfrac{5g}{-7} + 1\right) \le {}^-7\left(-\dfrac{23}{7}\right)$$
$$5g - 7 \le 23$$
$$5g \le 30$$
$$g \le 6$$

10. $0 < 1 - u < 1$

$^-1 < \quad - u < 0$ after subtracting 1 from all three parts

$1 > \quad u > 0$ after multiplying all three parts by $^-1$

$0 < \quad u < 1$

Page 231 Share and Summarize

Possible answer: Solve the inequality by doing the same thing to both sides. However, if you multiply or divide both sides by a negative number, reverse the inequality sign.

Pages 232–233 Problem Set E

1a. 1, 2, 3, 4

1b.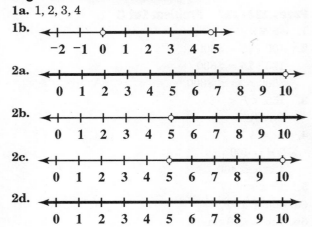

2a.

2b.

2c.

2d.

2e. Possible answer: The word *and* means that the values must satisfy both inequalities; these are the values where the graphs in Parts a and b overlap. The word *or* means that the graph should include any value that satisfies either inequality; this includes all the values from both Parts a and b (the entire number line).

3a.

3b.

3c. The graph in Part a includes values that are solutions of both inequalities. Since there are no values that are both greater than 10 and less than 5, this graph shows no values. The graph in Part b includes values that satisfy either inequality.

4a.

4b.

5a. $^-3, {}^-2, {}^-1, 0, 1, 2, 3$

5b.

5c. $^-4 \le x \le 4$

6. $\dfrac{2p}{5} < 10$

$2p < 50$

$p < 25$

7. $^-2(k - 5) \leq 10$
$^-2k + 10 \leq 10$
$^-2k \leq 0$
$k \geq 0$

Page 233   Problem Set F

1.

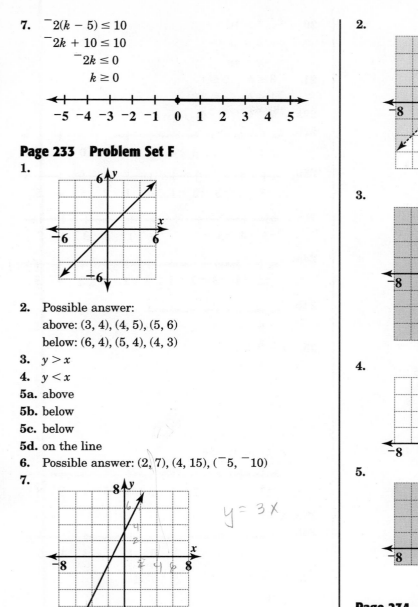

2. Possible answer:
above: $(3, 4)$, $(4, 5)$, $(5, 6)$
below: $(6, 4)$, $(5, 4)$, $(4, 3)$

3. $y > x$

4. $y < x$

5a. above

5b. below

5c. below

5d. on the line

6. Possible answer: $(2, 7)$, $(4, 15)$, $(^-5, ^-10)$

7.

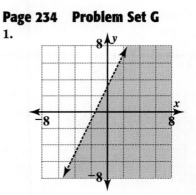

$y = 3x$

Points will appear above the line.

Page 234   Problem Set G

1.

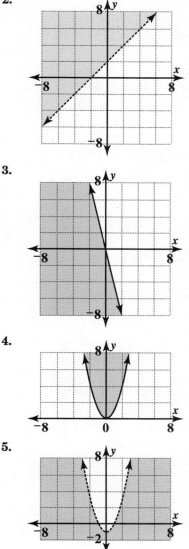

2.

3.

4.

5.

Page 234   Share and Summarize

1a. The graph of "$x \geq a$ and $x \leq b$" includes the values that satisfy both inequalities. The graph of "$x \geq a$ or $x \leq b$" includes the values that satisfy either inequality.

1b. Possible answer: $a = 4$, $b = 12$

1c. Possible answer: $a = 4$, $b = 0$

2. Possible answer: Graph the related equation. If the inequality symbol is $<$ or $>$, use a dashed line or curve. If it's $\leq$ or $\geq$, use a solid line or curve. Then test a point on one side of the line or curve. If the point satisfies the inequality, shade the side of the graph containing the point. If it does not satisfy the inequality, shade the other side. Examples will vary.

Pages 235–239   On Your Own Exercises

1. $n - 2 > 5$
$n > 7$
Possible answer: 8, 9, 10, 11, 12, 13

2a. $^-3, ^-2, ^-1, 0$

2b. Possible answer: $^-3.5, ^-2.999, ^-0.02$

3. $^-2n \geq 6$

$n \leq {}^-3$

Possible answer: $^-7, {}^-6, {}^-5, {}^-4, {}^-3$

4. $^-2 < p < 2$

Possible answer: $^-1.5, {}^-1, 0, 0.25, 1$

5. Possible answer: $6.2, 6.4, 6.6, 6.8, 6.9$

6. Possible answer: $13, 14, 15, 16, 17$

7. $m - 3 > 9$

$m > 12$

Possible answer: $12.5, 13, 14, 15, 16$

8. $1 \leq {}^-x \leq 5$

$^-1 \geq x \geq {}^-5$

$^-5 \leq x \leq {}^-1$

Possible answer: $^-5, {}^-4, {}^-3, {}^-2, {}^-1$

9. $^-5 < q < 5$

Possible answer: $^-3, {}^-2, 0, 1, 2$

10. $^-6 \leq b \leq 6$

Possible answer: $^-2, {}^-1, 3, 4, 5$

11. $|s| \geq 11$

$s \leq {}^-11$ and $s \geq 11$

Possible answer: $^-12, {}^-11, 15, 20, 25$

12. $1.5 \leq h \leq 2$

13. $500 \cdot \$0.12 = \$60$

$750 \cdot \$0.12 = \$90$

$60 \leq d \leq 90$

14a. $1 + 0.75t$

14b. $1 + 0.75t \leq 5$

15. $3.50 + 0.25n < 7.50$

16a. $1 - x = 0$

$x = 1$

16b. $1 - x < 0$

$-x < {}^-1$

$x > 1$

16c. $1 - x > 0$

$-x > {}^-1$

$x < 1$

17a. $1 - d = 1$

$^-d = 0$

$d = 0$

17b. $1 - d < 1$

$^-d < 0$

$d > 0$

17c. $1 - d > 1$

$^-d > 0$

$d < 0$

18. $5(e - 2) > 10$

$5e - 10 > 10$

$5e > 20$

$e > 4$

19. $\frac{f}{2} + 5 > 10$

$\frac{f}{2} > 5$

$f > 10$

20. $\frac{g + 2}{5} > 10$

$g + 2 > 50$

$g > 48$

21. $^-3 \leq h - 2 \leq 1$

$^-1 \leq h \leq 3$

22a. $^-7, {}^-6, {}^-5, {}^-4, {}^-3, {}^-2$

22b.

23a.

23b.

24a.

24b.

25. $r - 3 \geq 3$

$r \geq 6$

$^-(r - 3) \geq 3$

$-r + 3 \geq 3$

$-r \geq 0$

$r \leq 0$

$r \leq 0$ and $r \geq 6$

26a. $x \leq 3$

26b.

27. $\frac{-3p}{4} < 6$

$^-3p < 24$

$p > {}^-8$

28. $12 - 5q \geq 32$

$^-5q \geq 20$

$q \leq {}^-4$

29.

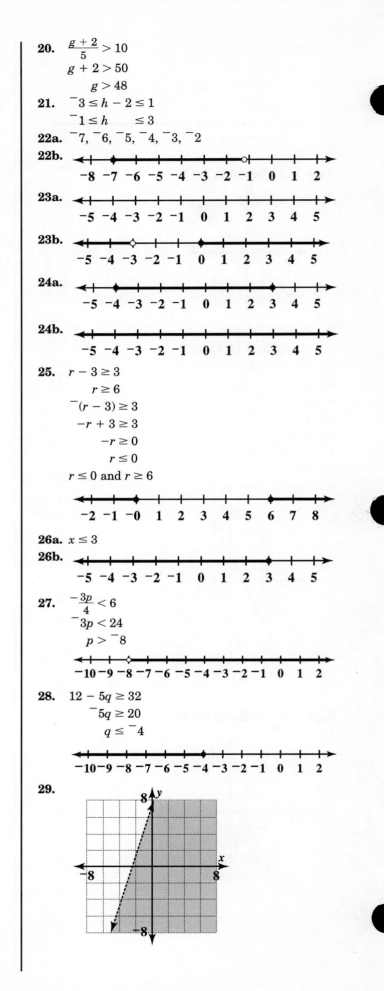

30.

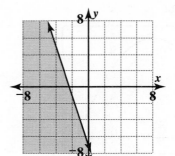

31.

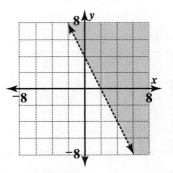

32. Make the curve dashed and shade the area above the curve.

33.

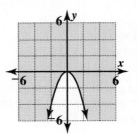

34.

Weight Class	Weight Range (pounds)	Inequality
Super heavyweight	over 201	$w > 201$
Heavyweight	179–201	$179 \leq w \leq 201$
Welterweight	140–147	$140 \leq w \leq 147$
Featherweight	120–125	$120 \leq w \leq 125$
Light flyweight	under 107	$w < 107$

35. $372 - 15 = 357 \qquad 372 + 15 = 387$
$425 - 15 = 410 \qquad 425 + 15 = 440$
$357 \leq x \leq 387$ and $410 \leq y \leq 440$

36. $y = 2(0) + 7 = 0 + 7 = 7$
$y = 2(10) + 7 = 20 + 7 = 27$
Possible answer: For x values in this range, y values range from 7 to 27. I would use $0 \leq y \leq 30$ on the y-axis. This would show the origin and allow me to use intervals of 2 or 5 on the y-axis.

37. $y = 2(^-5) - 10 = ^-10 - 10 = ^-20$
$y = 2(5) - 10 = 10 - 10 = 0$
Possible answer: For x values in this range, y values range from $^-20$ to 0. This would be a reasonable range for the y-axis.

38. $y = (^-5)^2 + 1 = 25 + 1 = 26$
$y = 0^2 + 1 = 0 + 1 = 1$
$y = 5^2 + 1 = 25 + 1 = 26$

Possible answer: For x values in this range, y values range from 1 to 26. I would use $0 \leq y \leq 30$ on the y-axis. This would show the origin and allow me to use intervals of 2 or 5 on the y-axis.

39. $y = ^-2(^-5) = 10$
$y = ^-2(0) = 0$
Possible answer: For x values in this range, y values range from 0 to 10. This would be a reasonable range for the y-axis.

40a.

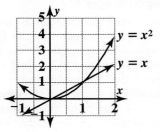

40b. 15 85 1,100

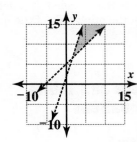

40c.

40d. The graph includes no points.

41. Possible answer: Graph $y = x^2$ and $y = x$ on the same set of axes. The graph of $y = x^2$ is below the graph of $y = x$ when $0 < x < 1$.

42.

43. $^-2y = 14x + \frac{1}{2}(6x + 12)$
$^-2y = 14x + 3x + 6$
$^-2y = 17x + 6$
$y = ^-8.5x - 3$

44. $\frac{1}{5}(10x + 5) - 2 + 9x - 3y = y$
$2x + 1 - 2 + 9x - 3y = y$
$11x - 1 - 3y = y$
$11x - 1 = 4y$
$2.75x - 0.25 = y$
$y = 2.75x - 0.25$

45.
$$\frac{6(x-7)}{2(3-y)} = 0.4$$
$$6(x-7) = 0.4 \cdot 2(3-y)$$
$$6x - 42 = 2.4 - 0.8y$$
$$6x - 44.4 = {}^-0.8y$$
$${}^-7.5x + 55.5 = y$$
$$y = {}^-7.5x + 55.5$$

46. $1.5a^{3+3} = 1.5a^6$

47. $m^{7-5} \cdot b^5 = m^2 b^5$

48. $2^2 \cdot (x^{-2})^2 = 4x^{-2 \cdot 2} = 4x^{-4}$

49. $({}^-1)^4 \cdot (m^2)^4 \cdot n^4 = 1 \cdot m^{2 \cdot 4} \cdot n^4 = m^8 n^4$

50. $a^{m \cdot n} \cdot b^{3 \cdot 0} = a^{mn} \cdot b^0 = a^{mn} \cdot 1 = a^{mn}$

51. $\dfrac{x^{2 \cdot {}^-2}y^{{}^-3 \cdot {}^-2}}{x^4 y^4} = \dfrac{x^{-4}y^6}{x^4 y^4} = x^{-8}y^2 \text{ or } \dfrac{y^2}{x^8}$

52. $r = 65m + 100$

53a. Graph Z

53b. Graph X

53c. Graph Y

54a.

Stage, n	0	1	2	3
Line Segments, s	2	8	32	128

54b. exponential (growth)

54c. $s = 2 \cdot 4^n$

Pages 238   In Your Own Words

Possible answer: Graphing an inequality requires more steps than graphing an equation. To graph an inequality, you must first graph the related equation. The related equation is graphed using a solid line or curve if the inequality symbol is $\leq$ or $\geq$ or using a dashed line or curve if the inequality symbol is $<$ or $>$. If a test point from one side of the line or curve satisfies the inequality, the side containing that point is then shaded. If it does not satisfy the inequality, the other side of the line or curve is shaded.

4-3 | Using Graphs and Tables to Solve Equations

Pages 242–243   Problem Set A

1a. Possible calculator screen:

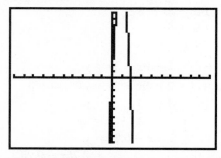

The top of the graph is not visible, and the graph is so narrow that it is difficult to see what it does between $x = 0$ and $x = 2$.

1b. Possible graph:

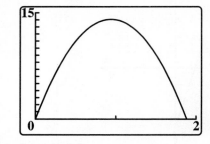

1c. about $(1, 14)$

2a. 0

2b. Possible calculator screen:

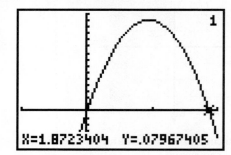

0 and about 1.9

2c. $30t - 16t^2 = 0$

2d. $t = 0$: $30(0) - 16(0^2) = 0$

$t = 1.9$: $30(1.9) - 16(1.9^2) = 57 - 57.76 = {}^-0.76$

$t = 0$ is exact but $t = 1.9$ is not.

3. The ball starts out at ground level (when $t = 0$) and returns to Earth approximately 1.9 s later.

4. Possible calculator screen:

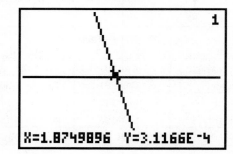

1.875

$30(1.875) - 16(1.875^2) = 56.25 - 56.25 = 0$

5. $0 \leq t \leq 1.875$; Possible explanations: The ball is bounced at $t = 0$, so t can't be less than 0, and the ball hits the ground at $t = 1.875$, so t can't be greater than 1.875. *Or*, for values of t outside this range, h is negative, which doesn't make sense for this situation.

Page 244   Problem Set B

1. Possible answer: Draw a horizontal line at $h = 3$, find where it intersects the curve, and estimate the values of t for each point of intersection.

2. The graph has 2 points with an h value of 3.

3. Possible calculator screens:

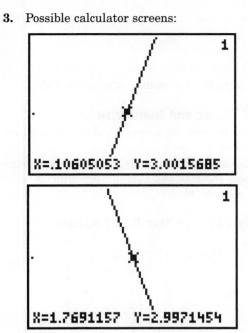

X=.10605053 Y=3.0015685

X=1.7691157 Y=2.9971454

0.11, 1.77

4. It is 3 ft high at about 0.11 s on the way up and at about 1.77 s on the way down.

5. The graph never reaches as high as $h = 20$.

6. Possible equation: $30t - 16t^2 = 30$

7. 2

8. Yes; it is the value of h at the highest point of the graph; $c \approx 14$ (when $t \approx 1$).

9. $0 \le h \le 14$ or $0 \le h \le 14.0625$; Possible explanation: The minimum height is 0, when the ball is on the ground. The maximum height, from Problem 8, is about 14 m.

Page 244 Share and Summarize

1. Possible answer: Use Trace to find estimates for solutions and Zoom to increase their accuracy. To solve the equation $20x^2 - 30 = 0$, make a graph of $y = 20x^2 - 30$. Then use Trace to find approximate values of x that make y equal to 0. Zoom in and trace again to get more accurate. $^-1.22$, 1.22

2. 0, 1, or 2

Page 247 Problem Set C

1a. $x = 1.5$, $\Delta x = 0.01$

1b.

x	y
1.5	3.75
1.51	3.7901
1.52	3.8304
1.53	3.8709
1.54	3.9116
1.55	3.9525
1.56	3.9936
1.57	4.0349
1.58	4.0764
1.59	4.1181
1.6	4.16

1c. 1.56 and 1.57; 1.56 is closer. When x is 1.56, the area is less than 0.01 away from 4. When x is 1.57, the area is more than 0.03 away from 4.

1d. width = 1.56 m or 156 cm
length = 1.56 + 1 = 2.56 m or 256 cm

2a. $x = 1.56$, $\Delta x = 0.001$

2b. Possible calculator screen:

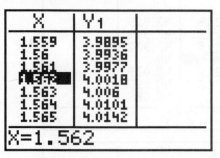

X=1.562

1.561 and 1.562

2c. 1.562; The area for 1.561 is 3.9977, which differs from 4 by 0.0023; the area for 1.562 is 4.0018, which differs from 4 by 0.0018.

3a. $x(x + 2) = 6$

3b. Possible calculator screen:

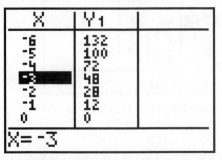

X=1.646

The exact answer is between 1 and 2; between 1.6 and 1.7, and between 1.64 and 1.65. 1.65 m is the width to the nearest centimeter.

Page 248 Problem Set D

1. Possible calculator screens:

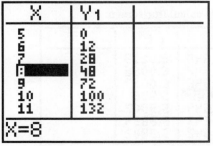

X= -3

X=8

The expression $2m(m - 5)$ is equal to 48 when $m = {}^-3$ and when $m = 8$.

${}^-3, 8$

$m = {}^-3: 2({}^-3)({}^-3 - 5) = {}^-6({}^-8) = 48$ ✓

$m = 8: 2(8)(8 - 5) = 16(3) = 48$ ✓

2. Possible calculator screens:

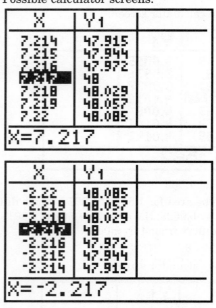

The expression $3t(t - 5)$ is equal to 48 when $t \approx 7.22$ and when $t \approx {}^-2.22$.

$7.22, {}^-2.22$

$t = 7.22: 3(7.22)(7.22 - 5) = 21.66(2.22) \approx 48$ ✓

$t = {}^-2.22: 3({}^-2.22)({}^-2.22 - 5) = {}^-6.66({}^-7.22) \approx 48$ ✓

3a. Scroll through the table to see whether there is a second value of x that gives a value of y equal or close to 4.

3b. Possible calculator screen:

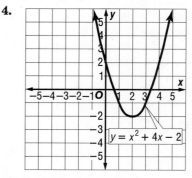

The expression $x(x + 1)$ is also equal to 4 when $x \approx {}^-2.56$.

${}^-2.56$

${}^-2.56({}^-2.56 + 1) = {}^-2.56({}^-1.56) \approx 4$ ✓

3c. Possible calculator screen:

The expression $x(x + 2)$ is also equal to 6 when $x \approx {}^-3.65$.

${}^-3.65$

${}^-3.65({}^-3.65 + 2) = {}^-3.65({}^-1.65) \approx 6$ ✓

3d. No; a tapestry cannot have a negative width.

Page 248　Share and Summarize

1. Possible answer: Equations i and iv, because they are linear.

2. Possible answer: Equations ii and iii, because they are more complex and may be very difficult to solve using algebra.

Pages 249–255　On Your Own Exercises

1a.
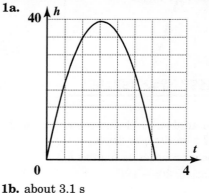

1b. about 3.1 s

1c. about 39 ft

1d. about 1.6 s

2a. Draw a horizontal line intersecting the graph at $t = 0.5$ and see where it intersects the graph again.

2b. about 1.4 s

3a. $h < 14.0625$

3b. $h > 14.0625$

3c. $h = 14.0625$

4.

$y = x^2 + 4x - 2$

4a. Possible answer: 0

4b. ${}^-2$

4c. Possible answer: ${}^-3$

5.

x	26	25	24	23	22	21	0	1	2	3	4	5	6
y	36	24	14	6	0	24	26	26	24	0	6	14	24

Solutions: ${}^-4, 5$

6.

x	29	28	27	26	25	24	23	22	21	0	1	2	3	4	5	6	7	8	9
y	93	75	59	45	33	23	15	9	5	3	3	5	9	15	23	33	45	59	75

Solutions: ${}^-6, 7$

7a. $^-1, 4$

7b. Possible answer: Look at values that increase by 0.1, between $^-2$ and $^-1$ and between 4 and 5.

7c. Possible calculator screens:

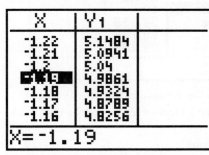

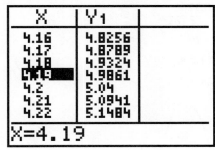

$^-1.2, 4.2$

8. $x^3 + 5x^2 + 4 = 5$

$0.5^3 + 5(0.5)^2 + 4 = 5.375$

$0.4^3 + 5(0.4)^2 + 4 = 4.384$

$0.45^3 + 5(0.45)^2 + 4 = 5.103625$

$0.43^3 + 5(0.43)^2 + 4 = 5.00407$

0.4

9a. between $^-7$ and $^-6$, between 4 and 5

9b. Possible calculator screens:

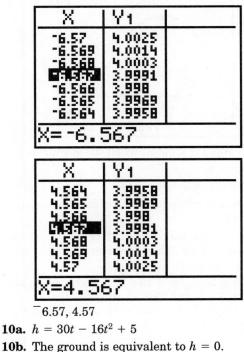

$^-6.57, 4.57$

10a. $h = 30t - 16t^2 + 5$

10b. The ground is equivalent to $h = 0$.

$30t - 16t^2 + 5 = 0$

10c. $30t - 16t^2 + 5 = 5$, or $30t - 16t^2 = 0$

11a. $100 - 16t^2 = 0$, or $100 = 16t^2$

11b. $16t^2 = 100$

$t^2 = 6.25$

$t = \sqrt{6.25}$

$t = 2.5$

12a. $h = vt - 16t^2$

$h = 70t - 16t^2$

Use a calculator to graph $h = 70t - 16t^2$. Then use the Trace and Table features to find the coordinates of the highest point of the parabola.

Possible calculator screens:

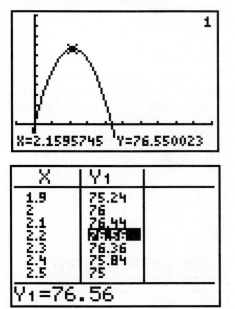

The highest point on the parabola has an h value of about 76.6.

No; the grappling hook reaches a maximum height of about 76.6 ft.

12b. Since an initial velocity of 70 fps is not enough to reach the cliff's edge, try substituting values for v into the equation $h = vt - 16t^2$ that are greater than 70.

Try $v = 80$.

$h = vt - 16t^2$

$h = 80t - 16t^2$

Use a calculator to graph $h = 80t - 16t^2$. Then use the Trace and Table features to find the coordinates of the highest point of the parabola.

Possible calculator screens:

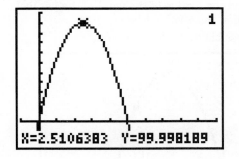

Chapter 4

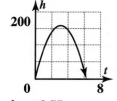

$Y_1=99.999984$

The highest point on the parabola has an
h value of about 100, so an initial velocity of 80
is a good estimate.

Possible answer: 80 fps

12c. $h = vt - 16t^2$

$h = 100t - 16t^2$

Use a calculator to graph $h = 100t - 16t^2$. Then
use the Trace and Table features to find the
coordinates of the highest point of the parabola.

Possible calculator screens:

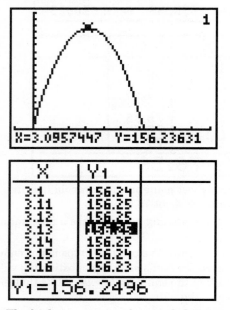

$Y_1=156.2496$

The highest point on the parabola has an
h value of about 156.

$156 - 100 = 56$

The hook will rise about 56 ft above the edge of
the cliff.

12d. On the graph of $h = 100t - 16t^2$ on the
calculator, use the Trace and Table features to
find the t value of the point of the parabola
when the h value is about 100.

Possible calculator screens:

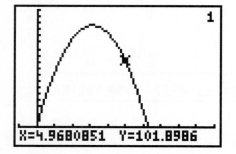

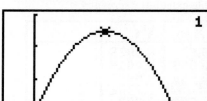

$X=5$

When the h value is 100, the t value is 5.
The hook catches the top of the cliff at about 5 s.

13a. $s = 16t^2$

$50 = 16t^2$

$t^2 = 3.125$

$t = \sqrt{3.125}$

$t \approx 1.77$

about 1.8 s

13b.

about 0.55 s

14a. $h = \frac{1}{2}(20 - 2w)$, or $h = 10 - w$

14b. $a = (10 - w)w$, or $a = 10w - w^2$

14c. Use a calculator to graph $a = 10w - w^2$. Then
use the Trace feature to find the coordinates of
the highest point of the parabola.

Possible calculator screen:

The a value is greatest when the w value is 5.

$h = 10 - w$

$h = 10 - 5 = 5$

The area is greatest when the dimensions are
5 ft by 5 ft.

14d. The closer the width gets to 0 or 10, the smaller
the area will be. When it reaches these values,
the area is 0.

14e. On the graph of $a = 10w - w^2$ on the calculator,
use the Trace and Table features to find the
w values of the point of the parabola when the
a value is about 15.

Possible calculator screens:

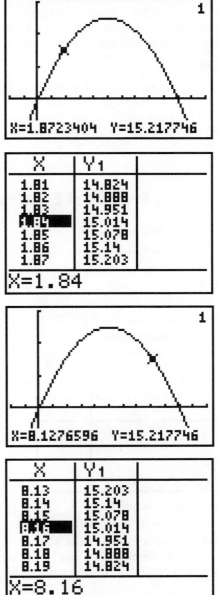

When the a value is about 15, the w values are about 1.8 and 8.2.

The dimensions of the frame are about 1.8 ft by 8.2 ft.

15a. $0 = 20t - 16t^2$ and $0 = 30t - 16t^2$

15b. Use the Table feature to find where y_1 crosses the x-axis.

Possible calculator screen:

X	Y₁	Y₂
1.22	.5856	12.786
1.23	.3936	12.694
1.24	.1984	12.598
1.25	0	12.5
1.26	-.2016	12.398
1.27	-.4064	12.294
1.28	-.6144	12.186

X=1.25

Use the Table feature to find where y_2 crosses the x-axis.

Possible calculator screen:

X	Y₁	Y₂
1.872	-18.63	.08986
1.873	-18.67	.05994
1.874	-18.71	.02998
1.875	-18.75	0
1.876	-18.79	-.03
1.877	-18.83	-.0601
1.878	-18.87	-.0901

X=1.875

$1.875 - 1.25 = 0.625$ s

16a. If the y values increase and then decrease, the greatest y value is the maximum.

16b. If the y values decrease and then increase, the least y value is the minimum.

16c. i.

-3	-2	-1	0	1	2	3
24	25	24	21	16	9	0

maximum, 25

ii.

-3	-2	-1	0	1	2	3
24	15	8	3	0	-1	0

minimum, ⁻1

iii.

-3	-2	-1	0	1	2	3
-7	0	5	8	9	8	5

maximum, 9

17. $m = \dfrac{4.5 - (^-0.5)}{^-1 - 9} = \dfrac{5}{^-10} = \dfrac{^-1}{2} = {^-}0.5$

$y = {^-}0.5x + b$

$^-0.5 = {^-}0.5(9) + b$

$^-0.5 = {^-}4.5 + b$

$4 = b$

$y = {^-}0.5x + 4$

18. $m = \dfrac{^-3 - (^-2)}{^-4 - 1} = \dfrac{^-1}{^-5} = \dfrac{1}{5} = 0.2$

$y = 0.2x + b$

$^-2 = 0.2(1) + b$

$^-2 = 0.2 + b$

$^-2.2 = b$

$y = 0.2x - 2.2$

19.

x	-3	-2	-1	0	1	2
y	-4	1	4	5	4	1
1st Differences		5	3	1	-1	-3
2nd Differences			-2	-2	-2	-2

quadratic

20.

x	-3	-2	-1	0	1	2
y	7	2	-1	-2	-2	-1
1st Differences		-5	-3	-1	0	1
2nd Differences			2	2	1	1

neither

21.

x				$^-3$	$^-2$	$^-1$	0	1	2
y				0	$^-0.5$	$^-1$	$^-1.5$	$^-2$	$^-2.5$
1st Differences				$^-0.5$	$^-0.5$	$^-0.5$	$^-0.5$	$^-0.5$	

linear

22a.

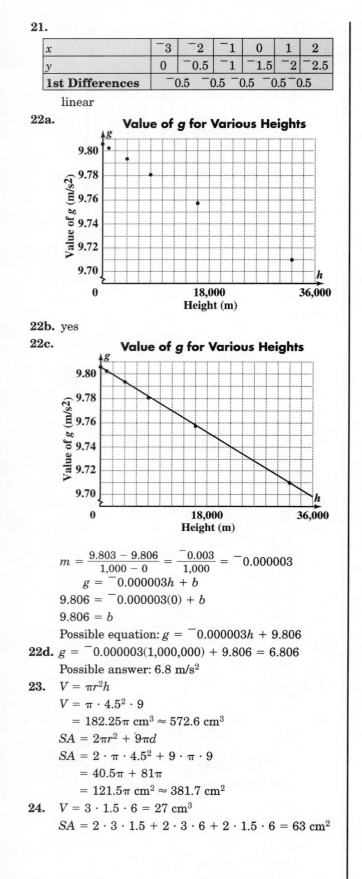

22b. yes

22c.

Value of g for Various Heights

$$m = \frac{9.803 - 9.806}{1{,}000 - 0} = \frac{^-0.003}{1{,}000} = {}^-0.000003$$
$$g = {}^-0.000003h + b$$
$$9.806 = {}^-0.000003(0) + b$$
$$9.806 = b$$

Possible equation: $g = {}^-0.000003h + 9.806$

22d. $g = {}^-0.000003(1{,}000{,}000) + 9.806 = 6.806$

Possible answer: 6.8 m/s^2

23. $V = \pi r^2 h$

$V = \pi \cdot 4.5^2 \cdot 9$

$\quad = 182.25\pi \text{ cm}^3 \approx 572.6 \text{ cm}^3$

$SA = 2\pi r^2 + 9\pi d$

$SA = 2 \cdot \pi \cdot 4.5^2 + 9 \cdot \pi \cdot 9$

$\quad = 40.5\pi + 81\pi$

$\quad = 121.5\pi \text{ cm}^2 \approx 381.7 \text{ cm}^2$

24. $V = 3 \cdot 1.5 \cdot 6 = 27 \text{ cm}^3$

$SA = 2 \cdot 3 \cdot 1.5 + 2 \cdot 3 \cdot 6 + 2 \cdot 1.5 \cdot 6 = 63 \text{ cm}^2$

Page 254   In Your Own Words

Possible answer: To estimate the solution(s) of an equation such as $3x^2 - 5 = 0$, in which one side of the equation is zero, you estimate for what x-value(s) the graph of the related equation $y = 3x^2 - 5$ has a y-value of zero. In other words, you estimate where the graph crosses the x-axis. To estimate the solution(s) of an equation such as $5x^2 + 8 = {}^-2$, in which neither side is zero, you estimate for what x-value(s) the graphs of the related equations, $y = 5x^2 + 8$ and $y = {}^-2$, intersect.

4-4   Solving Systems of Equations

Pages 257–258   Problem Set A

1a. Equation i: one solution, 2

$2x + 3 = 7$

$\quad 2x = 4$

$\quad\ x = 2$

Equation ii: two solutions, $^-2$, $^-3$

Possible calculator screen:

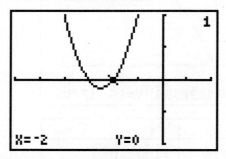

Equation iii: one solution, 2

When $x = 2$, $(2 - 2)^2 = 0^2 = 0$.

1b. These equations have an infinite number of solutions, each of which is an (x, y) pair that satisfies the equation. It is impossible to list them all.

1c. Yes; yes; the solutions of each equation are represented by the points on their graphs. Every ordered pair (x, y) on the graph represents one of the solutions.

1d. $2x + y = 7 \qquad\qquad 3x - y = 3$

$\qquad y = {}^-2x + 7 \qquad\quad {}^-y = {}^-3x + 3$

$\qquad\qquad\qquad\qquad\qquad\quad\ y = 3x - 3$

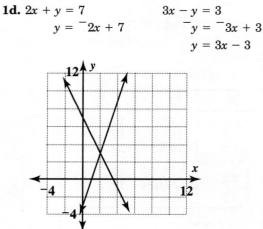

They meet at $(2, 3)$.

1e. $x = 2$ and $y = 3$; These are the coordinates of the point where the two lines meet.

2.
$$2y - x = 20 \qquad\qquad 2x = 5 - y$$
$$2y = x + 20 \qquad\quad y + 2x = 5$$
$$y = \tfrac{1}{2}x + 10 \qquad\quad y = {}^-2x + 5$$

Possible calculator screen:

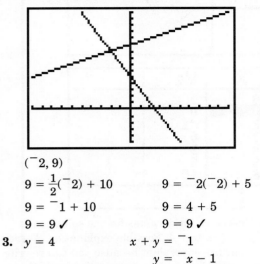

$({}^-2, 9)$

$$9 = \tfrac{1}{2}({}^-2) + 10 \qquad\quad 9 = {}^-2({}^-2) + 5$$
$$9 = {}^-1 + 10 \qquad\qquad\quad 9 = 4 + 5$$
$$9 = 9\ \checkmark \qquad\qquad\qquad 9 = 9\ \checkmark$$

3.
$$y = 4 \qquad\qquad x + y = {}^-1$$
$$y = {}^-x - 1$$

Possible calculator screen:

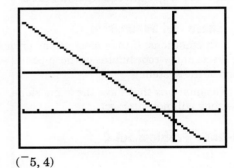

$({}^-5, 4)$

$$4 = 4\ \checkmark \qquad\qquad 4 = {}^-({}^-5) - 1$$
$$4 = 5 - 1$$
$$4 = 4\ \checkmark$$

4a.
$$x + y = 5 \qquad\qquad 2x = 12 - 2y$$
$$y = {}^-x + 5 \qquad\qquad 2y = {}^-2x + 12$$
$$y = {}^-x + 6$$

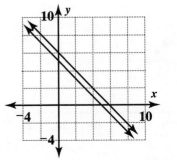

4b. no

4c. The slope of each line is ${}^-1$, so the lines are parallel.

4d. No; since the lines don't intersect, they have no points in common.

5. Possible answer: $y = 4x + 5$ and $2y - 8x = 3$
$$y = 4x + 5 \qquad\qquad 2y - 8x = 3$$
$$2y = 8x + 3$$
$$y = 4x + \tfrac{3}{2}$$

The slope of each line is 4, so the lines are parallel.

6a. Possible answers: $3x = 5y - 4$ and $4x + 2y = 7$ or $3x = 5y - 4$ and $y = {}^-2x + 5$
$$3x = 5y - 4 \qquad\qquad 4x + 2y = 7$$
$${}^-5y = {}^-3x - 4 \qquad\qquad 2y = {}^-4x + 7$$
$$y = \tfrac{3}{5}x + \tfrac{4}{5} \qquad\qquad y = {}^-2x + \tfrac{7}{2}$$

The slopes are not equal, so the lines intersect.

$$3x = 5y - 4 \qquad\qquad y = {}^-2x + 5$$
$${}^-5y = {}^-3x - 4$$
$$y = \tfrac{3}{5}x + \tfrac{4}{5}$$

The slopes are not equal, so the lines intersect.

6b. $4x + 2y = 7$ and $y = {}^-2x + 5$
$$4x + 2y = 7 \qquad\qquad y = {}^-2x + 5$$
$$2y = {}^-4x + 7$$
$$y = {}^-2x + \tfrac{7}{2}$$

The slope of each line is ${}^-2$, so the lines do not intersect.

7a.
$$2x - y = 4 \qquad\qquad 5x - 2.5y = 10$$
$${}^-y = {}^-2x + 4 \qquad\qquad {}^-2.5y = {}^-5x + 10$$
$$y = 2x - 4 \qquad\qquad y = 2x - 4$$

Since the equations represent the same line, the system has an infinite number of solutions. Although the system has an infinite number of solutions, unless students notice that the equations are equivalent, they will probably guess no solution.

7b.

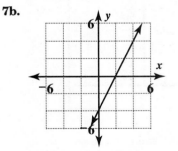

7c. They're the same line.

7d. an infinite number

7e. Possible answer: In Problem 4, there was no solution because the lines were parallel and went through different points. In this system, the lines have the same slope but go through the same points.

8a.
$$2A = B$$
$$4(A - 4) = B - 4$$

8b.
$$2A = B \qquad\qquad 4(A - 4) = B - 4$$
$$B = 2A \qquad\qquad 4A - 16 = B - 4$$
$$4A - 12 = B$$
$$B = 4A - 12$$

Ben's Age vs. Alex's Age

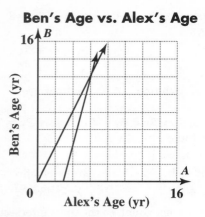

Alex is 6; Ben is 12.

Page 259   Problem Set B

1. $y - x - 1 = 0$

    $y = x + 1$

    Possible calculator screen:

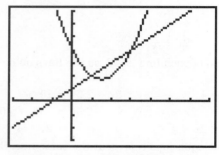

    (1, 2) and (3, 4); two solutions

2a. Possible calculator screen:

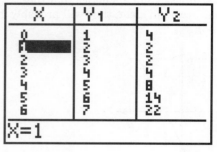

    1, 3

2b. The solutions are the same as the x values in Problem 1. Possible explanations: The table for the equations in Problem 1 is the same as the table for the equation in Problem 2. *Or*, if you solve the system equations for y, you get the two sides of the equation for this problem, so finding where the two equations have the same y value is the same as setting the right sides of the solved equations equal to each other.

2c. Possible calculator screens:

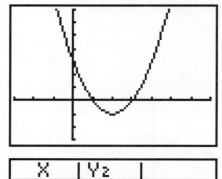

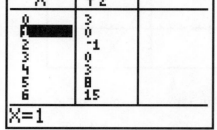

1, 3; These are the x values for the solutions of $x + 1 = x^2 - 3x + 4$. Possible explanation: These equations are equivalent because you can rewrite the equation in Part a by subtracting x and 1 from both sides to get the equation in Part c.

Page 259   Share and Summarize

1. Graph both equations. If they meet at one or more points, the x- and y-coordinates of those points are solutions of the system.

2. Select two equations that have the same slope, because they will not intersect.

Pages 260–261   Problem Set C

1. $6 + 10 = 16$

    $8 + 8 = 16$

    Possible answer: $t = 6$ and $d = 10$, or $t = 8$ and $d = 8$

2. $d + t = 16$

3.

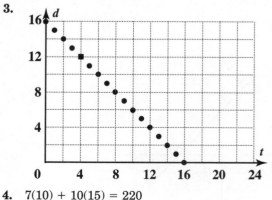

4. $7(10) + 10(15) = 220$

    $22(10) + 0(15) = 220$

    Possible answer: $t = 7$ and $d = 10$, or $t = 22$ and $d = 0$

5. $15d + 10t = 220$

6.

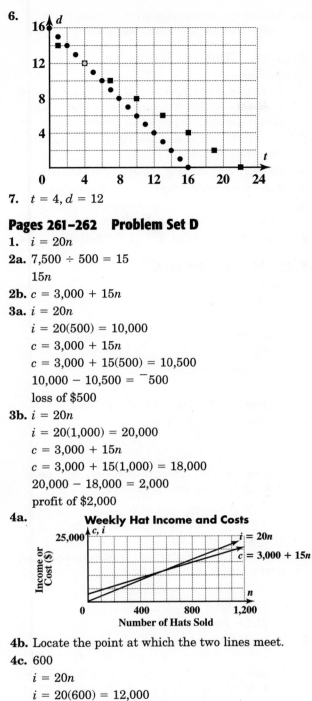

7. $t = 4, d = 12$

Pages 261–262   Problem Set D

1. $i = 20n$

2a. $7,500 \div 500 = 15$

$15n$

2b. $c = 3,000 + 15n$

3a. $i = 20n$

$i = 20(500) = 10,000$

$c = 3,000 + 15n$

$c = 3,000 + 15(500) = 10,500$

$10,000 - 10,500 = {}^-500$

loss of $500

3b. $i = 20n$

$i = 20(1,000) = 20,000$

$c = 3,000 + 15n$

$c = 3,000 + 15(1,000) = 18,000$

$20,000 - 18,000 = 2,000$

profit of $2,000

4a.

Weekly Hat Income and Costs

$i = 20n$

$c = 3,000 + 15n$

Income or Cost ($) — vertical axis, 25,000

Number of Hats Sold — horizontal axis, 0, 400, 800, 1,200

4b. Locate the point at which the two lines meet.

4c. 600

$i = 20n$

$i = 20(600) = 12,000$

$c = 3,000 + 15n$

$c = 3,000 + 15(600) = 12,000$

$12,000 - 12,000 = 0$

break even

4d. 800

$i = 20n$

$i = 20(800) = 16,000$

$c = 3,000 + 15n$

$c = 3,000 + 15(800) = 15,000$

$16,000 - 15,000 = 1,000$

profit of $1,000

4e. $20n = 3,000 + 15n$

$5n = 3,000$

$n = 600$

Page 262   Share and Summarize

1. Possible answer: Maria is making a sauce that requires 3 tomatoes for every onion used. Tomatoes cost $0.75 each and onions cost $0.32 each. Maria has $10 to spend. How many of each vegetable can she buy?

2. The break-even point is the number of sales for the point at which the income and cost graphs intersect.

3. The break-even point is the solution of the system.

Page 264   Problem Set E

1. $4b + a = 15$

$4b + (3 - b) = 15$

$3b + 3 = 15$

$3b = 12$

$b = 4$

$a = 3 - b$

$a = 3 - 4$

$a = {}^-1$

${}^-1 = 3 - 4$

${}^-1 = {}^-1 \checkmark$

$4(4) + {}^-1 = 15$

$16 - 1 = 15 \checkmark$

2. $8y + x = 16$

$8y + (2 - y) = 16$

$7y + 2 = 16$

$7y = 14$

$y = 2$

$x = 2 - y$

$x = 2 - 2$

$x = 0$

$0 = 2 - 2$

$0 = 0 \checkmark$

$8(2) + 0 = 16$

$16 = 16 \checkmark$

3. No; substituting $3 - b$ for a in the first equation will give the equation $3 - b = 3 - b$, which is true for every possible value of b. Evan did not consider the second equation.

Page 265   Problem Set F

1a. $y = 8 - x \ or \ y = 4x - 7$

1b.
$$4x - y = 7$$
$$4x - (8 - x) = 7$$
$$4x - 8 + x = 7$$
$$5x - 8 = 7$$
$$5x = 15$$
$$x = 3$$
$$y = 8 - x$$
$$y = 8 - 3$$
$$y = 5$$
$$(3, 5)$$
$$3 + 5 = 8$$
$$8 = 8 \checkmark$$
$$4(3) - 5 = 7$$
$$12 - 5 = 7 \checkmark$$

2. $x = 8 - y$
$$4x - y = 7$$
$$4(8 - y) - y = 7$$
$$32 - 4y - y = 7$$
$$32 - 5y = 7$$
$$^-5y = ^-25$$
$$y = 5$$
$$x = 8 - y$$
$$x = 8 - 5$$
$$x = 3$$
$$(3, 5)$$
yes

3a. $a + b = 10$

3b. $2a + 3b = 23$

3c. $a = 10 - b$
$$2a + 3b = 23$$
$$2(10 - b) + 3b = 23$$
$$20 - 2b + 3b = 23$$
$$b = 3$$
$$a = 10 - b$$
$$a = 10 - 3$$
$$a = 7$$

4a.

x is about 2.5, y is about 7.5.

4b. $y = 2x + 3$
$$2(2x + 3) + 5x = 27$$
$$4x + 6 + 5x = 27$$
$$9x = 21$$
$$x = 2\frac{1}{3}$$
$$y = 2\left(2\frac{1}{3}\right) + 3$$
$$y = 4\frac{2}{3} + 3$$
$$y = 7\frac{2}{3}$$
These are close to the estimates.

4c. Solving by substitution gives exact answers rather than approximate answers.

Page 265   Share and Summarize
Possible answer:
1. Rewrite one equation by doing the same thing to both sides so that one variable is equal to an expression that includes the other variable.
2. Substitute that expression for the first variable in the second equation.
3. Simplify both sides of the second equation.
4. Solve the equation for the second variable.
5. Substitute that value in the first equation, and solve that equation for the first variable.
6. Check that the solution satisfies both equations.

Page 268   Problem Set G
1.
$$9x + 3x = 3 + 9$$
$$12x = 12$$
$$x = 1$$
$$9(1) - 2y = 3$$
$$9 - 2y = 3$$
$$^-2y = ^-6$$
$$y = 3$$
Adding, you get $12x = 12$, so $x = 1$ and $y = 3$.

2. Multiply both sides by 4.
$$3m + 2 = 13.5$$
$$12m + 8 = 54$$

3. Possible answer: Multiply both sides by 2 and then subtract $8y$ from both sides.
$$x + 4y = 2$$
$$2x + 8y = 4$$
$$2x = ^-8y + 4$$

4. Possible answer: Subtract 1 from both sides and then multiply both sides by 3.
$$7d + 1 = 4p$$
$$7d = 4p - 1$$
$$21d = 12p - 3$$

5a. Multiply both sides of Equation A by 3 to get $3x + 6y = 27$ or by $^-3$ to get $^-3x - 6y = ^-27$.

5b. Possible answer: Multiply Equation B by 2 to get $6x + 2y = 14$ or by $^-2$ to get $^-6x - 2y = ^-14$.

5c. Possible answer: Eliminate y by multiplying Equation C by 3. Then add the equations.

5d. Possible answer: Eliminate y by multiplying Equation F by 2 (then add) or by $^-2$ (then subtract).

5e. Possible answer: Eliminate x by multiplying Equation G by 2 and Equation H by 5, and then subtract the resulting equations. Alternatively, multiply Equation G by $^-2$ and Equation H by 5, and then add the resulting equations.

6. System i:
$$x + 2y = 9$$
$$6x + 2y = 14$$
$$x - 6x = 9 - 14$$
$$^-5x = ^-5$$
$$x = 1$$

$x + 2y = 9$
$1 + 2y = 9$
$2y = 8$
$y = 4$
$(1, 4)$
$1 + 2(4) = 9$
$1 + 8 = 9$ ✓

System iii:
$35x - 6y = 1$
$14x + 6y = 20$
$35x + 14x = 1 + 20$
$49x = 21$
$x = \dfrac{3}{7}$
$7\left(\dfrac{3}{7}\right) + 3y = 10$
$3 + 3y = 10$
$3y = 7$
$y = \dfrac{7}{3}$
$\left(\dfrac{3}{7}, \dfrac{7}{3}\right)$
$7\left(\dfrac{3}{7}\right) + 3\left(\dfrac{7}{3}\right) = 10$
$3 + 7 = 10$
$10 = 10$ ✓

System iv:
$10x + 6y = 84$
$10x + 40y = 390$
$6y - 40y = 84 - 390$
$^-34y = {}^-306$
$y = 9$
$2x + 8(9) = 78$
$2x + 72 = 78$
$2x = 6$
$x = 3$
$(3, 9)$
$2(3) + 8(9) = 78$
$6 + 72 = 78$
$78 = 78$ ✓

Page 269   Problem Set H

1. substitution:
$3x = y + 7$
$y = 3x - 7$
$5x = 9y + 41$
$5x = 9(3x - 7) + 41$
$5x = 27x - 63 + 41$
$^-22x = {}^-22$
$x = 1$
$y = 3x - 7$
$y = 3(1) - 7$
$y = 3 - 7$
$y = {}^-4$
$(1, {}^-4)$

elimination:
$27x = 9y + 63$
$5x = 9y + 41$
$27x - 5x = 63 - 41$
$22x = 22$
$x = 1$
$3x = y + 7$
$3(1) = y + 7$
$3 = y + 7$
$y = 4$
$(1, {}^-4)$

Possible answer: Substitution is better because it's easy to solve the first equation for y and substitute that expression into the second equation.

2. substitution:
$5x - 3y = 10$
$5x = 10 + 3y$
$x = 2 + \dfrac{3}{5}y$
$15\left(2 + \dfrac{3}{5}y\right) + 6y = 30$
$30 + 9y + 6y = 30$
$15y = 0$
$y = 0$
$x = 2 + \dfrac{3}{5}y$
$x = 2 + \dfrac{3}{5}(0)$
$x = 2 + 0$
$x = 2$
$(2, 0)$

elimination:
$10x - 6y = 20$
$15x + 6y = 30$
$10x + 15x = 20 + 30$
$25x = 50$
$x = 2$
$5x - 3y = 10$
$5(2) - 3y = 10$
$10 - 3y = 10$
$^-3y = 0$
$y = 0$
$(2, 0)$

Possible answer: It's easiest to eliminate y by multiplying both sides of the first equation by 2 and then adding.

3a. $x + y = 4$
$y = {}^-x + 4$
$3x + 3y = 11$
$3y = {}^-3x + 11$
$y = {}^-x + \dfrac{11}{3}$

The lines are parallel, so there is no solution.

3b. $x + y = 4$

$\quad y = 4 - x$

$\quad\quad 3x + 3y = 11$

$\quad 3x + 3(4 - x) = 11$

$\quad 3x + 12 - 3x = 11$

$\quad\quad\quad 12 = 11$

Possible answer: Substituting $y = 4 - x$ into the second equation gives $3x + 12 - 3x = 11$, which simplifies to $12 = 11$, which is not true for any value of x.

3c. $3x + 3y = 12$

$\quad 3x + 3y = 11$

$\quad\quad\quad 0 = 1$

Possible result: $0 = 1$; both variables were eliminated, leaving a false statement.

3d. $3x + 3y = 12$

$\quad 3x + 3y = 12$

$\quad\quad\quad 0 = 0$

$0 = 0$ is true for any values of x and y. There are infinitely many solutions.

Page 269 Share and Summarize

1. Answers will vary. Examples should include one equation in which one variable is fairly easy to express in terms of the other.

2. Answers will vary.

3. Answers will vary. Equations whose graphs are parallel to each other have no common solutions.

Pages 270–274 Lab

1. $c = 24.95j + 11.95t$

2. They multiply the cost of the number of jeans in that column by $24.95 and add this to the number of T-shirts in Cell B3 (which is 0) times $11.95 to get the total cost of the jeans and T-shirts for that row and column.

3. $0.00, $24.95, $49.90, $74.85, $99.80, $124.75, $149.70

4a. All the formulas include 24.95*1 plus 11.95 times a variable. The variable changes from B3 to B4 to B5 and so on.

4b. Each finds the price for one pair of jeans plus the price of the number of T-shirts for that row.

5. 6 pairs of jeans and 0 T-shirts; $149.70

6. 2 T-shirts and 5 pairs of jeans; $148.65

7. 4 T-shirts and 4 pairs of jeans; $147.60

8. 6 T-shirts and 3 pairs of jeans; $146.55

9. 2 T-shirts and 4 pairs of jeans; $123.70

10. Possible answers: 5 T-shirts and 3 pairs of jeans for $134.60 *or* 4 T-shirts and 4 pairs of jeans for $147.60

11a. All the formulas include $F$1*1 and $A$9 times a variable. The variable changes from B3 to B4 to B5 and so on.

11b. They multiply the price of Item 1 ($F$1) by the number of this item that are bought (1) and add this to the price of Item 2 ($A$9) times the number of this item.

12. 3 pairs of shorts and 1 turtleneck, $73.80

13. 4 hats and 1 pair of socks, $29.95

14. Answers will vary.

15. Possible answer:

	A	B	C
1	Hourly rate	$6.25	
2			
3	**Day**	**Hours Worked**	**Dollars Earned**
4	Monday		=$B$1*B4
5	Tuesday		=$B$1*B5
6	Wednesday		=$B$1*B6
7	Thursday		=$B$1*B7
8	Friday		=$B$1*B8
9	Saturday		=$B$1*B9
10	Sunday		=$B$1*B10
11	Weekly total		=C4+C5+C6+C7 +C8+C9+C10

Pages 275–280 On Your Own Exercises

1a. i. $y = 2x + 4$

ii. $y + 2x = {}^-4$

$\quad\quad y = {}^-2x - 4$

iii. $x = 4 - \dfrac{y}{2}$

$\quad 2x = 8 - y$

$\quad\quad y = {}^-2x + 8$

iv. $2y - 4x = 10$

$\quad y - 2x = 5$

$\quad\quad\quad y = 2x + 5$

Equations i and iv,

Equations ii and iii

1b. The graphs of each pair are parallel lines, so there is no point at which they meet.

1c. Equations i and ii,

Equations i and iii,

Equations ii and iv,

Equations iii and iv

1d. The graphs of each pair are intersecting lines, so each pair has a common solution.

1e. Equations i and ii: $({}^-2, 0)$;

Equations i and iii: $(1, 6)$;

Equations ii and iv: $({}^-2.25, 0.5)$;

Equations iii and iv: $(0.75, 6.5)$

2a. $C = 2F$ and $C - 4 = F + 4$

2b. $C - 4 = F + 4$

$\quad 2F - 4 = F + 4$

$\quad\quad\quad F = 8$

$\quad C = 2F$

$\quad C = 2(8)$

$\quad C = 16$

Cheryl: 16; Felipe: 8

3a. $d = 5t + 4, d = 6t - 2$, where $d =$ number of diners and $t =$ number of tables

3b. $5t + 4 = 6t - 2$

$^-t = ^-6$

$t = 6$

$d = 5t + 4$

$d = 5(6) + 4$

$d = 30 + 4$

$d = 34$

$d = 5t + 4$

$34 = 5(6) + 4$

$34 = 30 + 4$

$34 = 34$ ✓

$d = 6t - 2$

$34 = 6(6) - 2$

$34 = 36 - 2$

$34 = 34$ ✓

34 friends, 6 tables

4a. bicycle: $d = 18t$

$d = 18(1.5)$

$= 27$ mi

car: $d = 50(t - 1)$

$d = 50t - 50$

$d = 50(1.5) - 50$

$= 75 - 50$

$= 25$ mi

The bicyclist will have traveled 27 mi; the car will have traveled 25 mi; the bicyclist will be ahead.

4b. bicycle: $d = 18(2)$

$= 36$ mi

car: $d = 50(2) - 50$

$= 100 - 10$

$= 50$ mi

After 2 h the car will be ahead, having traveled 50 mi while the bicyclist traveled 36 mi.

4c.

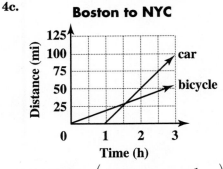

Boston to NYC

4d. about 28 mi $\left(\text{exact answer, } 28\frac{1}{8} \text{ mi}\right)$

4e. A bit longer than $1\frac{1}{2}$ h $\left(\text{exact answer, 1.5625 h, or } 1 \text{ h } 33\frac{3}{4} \text{ min}\right)$

4f. bicyclist: $d = 18t$; car $d = 50(t - 1)$, where d = distance from Boston and t = time after bicyclist left

4g. The time value would tell the time that the car overtook the bicyclist; the distance value would tell how far the bicyclist and the car had traveled.

5a. graph:

$g = ^-f + 20$

$g = ^-3f + 28$

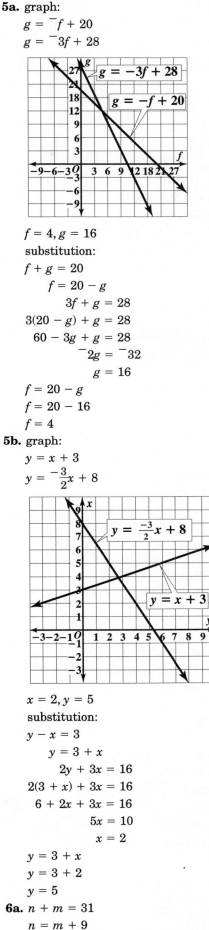

$f = 4, g = 16$

substitution:

$f + g = 20$

$f = 20 - g$

$3f + g = 28$

$3(20 - g) + g = 28$

$60 - 3g + g = 28$

$^-2g = ^-32$

$g = 16$

$f = 20 - g$

$f = 20 - 16$

$f = 4$

5b. graph:

$y = x + 3$

$y = \dfrac{-3}{2}x + 8$

$x = 2, y = 5$

substitution:

$y - x = 3$

$y = 3 + x$

$2y + 3x = 16$

$2(3 + x) + 3x = 16$

$6 + 2x + 3x = 16$

$5x = 10$

$x = 2$

$y = 3 + x$

$y = 3 + 2$

$y = 5$

6a. $n + m = 31$

$n = m + 9$

6b.
$$n + m = 31$$
$$m + 9 + m = 31$$
$$2m = 22$$
$$m = 11$$
$$n = m + 9$$
$$n = 11 + 9$$
$$n = 20$$

7a.
$$A + B = 11$$
$$0.25A + 0.35B = 3.15$$
$$A + B = 11$$
$$A = 11 - B$$
$$0.25A + 0.35B = 3.15$$
$$0.25(11 - B) + 0.35B = 3.15$$
$$2.75 - 0.25B + 0.35B = 3.15$$
$$0.10B = 0.40$$
$$B = 4$$
$$A = 11 - B$$
$$A = 11 - 4$$
$$A = 7$$

7b. 7 books at 25¢ and 4 books at 35¢

8.
$$x + x = 12 + 6$$
$$2x = 18$$
$$x = 9$$
$$x + y = 12$$
$$9 + y = 12$$
$$y = 3$$
Possible answer:
eliminate y; added; $x = 9$, $y = 3$

9.
$$3p + 3p = 13 + (^-5)$$
$$6p = 8$$
$$p = \frac{8}{6}, \text{ or } \frac{4}{3}$$
$$3p + 2q = 13$$
$$3\left(\frac{4}{3}\right) + 2q = 13$$
$$4 + 2q = 13$$
$$2q = 9$$
$$q = \frac{9}{2}$$
Possible answer:
eliminate q; added; $p = \frac{8}{6}$, or $\frac{4}{3}$; $q = \frac{9}{2}$

10.
$$4b - (^-2b) = 59 - 23$$
$$6b = 36$$
$$b = 6$$
$$5a + 4b = 59$$
$$5a + 4(6) = 59$$
$$5a + 24 = 59$$
$$5a = 35$$
$$a = 7$$
Possible answer:
eliminate a; subtracted; $a = 7$, $b = 6$

11.
$$9s - 4s = 3 - 8$$
$$5s = {^-5}$$
$$s = {^-1}$$
$$9s + 2t = 3$$
$$9(^-1) + 2t = 3$$
$${^-9} + 2t = 3$$
$$2t = 12$$
$$t = 6$$
Possible answer:
eliminate t; subtracted; $s = {^-1}$, $t = 6$

12.
$$6m + 2n = 14$$
$$m + 2n = 9$$
$$6m - m = 14 - 9$$
$$5m = 5$$
$$m = 1$$
$$3m + n = 7$$
$$3(1) + n = 7$$
$$3 + n = 7$$
$$n = 4$$
Possible answer:
Equation A; multiplied by 2; subtracted; $m = 1$, $n = 4$

13.
$$6x + y = {^-54}$$
$${^-6x} + 15y = 150$$
$$y + 15y = {^-54} + 150$$
$$16y = 96$$
$$y = 6$$
$$6x + y = {^-54}$$
$$6x + 6 = {^-54}$$
$$6x = {^-60}$$
$$x = {^-10}$$
Possible answer:
Equation D; multiplied by $^-3$; added; $x = {^-10}$, $y = 6$

14.
$$6a + 15b = 36$$
$$6a + 4b = 14$$
$$15b - 4b = 36 - 14$$
$$11b = 22$$
$$b = 2$$
$$2a + 5(2) = 12$$
$$2a + 10 = 12$$
$$2a = 2$$
$$a = 1$$
Possible answer:
both; multiplied Equation E by 3 and Equation F by 2; subtracted; $a = 1$, $b = 2$

15.
$$4y = 3x - 16$$
$$4y = 2x + 3$$
$$0 = 3x - 2x - 16 - 3$$
$$0 = x - 19$$
$$x = 19$$

$$y = \frac{3}{4}x - 4$$
$$y = \frac{3}{4}(19) - 4$$
$$y = 14.25 - 4$$
$$y = 10.25$$

Possible answer:

Equation G; multiplied by 4; subtracted; $x = 19$, $y = 10.25$

16a. $a + d = 1,000$ and $30a + 40d = 38,000$, where a = tickets bought in advance and d = tickets bought at the door

16b.

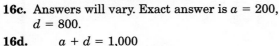
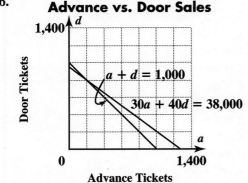

Advance vs. Door Sales

Door Tickets (vertical axis), Advance Tickets (horizontal axis)

1,400 (top), d axis, a axis, $a + d = 1,000$, $30a + 40d = 38,000$, 0, 1,400

16c. Answers will vary. Exact answer is $a = 200$, $d = 800$.

16d.
$$a + d = 1,000$$
$$200 + 800 = 1,000$$
$$1,000 = 1,000 \checkmark$$
$$30a + 40d = 38,000$$
$$30(200) + 40(800) = 38,000$$
$$6,000 + 32,000 = 38,000$$
$$38,000 = 38,000 \checkmark$$

17a. Graph C: Tyrone
Graph B: Manuela
Graph A: Kevin

17b. Manuela passed Tyrone at a distance of about 22 mi, about 3.8 h after Tyrone left the hotel. Kevin passed Manuela at a distance of about 9 mi, about 0.7 h after Manuela left the hotel (2.7 h after Tyrone left). Kevin passed Tyrone at a distance of about 17 mi, about 3 h after Tyrone left the hotel.

17c. Tyrone: $\frac{28 - 0}{5 - 0} = \frac{28}{5} = 5.6$
about 5.6 mph

Manuela: $\frac{30 - 0}{4.5 - 2} = \frac{30}{2.5} = 12$
about 12 mph

Kevin: $\frac{35 - 0}{3.5 - 2.5} = \frac{35}{1} = 35$
about 35 mph

17d. Answers will depend on student estimates for Part c. Possible answer:

Tyrone: $D = 5.6T + b$
$$0 = 5.6(0) + b$$
$$0 = 0 + b$$
$$b = 0$$
$$D = 5.6T$$

Manuela: $D = 12T + b$
$$0 = 12(2) + b$$
$$0 = 24 + b$$
$$b = {}^-24$$
$$D = 12T - 24$$

Kevin: $D = 35T + b$
$$0 = 35(2.5) + b$$
$$0 = 87.5 + b$$
$$b = {}^-87.5$$
$$D = 35T - 87.5$$

17e. $D = 5.6T$
$$D = 12T - 24$$
$$5.6T = 12T - 24$$
$${}^-6.4T = {}^-24$$
$$T = 3.75$$
$$D = 5.6T$$
$$D = 5.6(3.75)$$
$$D = 21$$

18. Possible answer: Bill bought a total of 12 pens and pencils. If pencils cost \$0.25 and pens cost \$1.00, and Bill spent \$7.50, how many of each did he buy? If a = number of pencils and b = number of pens, $a + b = 12$ and $0.25a + b = 7.5$.

$$a + b = 12$$
$$a = 12 - b$$
$$0.25a + b = 7.5$$
$$0.25(12 - b) + b = 7.5$$
$$3 - 0.25b + b = 7.5$$
$$0.75b = 4.5$$
$$b = 6$$
$$a = 12 - b$$
$$a = 12 - 6$$
$$a = 6$$

19.

$(^-1, 1)$ and $(1, 1)$

20.
$$9c + 7a = 107$$
$$7c + 9a = 101$$
$$63c + 49a = 749$$
$$63c + 81a = 909$$
$$49a - 81a = 749 - 909$$
$${}^-32a = {}^-160$$
$$a = 5$$

$$9c + 7a = 107$$
$$9c + 7(5) = 107$$
$$9c + 35 = 107$$
$$9c = 72$$
$$c = 8$$

The price of a citron is 8; the price of a wood apple is 5.

21a. let R = cost of a ride and G = cost of a game; $4R + 3G = 13.50$; $2R + 5G = 15.50$

21b. $2R + 5G = 15.50$
$$5G = 15.50 - 2R$$
$$G = 3.10 - \frac{2}{5}R$$
$$4R + 3G = 13.50$$
$$4R + 3\left(3.10 - \frac{2}{5}R\right) = 13.50$$
$$4R + 9.30 - \frac{6}{5}R = 13.50$$
$$2.8R = 4.20$$
$$R = 1.50$$
$$2R + 5G = 15.50$$
$$2(1.50) + 5G = 15.50$$
$$3 + 5G = 15.50$$
$$5G = 12.50$$
$$G = 2.50$$
ride: \$1.50; game: \$2.50

22a. $8 = A + 120B$

22b. $17 = A + 300B$

22c. $8 = A + 120B$
$$A = 8 - 120B$$
$$17 = A + 300B$$
$$17 = 8 - 120B + 300B$$
$$9 = 180B$$
$$B = 0.05$$
$$A = 8 - 120B$$
$$A = 8 - 120(0.05)$$
$$A = 8 - 6$$
$$A = 2$$
fixed charge = \$2.00,
variable charge = \$0.05

23. $E + K = 11$
$$E - K = 3$$
$$E + E = 11 + 3$$
$$2E = 14$$
$$E = 7$$
$$E + K = 11$$
$$7 + K = 11$$
$$K = 4$$
Evan: 7, Keenan: 4;
Possible equations: $E + K = 11$, $E - 3 = K$

24a. $9A + 5C = 62$, $A + C = 10$

24b. $9A + 5C = 62$
$$5A + 5C = 50$$
$$9A - 5A = 62 - 50$$
$$4A = 12$$
$$A = 3$$

$$A + C = 10$$
$$3 + C = 10$$
$$C = 7$$
3 adults, 7 children

25a. $y = mx + b$
$$^-2 = m(1) + b$$
$$^-2 = m + b$$

25b. $y = mx + b$
$$4 = m(3) + b$$
$$4 = 3m + b$$

25c. $^-2 = m + b$
$$b = {}^-2 - m$$
$$4 = 3m + b$$
$$4 = 3m + (^-2 - m)$$
$$4 = 3m - 2 - m$$
$$6 = 2m$$
$$3 = m$$
$$^-2 = 3 + b$$
$$^-5 = b$$
$$y = 3x - 5$$

25d. $y = mx + b$
$$5 = {}^-x + b$$
$$^-3 = 3x + b$$
$$b = 5 + x$$
$$^-3 = 3x + (5 + x)$$
$$^-3 = 3x + 5 + x$$
$$^-8 = 4x$$
$$^-2 = x$$
$$b = 5 - 2$$
$$b = 3$$
$$y = {}^-2x + 3$$

26. $y = {}^-2x + b$
$$0 = {}^-2(5) + b$$
$$0 = {}^-10 + b$$
$$b = 10$$
$$y = {}^-2x + 10$$

27. $y = 0.5x + b$
$$0 = 0.5(^-2.5) + b$$
$$0 = {}^-1.25 + b$$
$$b = 1.25$$
$$y = 0.5x + 1.25$$

28. inverse variation, $xy = 2.5$

29. linear, $y = 2.5x - 2.5$

30. quadratic, $y = 0.25x^2$

31. $2\pi r = C$
$$2\pi r = 19$$
$$r = \frac{9.5}{\pi}$$
$$V = \pi r^2 h$$
$$V = \pi \cdot \left(\frac{9.5}{\pi}\right)^2 \cdot 9$$
$$V = \frac{812.25}{\pi} \text{ m}^3 \approx 258.5 \text{ m}^3$$

32. $2\pi r = C$

$2\pi r = 34$

$r = \dfrac{17}{\pi}$

$h = 2r$

$h = 2 \cdot \dfrac{17}{\pi}$

$h = \dfrac{34}{\pi}$

$V = \pi r^2 h$

$V = \pi \cdot \left(\dfrac{17}{\pi}\right)^2 \cdot \dfrac{34}{\pi}$

$V = \dfrac{9{,}826}{\pi^2} \text{ m}^3 \approx 995.6 \text{ m}^3$

33. similar, because the four sides of each figure are the same length, and all squares are similar

34. similar, because all equilateral triangles are similar

35. neither, because the angles are not congruent

36. $\dfrac{10}{15} = \dfrac{2}{3}$

$\dfrac{5}{7.5} = \dfrac{2}{3}$

$\dfrac{8}{12} = \dfrac{2}{3}$

similar, because corresponding sides have a common ratio

37. congruent and similar, because corresponding sides and angles are congruent

38. congruent and similar, because corresponding sides and angles are congruent

Page 279   In Your Own Words

Possible answer: If one of the variables in one of the equations has a coefficient of 1, then substitution can easily be used to solve the system. Systems in which multiplying both sides of one equation by a constant makes it easy to eliminate one of the variables by adding or subtracting are best solved using elimination. If the equations in the system have none of these characteristics, graphing might be the best alternative.

Review and Self-Assessment

Pages 281–284   Strategies and Applications

1. Possible answer: Make a flowchart showing the operations needed to get from the input to the output. Start from the output and work backward, undoing each operation, until you have found the input. For example, here is a flowchart for $2n - 1 = 16$.

To solve the equation, start with 16. Since 1 is subtracted from the value in the second oval to get 16, that value must be 17. Since the input is multiplied by 2 to get 17, the input is 34.

2. Possible answer: Apply the same operation to both sides of the equation. Try to get the variable alone on one side of the equation.

$2n - 1 = 16 + n$

$n - 1 = 16$ after subtracting n from both sides

$n = 17$ after adding 1 to both sides

3. $x + (x + 1) + (x + 2) = 57$

$3x + 3 = 57$

$3x = 54$

$x = 18$

$x + 1 = 18 + 1 = 19$

$x + 2 = 18 + 2 = 20$

The three numbers are 18, 19, and 20.

4. 3, 4, 5, 6, 7

5. 8 is less than x, which is less than or equal to 11, or x is greater than 8 and less than or equal to 11; 9, 10, 11.

6. $2m - 800 \geq 1{,}300$

$2m \geq 2{,}100$

$m \geq 1{,}050$

7. $1{,}500 + 40n \leq 7{,}500$

$40n \leq 6{,}000$

$n \leq 150$ people

8a. yes

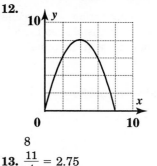

8b. no

9. Possible answer: Graph the corresponding equation. If the inequality involves $<$ or $>$, use a dashed line or curve. If it involves $\leq$ or $\geq$, draw a solid line or curve. Then test a point on one side of the line or curve, If it satisfies the inequality, shade the side of the graph containing it. If it doesn't satisfy the inequality, shade the other side. Examples will vary.

10. Possible answer: Graph the function, and then use Trace to find an initial estimate of the solution. Use Zoom to increase the accuracy of the estimate.

11. $h = 5$ at approximately $t = 0.6, 1.6$

12.

13. $\dfrac{11}{4} = 2.75$

2.75 is between 2.64 and 2.99 on the table.

The solution is between 1.2 and 1.3.

14. One solution is $x = 2$; the other is between $x = {}^-2$ and $x = {}^-1$.

15.
$$y - 1 = {}^-x$$
$$y = {}^-x + 1$$
$$y - x^2 = {}^-1$$
$$y = x^2 - 1$$

Possible calculator screen:

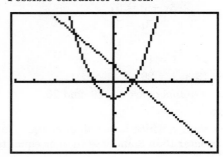

(1, 0) and $({}^-2, 3)$

16a. A: $C = 0.75b + 15$
B: $C = 1.05b$

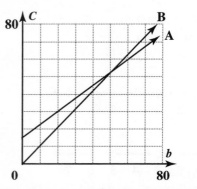
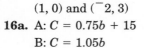

16b. For fewer than 50 bricks, Store B charges less. For more than 50 bricks, Store A charges less. For 50 bricks, they charge the same amount.

17.
$$2x - 2y = 5$$
$$2x - 2({}^-x - 3) = 5$$
$$2x + 2x + 6 = 5$$
$$4x = {}^-1$$
$$x = {}^-0.25$$

$$y = {}^-x - 3$$
$$y = {}^-({}^-0.25) - 3$$
$$y = 0.25 - 3$$
$$y = {}^-2.75$$

Possible answer: I used substitution because one equation already gives y in terms of x, so I can substitute that expression for y in the other equation.

Pages 284–285 Demonstrating Skills

18.
$$4 + 1 = 5$$
$$5 \cdot 3 = 15$$
$$15 - 3 = 12$$
$$12 \cdot 2 = 24$$

$$\frac{1}{3}\left(3 + \frac{24}{2}\right) - 1 = \frac{1}{3}(3 + 12) - 1$$
$$= \frac{1}{3}(15) - 1$$
$$= 5 - 1$$
$$= 4 \checkmark$$

19.
$$1 - 2p = 2 + 2p$$
$$1 - 4p = 2 \qquad \text{after subtracting } 2p \text{ from both sides}$$
$${}^-4p = 1 \qquad \text{after subtracting 1 from both sides}$$
$$p = {}^-0.25 \quad \text{after dividing both sides by } {}^-4$$
$$1 - 2({}^-0.25) = 2 + 2({}^-0.25)$$
$$1 + {}^-0.5 = 2 - 0.5$$
$$1.5 = 1.5 \checkmark$$

20.
$$3(j + 1) - 2(2 - j) \le 9$$
$$3j + 3 - 4 + 2j \le 9$$
$$5j \le 10$$
$$j \le 2$$

21.
$$6(k - 5) - 2 \le 10$$
$$6k - 30 - 2 \le 10$$
$$6k \le 42$$
$$k \le 7$$

22.
$${}^-2(b + 1) > {}^-5$$
$${}^-2b - 2 > {}^-5$$
$${}^-2b > {}^-3$$
$$b < 1.5$$

23.

![Number line from −5 to 5 with open circle at 2 and arrow pointing left]

-5 -4 -3 -2 -1 0 1 2 3 4 5

24.
$$\frac{t}{2} + 2 > 3$$
$$\frac{t}{2} > 1$$
$$t > 2$$

![Number line from −2 to 5 with open circle at 2 and arrow pointing right]

-2 -1 0 1 2 3 4 5

25.

![Coordinate plane graph with shaded region above a line, axes from −12 to 12]

26.

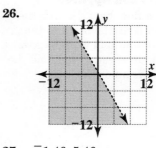

27. $^-1.46, 5.46$

28. $1.78, {}^-0.28$

29. $3y + 1 = 2x$

$3y + 1 = 2(y + 8)$

$3y + 1 = 2y + 16$

$\quad\quad y = 15$

$x = y + 8$

$x = 15 + 8$

$x = 23$

$(23, 15)$

$23 = 15 + 8$

$23 = 23$ ✓

$3(15) + 1 = 2(23)$

$\quad 45 + 1 = 46$

$\quad\quad 46 = 46$ ✓

30. $4x - 10y = 2$

$6x + 10y = 18$

$4x + 6x = 2 + 18$

$\quad 10x = 20$

$\quad\quad x = 2$

$4x - 10y = 2$

$4(2) - 10y = 2$

$8 - 10y = 2$

$^-10y = {}^-6$

$\quad\quad y = 0.6$

$(2, 0.6)$

$4(2) - 10(0.6) = 2$

$\quad\quad 8 - 6 = 2$

$\quad\quad\quad 2 = 2$ ✓

$3(2) + 5(0.6) = 9$

$\quad\quad 6 + 3 = 9$

$\quad\quad\quad 9 = 9$ ✓

31. $\quad\quad y - x = 2$

$(^-x + 1) - x = 2$

$\quad ^-2x + 1 = 2$

$\quad\quad ^-2x = 1$

$\quad\quad\quad x = {}^-0.5$

$y = {}^-x + 1$

$y = {}^-(^-0.5) + 1$

$y = 0.5 + 1$

$y = 1.5$

$(^-0.5, 1.5)$

$^-(^-0.5) + 1 = 1.5$

$\quad 0.5 + 1 = 1.5$

$\quad\quad\quad 1.5 = 1.5$ ✓

$1.5 - (^-0.5) = 2$

$1.5 + 0.5 = 2$

$\quad\quad 2 = 2$ ✓

32. $\quad\quad 3x = 3y + 1$

$3(1 - y) = 3y + 1$

$3 - 3y = 3y + 1$

$\quad\quad ^-6y = {}^-2$

$\quad\quad\quad y = \dfrac{1}{3}$

$x = 1 - y$

$x = 1 - \dfrac{1}{3}$

$x = \dfrac{2}{3}$

$\left(\dfrac{2}{3}, \dfrac{1}{3}\right)$

$3\left(\dfrac{2}{3}\right) = 3\left(\dfrac{1}{3}\right) + 1$

$\quad\quad 2 = 1 + 1$

$\quad\quad 2 = 2$ ✓

$\dfrac{2}{3} = 1 - \dfrac{1}{3}$

$\dfrac{2}{3} = \dfrac{2}{3}$ ✓

33. $^-3y + x = 3$

$\quad\quad x = 3 + 3y$

$\quad\quad 3.5y - 1.5x = 6$

$3.5y - 1.5(3 + 3y) = 6$

$3.5y - 4.5 - 4.5y = 6$

$\quad\quad\quad\quad ^-y = 10.5$

$\quad\quad\quad\quad\quad y = {}^-10.5$

$x = 3 + 3y$

$x = 3 + 3(^-10.5)$

$x = 3 + (^-31.5)$

$x = {}^-28.5$

$(^-28.5, {}^-10.5)$

$3.5(^-10.5) - 1.5(^-28.5) = 6$

$\quad ^-36.75 + 42.75 = 6$

$\quad\quad\quad\quad 6 = 6$ ✓

$^-3(^-10.5) + (^-28.5) = 3$

$\quad\quad 31.5 - 28.5 = 3$

$\quad\quad\quad\quad 3 = 3$ ✓

Chapter 5 Transformational Geometry

5-1 Reflection

Pages 290–291 Problem Set A

1.

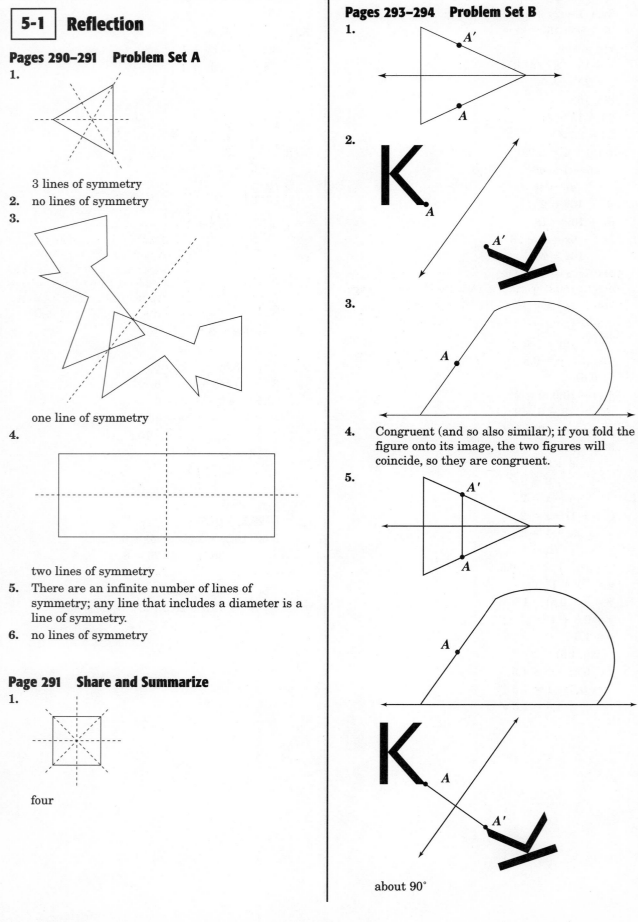

3 lines of symmetry

2. no lines of symmetry

3.

one line of symmetry

4.

two lines of symmetry

5. There are an infinite number of lines of symmetry; any line that includes a diameter is a line of symmetry.

6. no lines of symmetry

Page 291 Share and Summarize

1.

four

Pages 293–294 Problem Set B

1.

2.

3.

4. Congruent (and so also similar); if you fold the figure onto its image, the two figures will coincide, so they are congruent.

5.

about 90°

6a. 1: 0.8 cm; 2: 1 cm; 3: 1.4 cm

6b. 1: 0.8 cm; 2: 1 cm, 3: 1.4 cm

7. The line of symmetry is perpendicular to this segment and cuts it in half.

Page 295   Problem Set C

1a.

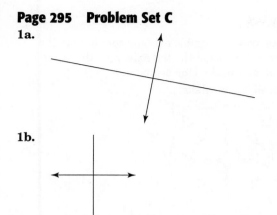

1b.

2. Possible answer: I folded the page to find the midpoint, and then used a corner of another page to draw a right angle through the midpoint.

3. A segment only has one midpoint, and only one line can be drawn through that point that is perpendicular to the segment. So a segment has one perpendicular bisector.

Page 295   Share and Summarize

The line of reflection is the perpendicular bisector of the segment.

Page 296   Problem Set D

1.

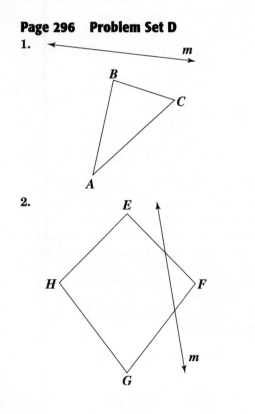

2.

3.

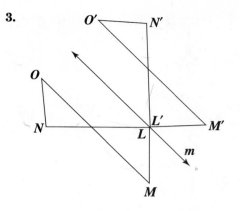

Page 296   Share and Summarize

Possible answer: First reflect point A. Draw a segment perpendicular to the line with one endpoint at point A. Measure the distance from point A to the line, and mark point A' on the other side of the line so the distance from point A' to the line is the same as from point A to the line. Do the same with points B and C, making points B' and C'. Connect points A' and B', points B' and C', and points A' and C'.

Pages 297–301   On Your Own Exercises

1.

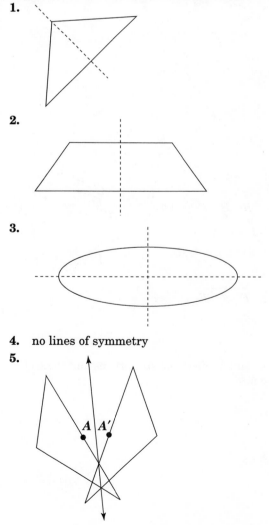

2.

3.

4. no lines of symmetry

5.

6.

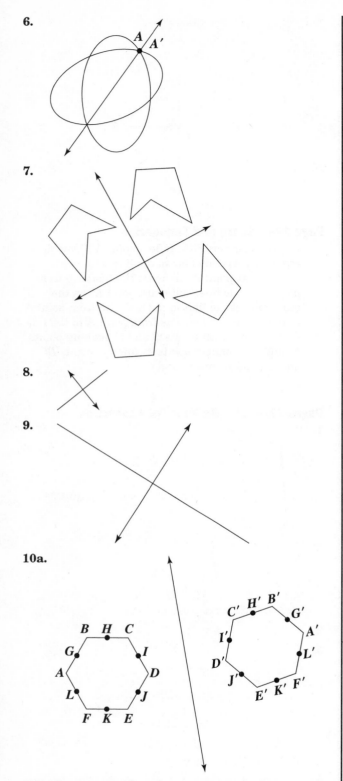

7.

8.

9.

10a.

10b. Six points; reflect the six vertices and connect them.

11a.

11b. four points; Possible explanation: Reflect the three vertices of the triangle, plus the other endpoint of the long segment.

12. Possible snowflake:

13a. Four: two through the diagonals of the base; two that cut opposite sides of the base at their midpoints. All four planes are perpendicular to the base.

13b. Infinitely many; any plane that contains a diameter of the sphere is a plane of symmetry.

13c. Seven; one is parallel to the bases and through the middle of the sides. The other six are perpendicular to the bases; three go through the diagonals and three cut opposite sides at their midpoints.

14a. Yes; the line of symmetry is perpendicular to the side of the table, through the point where the 8 ball hit it.

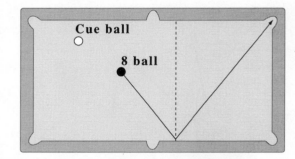

14b. yes; Possible explanation: I traced the angle and checked that it was the same as the other angle.

15. Kai is correct. He could use the "spikes" (points G, I, K, M, O) and connect every other one, or he could use the inner vertices (points H, J, L, N, P) and extend the sides of the resulting pentagon to their intersections.

16. Possible answers: a fork, a spoon, a pencil, a starfish, a plain T-shirt

17a.

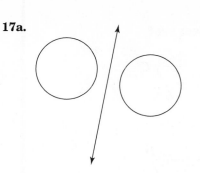

Number of points will vary.

17b. Answers will vary. Most likely they do not match exactly.

17c. Possible answer: No number of points is enough to reflect a circle because you can't connect the segments with straight lines.

18. $4^2 = 4 \cdot 4 = 16$

19. $\left(\frac{1}{9}\right)^2 = \frac{1}{9} \cdot \frac{1}{9} = \frac{1}{81}$

20. $\left(9 \cdot \frac{1}{3}\right)^3 = 3^3 = 3 \cdot 3 \cdot 3 = 27$

21. $\left(\frac{3}{2} \cdot \frac{2}{3}\right)^2 = 1^2 = 1 \cdot 1 = 1$

22. Possible equation: $y = 7x$

23. $y = \frac{1}{2}x$

Possible equation: $y = \frac{1}{2}x + 2$

24. Possible equation: $x = 1$

25a. 100°

25b. 220°

25c. 270°

25d. 50°

25e. 30°

25f. 80°

26a. $12 \cdot 2 = 24$

$24 \cdot 2 = 48$

$48 \cdot 2 = 96$

$96 \cdot 2 = 192$

This is an exponential relationship. The starting value is 12 and the growth factor is 2.

$A = 12(2^w)$

26b. $A = 12(2^7) = 1,536$

$A = 12(2^8) = 3,072$

during Week 8

Page 300   In Your Own Words

Possible answer: An object in my home that has at least one line of symmetry is my dresser. The front of the dresser has one vertical line of symmetry and it runs through the middle of the object.

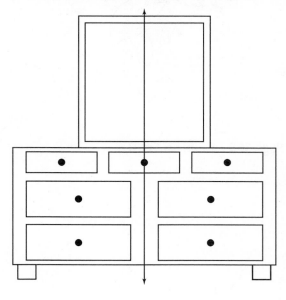

5-2   Rotation

Pages 302–303   Problem Set A

1a–c. Snowflakes will vary.

2. The snowflake matched with only a quarter turn. no

3. four

4. $360° \div 4 = 90°$

Page 304   Problem Set B

1. The figure exactly matches itself 6 times in 360°. $360° \div 6 = 60°$

2. The figure exactly matches itself 8 times in 360°. $360° \div 8 = 45°$

3. The figure exactly matches itself 2 times in 360°. $360° \div 2 = 180°$

Page 304   Share and Summarize

$6 \cdot 60° = 360°$

$8 \cdot 45° = 360°$

$2 \cdot 180° = 360°$

The number of identical elements multiplied by the angle of rotation is 360°.

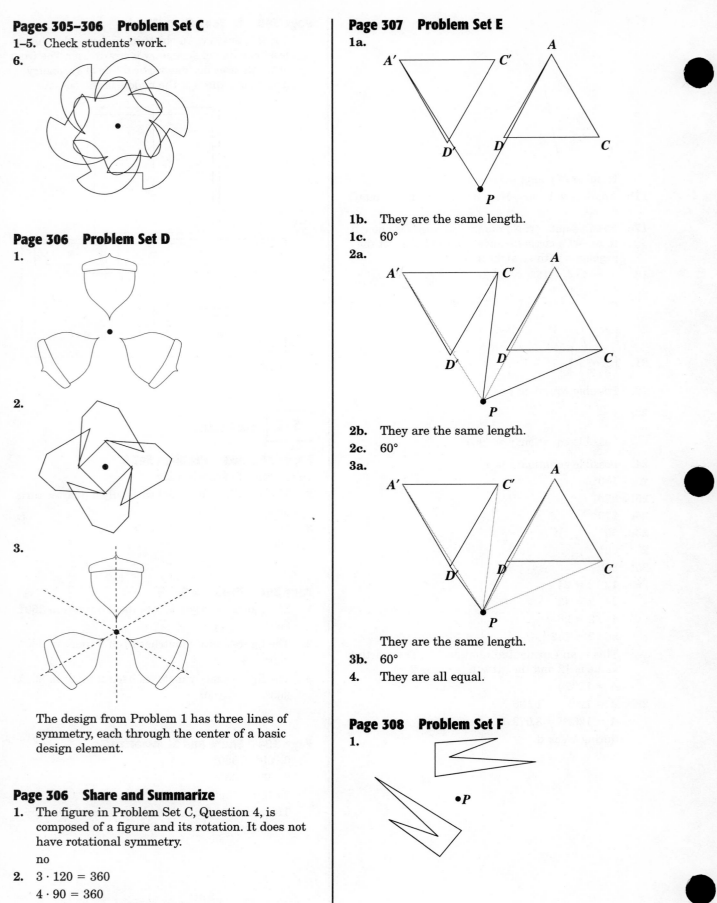

Pages 305–306   Problem Set C

1–5. Check students' work.

6.

Page 306   Problem Set D

1.

2.

3.

The design from Problem 1 has three lines of symmetry, each through the center of a basic design element.

Page 306   Share and Summarize

1. The figure in Problem Set C, Question 4, is composed of a figure and its rotation. It does not have rotational symmetry.

no

2. $3 \cdot 120 = 360$

$4 \cdot 90 = 360$

Yes; the product of these is 360°.

Page 307   Problem Set E

1a.

1b. They are the same length.

1c. 60°

2a.

2b. They are the same length.

2c. 60°

3a.

They are the same length.

3b. 60°

4.   They are all equal.

Page 308   Problem Set F

1.

2.

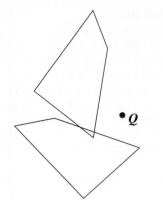

3. congruent (so also similar); Possible explanation: Rotating these figures did not change their size or shape.

Page 308   Share and Summarize

1. the angle of rotation

2. Possible answer: I would draw a line from each endpoint to the center of rotation. For each endpoint, I would draw another line from the center so that the angle it makes with the corresponding line is the given angle. If the angle is negative, I'd measure the angle in the clockwise direction; otherwise I'd measure in the counterclockwise direction. Then I would measure the distance from the endpoint to the centerpoint, and mark off that distance on the new line. That gives me the images of the endpoints. I'd connect them to get the image of the segment.

Pages 309–312   On Your Own Exercises

1a. 5

1b. $360° \div 5 = 72°$

1c. $72° \cdot 5 = 360°$

The angle measure multiplied by the number of elements is 360°.

2a. 9

2b. $360° \div 9 = 40°$

2c. $40° \cdot 9 = 360°$

The angle measure multiplied by the number of elements is 360°.

3a. Designs will vary depending on the center of rotation, but should have five copies of the basic design element.

3b. Designs will vary but should have five copies of the basic design element.

4.

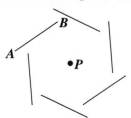

5.

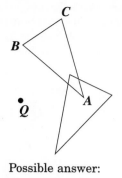

6. Possible answer:

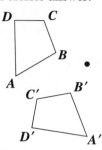

7. Possible answer:

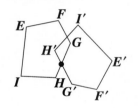

8a.

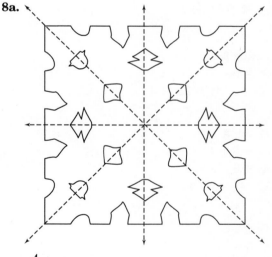

4

8b. They are the same lines.

8c. Eight; there are two in each "quadrant" of the paper, one on each side of the diagonal line.

8d. 90°

9a. four; one through the centers of the bases, and one through the centers of each of the three rectangular faces and the midpoint of the opposite edge

9b. for the one through the bases, 120°; for the others, 180°

10a–c. Designs will vary. Answers will vary.

11. Possible answer: hubcaps, some flowers, equilateral triangles, snowflakes, plates with designs on them, a Ferris wheel, a sea star, a sand dollar; Many will probably have line symmetry as well.

12a. 3

12b. 8

12c. 45°

12d. 45

12e. $135 \div 45 = 3$

$360 \div 45 = 8$

12f. The smaller angle measure is the GCF; the number of full circles is $135 \div$ GCF; the number of elements is $360 \div$ GCF.

12g. The GCF of 360 and 80 is 40.

40°

13. $8 = 2 \cdot 2 \cdot 2$

$\sqrt[3]{8} = 2$

$c = 3$

14. $81 = 3 \cdot 3 \cdot 3 \cdot 3$

$\sqrt[4]{81} = 3$

$c = 4$

15. $1 \cdot 1 \cdot 1 \cdot 1 = 1$

$\sqrt[4]{1} = 1$

$c = 1$

16a. $x - \frac{3}{5} = 2y$

$2y = x - \frac{3}{5}$

$y = \frac{1}{2}x - \frac{3}{10}$

Graph B

16b. $3y - 4x - 1 = 8x - y$

$4y = 12x + 1$

$y = 3x + \frac{1}{4}$

Graph A

16c. $x + 5 = 4y + 8$

$4y + 8 = x + 5$

$4y = x - 3$

$y = \frac{1}{4}x - \frac{3}{4}$

Graph C

17. $9 \cdot 3 = 27$

$27 \cdot 3 = 81$

$81 \cdot 3 = 243$

$243 \cdot 3 = 729$

This is an exponential relationship. The starting value is 9 and the growth factor is 3.

$A = 9(3^t)$

Page 311   In Your Own Words

Possible answer: Rotation and reflection are similar because they both geometrically transform objects across a plane. The image is congruent to the original object after both transformations. The procedures for rotating and reflecting objects are different. To reflect an object, flip it over a line of reflection. To rotate an object, turn it around a center of rotation (clockwise or counterclockwise) by an angle of rotation. Two examples are shown below.

reflection over line ℓ 90° rotation about point A

5-3 Translation and Combining Transformations

Page 315   Problem Set A

1.

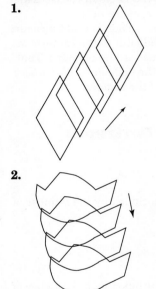

2.

3. Drawings will vary.

4. Congruent (so also similar); each image was created by tracing the original figure exactly, so they're the same size and shape.

Page 315   Problem Set B

1.

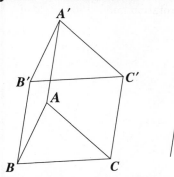

2. All lengths are 2.2 cm; they're the same.

3. They would all be parallel.

4. Draw a line parallel to the vector and through the point. Measure the length of the vector. Then find a new point on the line by moving out from the original point, in the direction the vector points, a distance equal to the vector length. That is the image point.

Page 315   Share and Summarize

Possible answer: A translation is a transformation in which you move a figure without turning or flipping it. You need a vector, which tells you how far to move the figure and in what direction.

Page 316   Problem Set C

1.

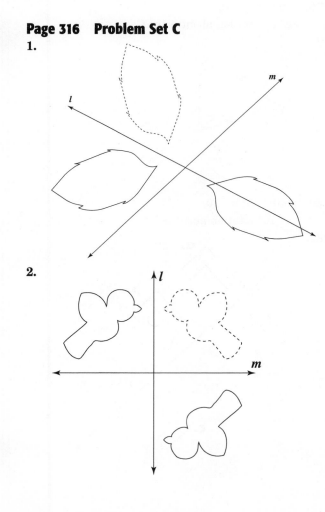

2.

3.

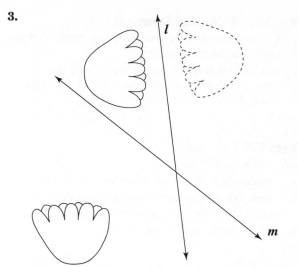

4. A rotation about the intersection of the two lines.

Page 317   Problem Set D

1a.

1b.

2a.

2b.

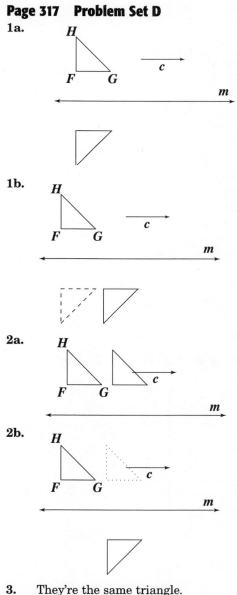

3. They're the same triangle.

Page 318 Share and Summarize

1. The final image is a rotation of the original figure about the intersection point.

2. In a glide reflection, you reflect over a line and then translate by a vector parallel to that line. Examples will vary.

Pages 318–321   Lab

1–7. Answers will vary.

8. translate in the same direction and distance

9. translate in the same direction and distance, and then reflect in the same line

10. rotate through the same angle

Pages 322–328   On Your Own Exercises

1.

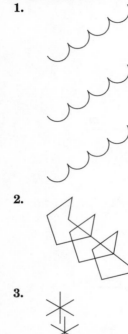

2.

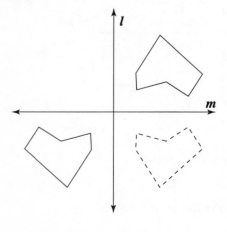

3.

4. Do nothing; the final image is the original figure.

5a.

5b. a rotation with the intersection of the lines as the center of rotation and a 180° angle of rotation

6a.

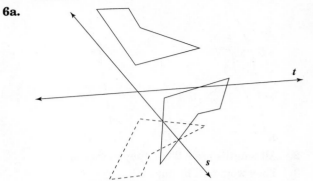

6b. a rotation with the intersection of the lines as the center of rotation

7a.

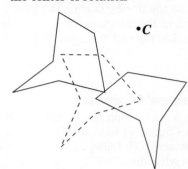

7b. $30 + 40 = 70$

a 70° rotation about point C

7c.

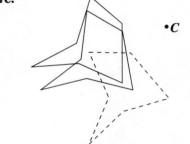

7d. $^-40 + 30 = {}^-10$

a $^-10°$ rotation about point C

8a.

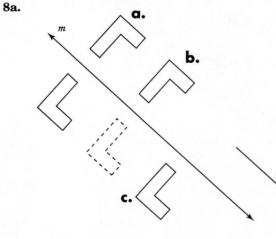

8b.

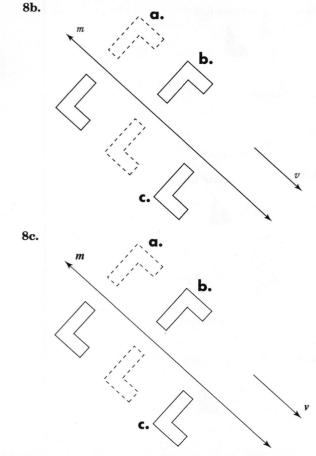

8c.

8d. a translation in the direction of the vector but with twice the length

9. Choose a point in the original figure, such as the center point of the snowflake. Draw a ray from that point on the original snowflake to the same point on the first copy. This is the translation vector.

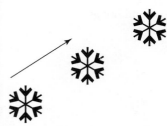

10. Choose a point in the original figure, such as the nose of the face. Draw a ray from that point on the original face to the same point on the first copy. This is the translation vector.

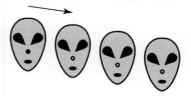

11a. Yes; a line of reflection is the line that could be used to fold one figure exactly onto the other.

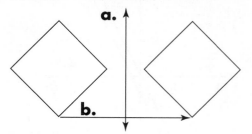

11b. Yes; a translation vector gives the distance and direction that will move every point on the original figure to the new figure.

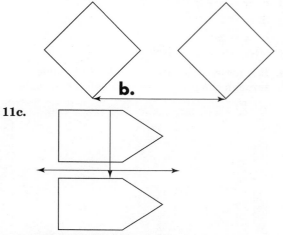

11c.

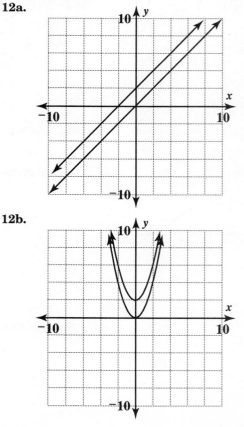

11d. Designs will vary.

11e. It must have a line of symmetry. In particular, it must have a line of symmetry parallel to the line of reflection (and perpendicular to the vector of translation).

12a.

12b.

Chapter 5

12c.

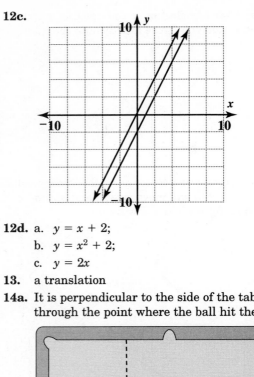

12d. a. $y = x + 2$;
     b. $y = x^2 + 2$;
     c. $y = 2x$

13. a translation

14a. It is perpendicular to the side of the table, through the point where the ball hit the side.

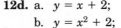

$\angle 1 = \angle 2$

14b.

Target pocket

14c.

First image

Second image

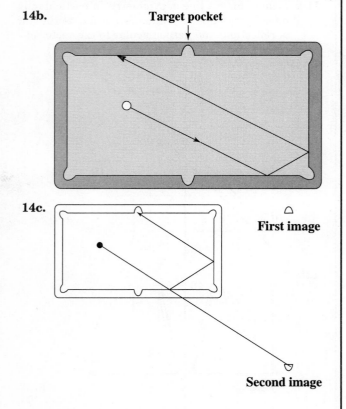

15a.

second image

$\cdot Q$

$\cdot P$

first image

15b.

second image

$\cdot Q$

$\cdot P$

first image

20°

15c.

image

$\cdot Q$

$\cdot P$

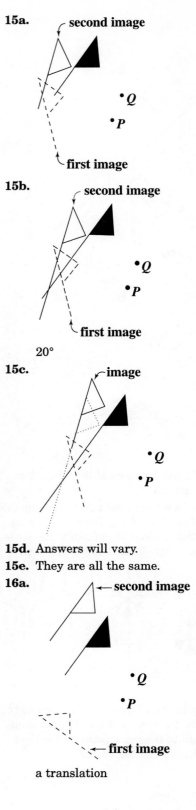

15d. Answers will vary.

15e. They are all the same.

16a.

second image

$\cdot Q$

$\cdot P$

first image

a translation

16b.

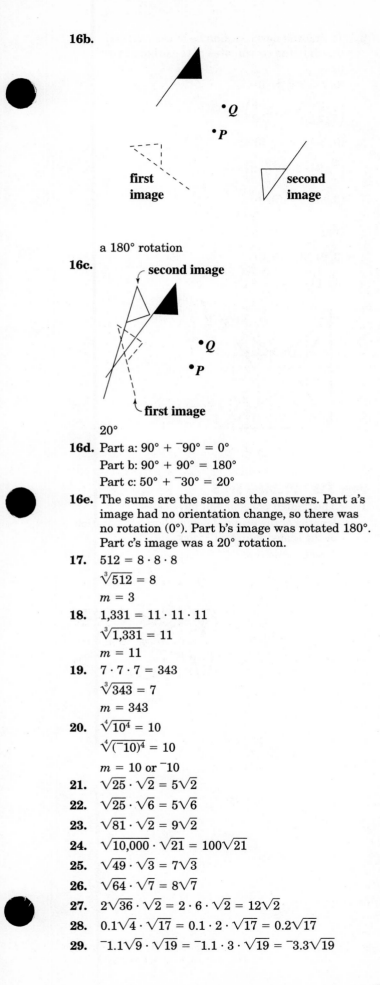

first image

second image

a 180° rotation

16c.

second image

•Q

•P

first image

20°

16d. Part a: 90° + ⁻90° = 0°

Part b: 90° + 90° = 180°

Part c: 50° + ⁻30° = 20°

16e. The sums are the same as the answers. Part a's image had no orientation change, so there was no rotation (0°). Part b's image was rotated 180°. Part c's image was a 20° rotation.

17. $512 = 8 \cdot 8 \cdot 8$

$\sqrt[3]{512} = 8$

$m = 3$

18. $1{,}331 = 11 \cdot 11 \cdot 11$

$\sqrt[3]{1{,}331} = 11$

$m = 11$

19. $7 \cdot 7 \cdot 7 = 343$

$\sqrt[3]{343} = 7$

$m = 343$

20. $\sqrt[4]{10^4} = 10$

$\sqrt[4]{(^-10)^4} = 10$

$m = 10 \text{ or } ^-10$

21. $\sqrt{25} \cdot \sqrt{2} = 5\sqrt{2}$

22. $\sqrt{25} \cdot \sqrt{6} = 5\sqrt{6}$

23. $\sqrt{81} \cdot \sqrt{2} = 9\sqrt{2}$

24. $\sqrt{10{,}000} \cdot \sqrt{21} = 100\sqrt{21}$

25. $\sqrt{49} \cdot \sqrt{3} = 7\sqrt{3}$

26. $\sqrt{64} \cdot \sqrt{7} = 8\sqrt{7}$

27. $2\sqrt{36} \cdot \sqrt{2} = 2 \cdot 6 \cdot \sqrt{2} = 12\sqrt{2}$

28. $0.1\sqrt{4} \cdot \sqrt{17} = 0.1 \cdot 2 \cdot \sqrt{17} = 0.2\sqrt{17}$

29. $^-1.1\sqrt{9} \cdot \sqrt{19} = ^-1.1 \cdot 3 \cdot \sqrt{19} = ^-3.3\sqrt{19}$

30a. (1, 4), (4, 2)

$d = \sqrt{(4-1)^2 + (2-4)^2}$

$= \sqrt{3^2 + (^-2)^2}$

$= \sqrt{9 + 4}$

$= \sqrt{13} \approx 3.6$

30b. (1, ⁻3), (3, 1)

$d = \sqrt{(3-1)^2 + (1 - ^-3)^2}$

$= \sqrt{2^2 + 4^2}$

$= \sqrt{4 + 16}$

$= \sqrt{20}$

$= \sqrt{4} \cdot \sqrt{5}$

$= 2\sqrt{5} \approx 4.5$

30c. (⁻4, 1), (⁻1, ⁻5)

$d = \sqrt{(^-1 - ^-4)^2 + (^-5 - 1)^2}$

$= \sqrt{3^2 + (^-6)^2}$

$= \sqrt{9 + 36}$

$= \sqrt{45}$

$= \sqrt{9} \cdot \sqrt{5}$

$= 3\sqrt{5} \approx 6.7$

30d. (⁻5, 3), (⁻1, 4)

$d = \sqrt{(^-1 - ^-5)^2 + (4 - 3)^2}$

$= \sqrt{4^2 + 1^2}$

$= \sqrt{16 + 1}$

$= \sqrt{17} \approx 4.1$

31. $6(x - 5) \div \dfrac{1}{2} = 36$

$(6x - 30) \div \dfrac{1}{2} = 36$

$2(6x - 30) = 36$

$12x - 60 = 36$

$12x = 96$

$x = 8$

32. $\dfrac{^-0.5(2x + 10)}{2} = ^-3.5$

$^-0.5(2x + 10) = ^-7$

$^-x - 5 = ^-7$

$^-x = ^-2$

$x = 2$

33. $7 \cdot 12 = 84$

$7 \text{ ft} = 84 \text{ in.}$

$10 \cdot 12 = 120$

$10 \text{ ft} = 120 \text{ in.}$

$84 \leq h \leq 120$

34. $12 \div 100 = 0.12$

$12 \text{ cm} = 0.12 \text{ m}$

$0.12^3 = 0.001728$

$1.5^3 = 3.375$

$0.001728 \leq v \leq 3.375$

35a. $96s^2 = 6 \cdot 12$

117

35b. $96s^2 = 6 \cdot 12$

Convert to inches.

$96s^2 = 72 \cdot 144$

$96s^2 = 10{,}368$

$s^2 = 108$

$s = \sqrt{108} \approx 10.4$

$\sqrt{108}$ in., or about 10.4 in.

Page 326   In Your Own Words

Possible answer: You can always transform one triangle into another that is congruent on the same sheet of paper by using combinations of transformations. This involves using more than one line of reflection, center of rotation, and/or vector size. The transformation also requires more than one image. Also, some objects may be transformed in different ways. For example, two reflections over perpendicular lines produces the same transformation as a rotation of 180°, two reflections over intersecting lines produces the same transformation as a rotation of a certain degree measure, two reflections over parallel lines produces the same transformation as a translation, and a translation with a reflection produces the same transformation as a glide reflection.

5-4   Dilation

Page 331   Problem Set A

1. To find the new coordinates of each vertex, multiply the coordinates of the original vertices by $\frac{1}{3}$.

$(0, 0) \cdot \dfrac{1}{3} = (0, 0)$

$\left(1, \dfrac{3}{2}\right) \cdot \dfrac{1}{3} = \left(\dfrac{1}{3}, \dfrac{1}{2}\right)$

$(0, 3) \cdot \dfrac{1}{3} = (0, 1)$

$\left(\dfrac{3}{2}, 2\right) \cdot \dfrac{1}{3} = \left(\dfrac{1}{2}, \dfrac{2}{3}\right)$

$(3, 3) \cdot \dfrac{1}{3} = (1, 1)$

$\left(2, \dfrac{3}{2}\right) \cdot \dfrac{1}{3} = \left(\dfrac{2}{3}, \dfrac{1}{2}\right)$

$(3, 0) \cdot \dfrac{1}{3} = (1, 0)$

$\left(\dfrac{3}{2}, 1\right) \cdot \dfrac{1}{3} = \left(\dfrac{1}{2}, \dfrac{1}{3}\right)$

2. To find the new coordinates of each vertex, multiply the coordinates of the original vertices by 3.

$(0, 0) \cdot 3 = (0, 0)$

$\left(1, \dfrac{3}{2}\right) \cdot 3 = \left(3, \dfrac{9}{2}\right)$

$(0, 3) \cdot 3 = (0, 9)$

$\left(\dfrac{3}{2}, 2\right) \cdot 3 = \left(\dfrac{9}{2}, 6\right)$

$(3, 3) \cdot 3 = (9, 9)$

$\left(2, \dfrac{3}{2}\right) \cdot 3 = \left(6, \dfrac{9}{2}\right)$

$(3, 0) \cdot 3 = (9, 0)$

$\left(\dfrac{3}{2}, 1\right) \cdot 3 = \left(\dfrac{9}{2}, 3\right)$

Page 333   Problem Set B

1. The dilated polygon will have sides $\frac{1}{2}$ the lengths of the original polygon's sides. Location of the scaled figure will vary.

Possible answer:

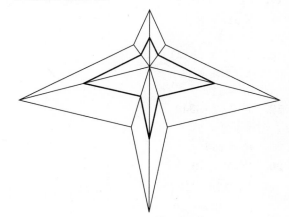

2a. Answers will vary.
Possible answer using a factor of $\frac{2}{3}$:

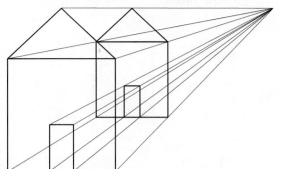

2b. The dilated figure will have line lengths 2 times those of the original figure. Location of the scaled figure will vary.
Possible answer:

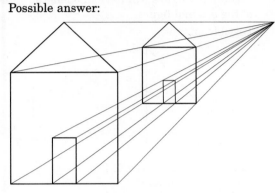

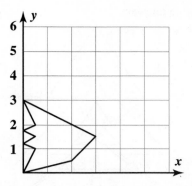

The dilated figure produced should have sides $\frac{1}{2}$ the length of the original figure's sides.

2.

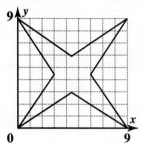

The dilated figure produced should have sides $\frac{1}{2}$ the length of the original figure's sides.

Pages 334–338   On Your Own Exercises

1a. $2 \cdot 1.5 = 3$

3 in.

1b. $1.5 = \frac{3}{2}$

The scale factor from small to large is $\frac{3}{2}$, so the scale factor from large to small is $\frac{2}{3}$.

$\frac{2}{3} \cdot 2 = \frac{4}{3} = 1\frac{1}{3}$

$1\frac{1}{3}$ in.

2a. The reciprocal of $\frac{1}{3}$ is 3.

3

2b. The reciprocal of 5 is $\frac{1}{5}$.

$\frac{1}{5}$

2c. The reciprocal of 1 is 1.

1

3a. finding the midpoints of the segments

3b. Find the points $\frac{1}{3}$ of the way from point F to the vertices.

3c. The dilated polygon will have sides $\frac{1}{3}$ the length of the original polygon's sides. Location of the dilated figure will vary.

Page 333   Share and Summarize

1. To find the new coordinates of each vertex, multiply the coordinates of the original vertices by 3.

$(0, 0) \cdot \frac{1}{2} = (0, 0)$

$(1, 2) \cdot \frac{1}{2} = \left(\frac{1}{2}, 1\right)$

$\left(0, \frac{5}{2}\right) \cdot \frac{1}{2} = \left(0, \frac{5}{4}\right)$

$(1, 3) \cdot \frac{1}{2} = \left(\frac{1}{2}, \frac{3}{2}\right)$

$\left(0, \frac{7}{2}\right) \cdot \frac{1}{2} = \left(0, \frac{7}{4}\right)$

$(1, 4) \cdot \frac{1}{2} = \left(\frac{1}{2}, 2\right)$

$(0, 6) \cdot \frac{1}{2} = (0, 3)$

$(6, 3) \cdot \frac{1}{2} = \left(3, \frac{3}{2}\right)$

$(4, 1) \cdot \frac{1}{2} = \left(2, \frac{1}{2}\right)$

Possible answer:

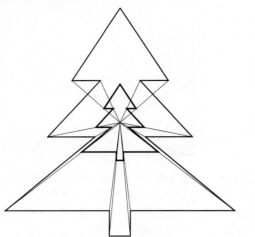

4. To find the new coordinates of each vertex, multiply the coordinates of the original vertices by 2.

$(2, 0) \cdot 2 = (4, 0)$

$(0, 4) \cdot 2 = (0, 8)$

$(1, 4) \cdot 2 = (2, 8)$

$(2, 2) \cdot 2 = (4, 4)$

$(3, 3) \cdot 2 = (6, 6)$

$(4, 2) \cdot 2 = (8, 4)$

$(5, 4) \cdot 2 = (10, 8)$

$(6, 4) \cdot 2 = (12, 8)$

$(4, 0) \cdot 2 = (8, 0)$

$(3, 2) \cdot 2 = (6, 4)$

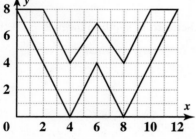

5a. The dilated polygon will have sides $\frac{1}{4}$ the length of the original polygon's sides. Location of the dilated figure will vary.

Possible answer:

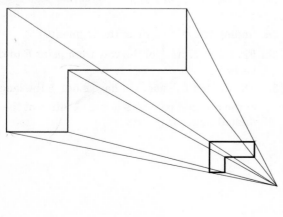

5b. The dilated polygon will be the same size as the original polygon.

Possible answer:

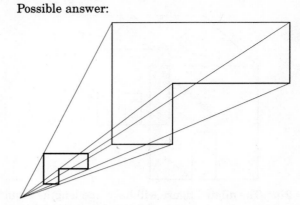

5c. They are congruent.

6a. The dilated figure will have line lengths $\frac{1}{3}$ those of the original figure.

Possible answer:

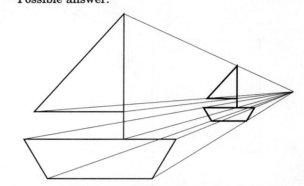

6b. The dilated figure will have line lengths 2 times those of the original figure.

Possible answer:

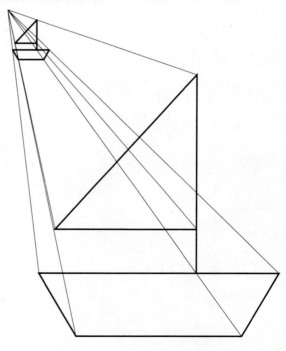

6c. The dilated figure is twice as big as the original figure.
$\frac{1}{3} \cdot 6 = 2$

7. Answers will vary.

8a. Each line segment in the image is 4 times longer than the original.
4

8b. $2 \cdot 2 = 4$
$4 \cdot 1 = 4$
$8 \cdot \frac{1}{2} = 4$
Possible answer: 2 and 2, 4 and 1, 8 and $\frac{1}{2}$; Any pair of numbers with a product of 4 will work.

9. If you multiply coordinates by 0, the resulting coordinate is (0, 0).
a point at (0, 0)

10a–d. Check students' work.

10e. Possible answer:

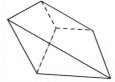

10f. Step c; you create a figure similar to the one you started with.

11. 1 mi = 5,280 ft
5,280 ft = 63,360 in.
The largest map is 8.5 in. by 8.5 in. since the park is square.
63,360 ÷ 8.5 = 7,454.12
The smallest possible scale factor is 7,455.
7,455

12a. $50\% \cdot 50\% = 25\% = \frac{1}{4}$
Use the 50% setting twice.

12b. $200\% \cdot 150\% = 300\% = 3$
Possible answer: Use 200% and then 150%.

12c. $150\% \cdot 50\% = 75\%$
Possible answer: Enlarge it to 150% and then reduce to 50% of that.

13. $3 \cdot 3 \cdot 3 \cdot 3 = 81$
$3^4 = 81$
$t = 3$

14. $2 \cdot 2 \cdot 2 \cdot 2 \cdot 2 = 32$
$2^5 = 32$
$t = 2$

15. $3 \cdot 3 \cdot 3 \cdot 3 \cdot 3 \cdot 3 = 729$
$3^6 = 729$
$t = 6$

16. $4 \cdot 4 \cdot 4 \cdot 4 \cdot 4 = 1,024$
$4^5 = 1,024$
$t = 5$

17a. $367.5 \cdot 12 = 4,410$
367.5 ft = 4,410 in.
$4,410 \div 600 = 7.35$

$4,410 \div 800 = 5.5125$
about 5.5 to 7.4

17b. $363.4 \div 367.5 \approx 0.9888$
about 98.9%

18. $1.2 \cdot 2 = 2.4$
$2.4 \cdot 2 = 4.8$
$4.8 \cdot 2 = 9.6$
$9.6 \cdot 2 = 19.2$
This is an exponential relationship. The starting value is 1.2 and the growth factor is 2.
$y = 1.2(2^x)$

19. $21 \cdot 3 = 63$
$63 \cdot 3 = 189$
$189 \cdot 3 = 567$
$567 \cdot 3 = 1,701$
$21 \div 3 = 7$
This is an exponential relationship. The starting value is 7 and the growth factor is 3.
$y = 7(3^x)$

20a. mean: $80.3 \div 5 = 16.06$
median: 14.5, 15.6, 15.9, 16.2, 18.1
The middle value in the ordered set is 15.9.

20b. Possible answer: 15.6, 20.2

20c. Possible answer: 16.06, 16.06

21. $V = \pi r^2 h$
$V = \pi r^2 \cdot 4r$
$= 4\pi r^3$

22. $V = \pi r^2 h$
$V = \pi \cdot \left(\frac{1}{2}d\right)^2 \cdot 2d$
$= \pi \cdot \frac{1}{4}d^2 \cdot 2d$
$= \frac{1}{2}\pi d^3$

Page 337   In Your Own Words

Possible answer: The triangle on the right is twice as big as the triangle on the left. So, the scale factor is 2. You can test whether the two triangles are similar by measuring the lengths of the line segments from the vanishing point P. The length of the line segment between point P and one vertex of the smaller triangle should be congruent to the line segment from the same vertex to the corresponding vertex of the larger triangle.

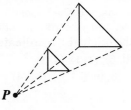

Pages 340–341   Problem Set A

1a. The *x*-coordinate stays the same, and the *y*-coordinate of the image is the opposite of the original *y*-coordinate.

1b. ($^-$1, 2); ($^-$4, 4); ($^-$5, 1); ($^-$3.5, 2.5)

1c. ($^-$1, $^-$2); ($^-$4, $^-$4); ($^-$5, $^-$1); ($^-$3.5, $^-$2.5)

1d.

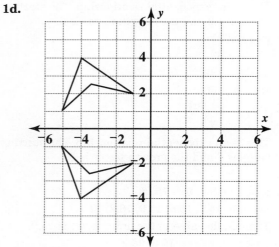

2a. The *x*-coordinate and the *y*-coordinate are reversed. The *x*-coordinate of the image is the *y*-coordinate of the original, and the *y*-coordinate of the image is the *x*-coordinate of the original.

2b. (0, 0); (2, 3); (0, 2); ($^-$1, 5); ($^-$4, 1)

2c. (0, 0), (3, 2); (2, 0); (5, $^-$1); (1, $^-$4)

2d.

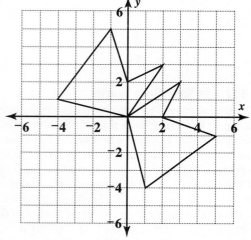

3a. The *x*-coordinate of the image is the opposite of the original *y*-coordinate, and *y*-coordinate of the image is the same as the original *x*-coordinate.

3b. (0, $^-$1); ($^-$4, 2); ($^-$1, 1); (0, 5); (1, 1); (4, 1)

3c. (1, 0); ($^-$2, $^-$4); ($^-$1, $^-$1); ($^-$5, 0); ($^-$1, 1); ($^-$1, 4)

3d.

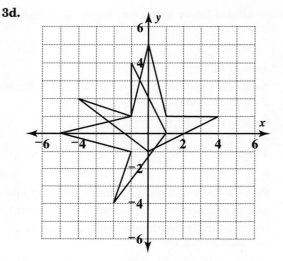

4a. Problem 1: Line is *x*-axis.

Problem 2: Line is *y* = *x*.

4b. Problem 3: Center is (0, 0), angle is 90°.

Page 342   Problem Set B

1a.

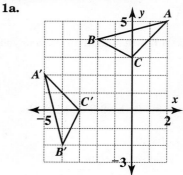

1b. rotation; 90° about the origin

1c. $A(2, 5) \rightarrow A'(^-5, 2)$
$B(^-2, 4) \rightarrow B'(^-4, ^-2)$
$C(0, 3) \rightarrow C'(^-3, 0)$

In each pair, the *x*- and *y*-coordinates are reversed and the original *y*-coordinate changes sign.

(^-y, *x*)

2a.

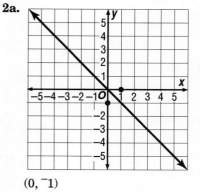

(0, $^-$1)

2b.

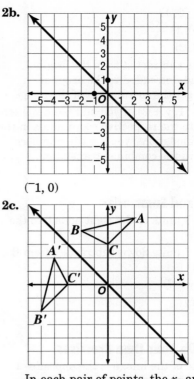

($^-$1, 0)

2c.

In each pair of points, the x- and y-coordinates are reversed and the sign changes.

$(x, y) \rightarrow (^-y, ^-x)$

$(2, 5) \rightarrow (^-5, 2)$

$(^-2, 4) \rightarrow (^-4, 2)$

$(0, 3) \rightarrow (^-3, 0)$

Page 342   Share and Summarize

1. Reflecting over the y-axis will change the sign of the x-coordinate.

   (2, 4.3)

2. Rotating about the origin with a 90° of rotation will reverse the coordinates and change the sign of the original y-coordinate.

   ($^-$3, 1)

3. Possible answer: The figure was tilted but not flipped.

4. Possible answer: I saw that the x- and y-coordinates were switched. In both cases, the 1s changed signs, so I needed to use the opposite for each coordinate.

Page 343   Problem Set C

1. $C(^-3, 0); D(^-2, 1), E(^-1, ^-1)$

   $C'(^-3 + 2, 0) = (^-1, 0)$

   $D'(^-2 + 2, 1) = (0, 1)$

   $E'(^-1 + 2, ^-1) = (1, ^-1)$

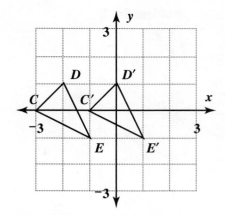

2. $F(^-1, ^-2), G(0, ^-1), H(1, ^-2)$

   $F'(^-1, ^-2 + 3) = (^-1, 1)$

   $G'(0, ^-1 + 3) = (0, 2)$

   $H'(1, ^-2 + 3) = (1, 1)$

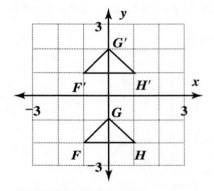

3. $J(1, 1), K(2, 3), L(3, 2)$

   $J'(1 - 2, 1 - 2) = (^-1, ^-1)$

   $K'(2 - 2, 3 - 2) = (0, 1)$

   $L'(3 - 2, 2 - 2) = (1, 0)$

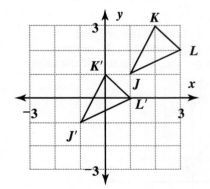

1a.

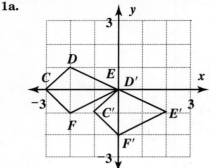

1b. $C(^-3, 0) \to C'(^-1, ^-1)$

$D(^-2, 1) \to D'(0, 0)$

$E(0, 0) \to E'(2, ^-1)$

In each pair, 2 is added to the original
x-coordinate, and 1 is subtracted from the original
y-coordinate to get the image coordinates of the
image.

$(x, y) \to (x + 2, y - 1)$

2a.

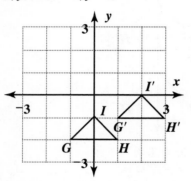

2b. $G(^-1, ^-2) \to G'(1, ^-1)$

$H(1, ^-2) \to H'(3, ^-1)$

$I(0, ^-1) \to I'(2, 0)$

In each pair, 2 is added to the original
x-coordinate, and 1 is added to the original
y-coordinate to get the coordinates of the image.

$(x, y) \to (x + 2, y + 1)$

2c.

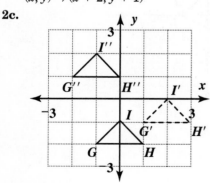

2d. $G'(1, ^-1) \to G''(^-2, 1)$

$H'(3, ^-1) \to H''(0, 1)$

$I'(2, 0) \to I''(^-1, 2)$

In each pair, 3 is subtracted from the original
x-coordinate, and 2 is added to the original
y-coordinate to get the coordinates of the image.

$(x, y) \to (x - 3, y + 2)$

2e. $G(^-1, ^-2) \to G''(^-2, 1)$

$H(1, ^-2) \to H''(0, 1)$

$I(0, ^-1) \to I''(^-1, 2)$

In each pair, 1 is subtracted from the original
x-coordinate, and 3 is added to the original
y-coordinate to get the coordinates of the image.

Yes; $(x, y) \to (x - 1, y + 3)$; if you add the numbers
that are added to the respective coordinates in the
two separate translations, you get the numbers
that are added in the combined translation.

Page 345   Share and Summarize

1. Moving a point 5 units to the right adds 5 to the
x-coordinate.

Moving a point 7 units down subtracts 7 from the
y-coordinate.

$(x, y) \to (x + 5, y - 7)$

2. Answer will vary.

Pages 346–352   On Your Own Exercises

1a. The x-coordinate of the image is the opposite of
the original x-coordinate, and the y-coordinate
of the image is the opposite of the original
y-coordinate.

1b. $(0, 5)$, $(4, 3)$, and $(2, ^-1)$

1c. $(0, ^-5)$, $(^-4, ^-3)$, and $(^-2, 1)$

1d.

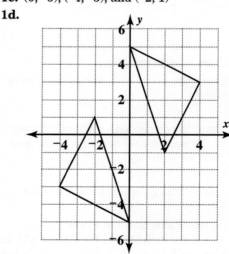

1e. rotation

2a. The x-coordinate of the image is the opposite of
the original x-coordinate, and the y-coordinate of
the image is the same as the original
y-coordinate.

2b. $(^-2, 3.5)$, $(0.5, 3.5)$, $(^-1.5, ^-2.5)$, $(^-3.5, ^-1)$

2c. $(2, 3.5)$, $(^-0.5, 3.5)$, $(1.5, ^-2.5)$, $(3.5, ^-1)$

2d.

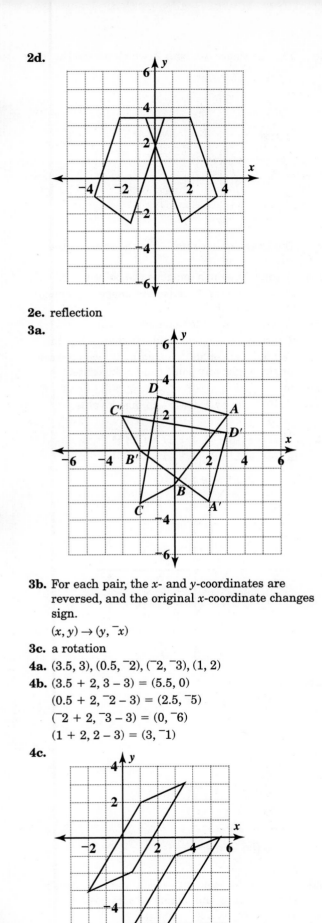

2e. reflection

3a.

3b. For each pair, the x- and y-coordinates are reversed, and the original x-coordinate changes sign.

$(x, y) \rightarrow (y, ^-x)$

3c. a rotation

4a. $(3.5, 3), (0.5, ^-2), (^-2, ^-3), (1, 2)$

4b. $(3.5 + 2, 3 - 3) = (5.5, 0)$

$(0.5 + 2, ^-2 - 3) = (2.5, ^-5)$

$(^-2 + 2, ^-3 - 3) = (0, ^-6)$

$(1 + 2, 2 - 3) = (3, ^-1)$

4c.

4d. translation

5a. $(1, 1), (0, 0), (^-3, ^-1), (^-1, 4), (1, 4)$

5b. $(1 - 1, 1 - 1) = (0, 0)$

$(0 - 1, 0 - 1) = (^-1, ^-1)$

$(^-3 - 1, ^-1 - 1) = (^-4, ^-2)$

$(^-1 - 1, 4 - 1) = (^-2, 3)$

$(1 - 1, 4 - 1) = (0, 3)$

5c.

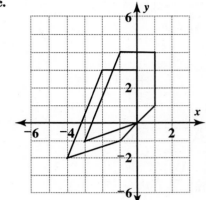

5d. translation

6. $(x + 2 - 1, y - 3 - 1) = (x + 1, y - 4)$

right 1 unit and down 4 units

7a.

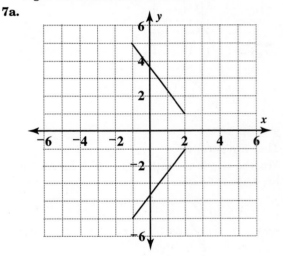

7b. original: $(2, ^-1), (^-1, ^-5)$

$d = \sqrt{(2 - ^-1)^2 + (^-1 - ^-5)^2}$

$\quad = \sqrt{3^2 + 4^2}$

$\quad = \sqrt{9 + 16}$

$\quad = \sqrt{25} = 5$

7c. image: $(2, 1), (^-1, 5)$

$d = \sqrt{(2 - ^-1)^2 + (1 - 5)^2}$

$\quad = \sqrt{3^2 + (^-4)^2}$

$\quad = \sqrt{9 + 16}$

$\quad = \sqrt{25} = 5$

yes

7d. When you use a GeoMirror or fold, you trace the original segment exactly, so you don't change its size.

Chapter 5

8a.

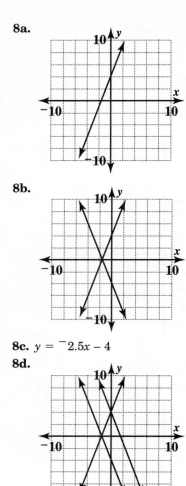

8b.

8c. $y = {}^{-}2.5x - 4$

8d.

8e. $y = {}^{-}2.5x + 4$

8f. They are parallel.

8g. Yes; the slopes are both ${}^{-}2.5$, which means the lines are parallel.

9a.

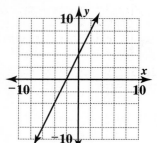

9b.

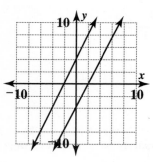

9c. They are parallel.

9d. $y = 2x - 4$

9e. Yes; the slopes are both 2, which means the lines are parallel.

10.

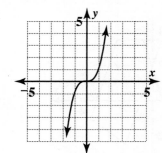

The image under rotation is the same as the original image.

11a. Nothing; a point's image is the point itself.

11b. Possible answer: because the image is identical to the original

11c. Rotating 0° wouldn't change a point. Rotating a full circle wouldn't change a point. Any multiple of 360°, including 0°, would work for the angle; any point can be the center.

11d. no

11e. Multiplying by 1 doesn't change a value. yes, 1

12a. $({}^{-}5, 4) \rightarrow ({}^{-}5 + 3, 4 + 1) = ({}^{-}2, 5)$
$(1, {}^{-}4) \rightarrow (1 + 3, {}^{-}4 + 1) = (4, {}^{-}3)$

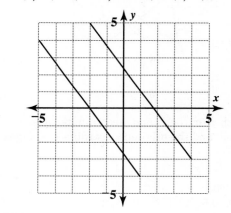

12b. $({}^{-}5, 4), (1, {}^{-}4)$
$d = \sqrt{({}^{-}5 - 1)^2 + (4 - {}^{-}4)^2}$
$= \sqrt{({}^{-}6^2) + 8^2}$
$= \sqrt{36 + 64}$
$= \sqrt{100} = 10$

12c. $({}^{-}2, 5), (4, {}^{-}3)$
$d = \sqrt{({}^{-}2 - 4)^2 + (5 - {}^{-}3)^2}$
$= \sqrt{({}^{-}6)^2 + 8^2}$
$= \sqrt{36 + 64}$
$= \sqrt{100} = 10$

yes

12d. You copy the segment exactly and just move it. The only thing that changes is its position.

13a. $(0, {}^{-}3) \rightarrow (0, {}^{-}3 - 3) = (0, {}^{-}6)$
$({}^{-}3, {}^{-}1) \rightarrow (3, {}^{-}1 - 3) = (3, {}^{-}4)$
$({}^{-}4, {}^{-}2) \rightarrow (4, {}^{-}2 - 3) = (4, {}^{-}5)$
$({}^{-}3, 5) \rightarrow (3, 5 - 3) = (3, 2)$

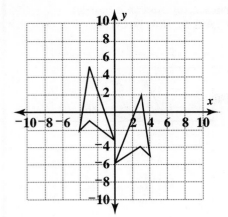

13b. glide reflection

14. As the x value changes by a constant, 1, the y value also changes by a constant, ‾2.2.

   yes

15. As the x value changes by a constant, 1, the y value does not change by a constant.

   no

16. As the x value changes by a constant, 1, the y value also changes by a constant, 9.

   yes

17a. $100 \div 2 = 50$

   $50 \div 2 = 25$

   $25 \div 2 = 12.5$

   $12.5 \div 2 = 6.25$

   $6.25 \div 2 = 3.125$

Cut Number	0	1	2	3	4	5
Line Length (m)	100	50	25	12.5	6.25	3.125

17b. $100 \cdot \frac{1}{2} = 50$

   $50 \cdot \frac{1}{2} = 25$

   $25 \cdot \frac{1}{2} = 12.5$

   $12.5 \cdot \frac{1}{2} = 6.25$

   $6.25 \cdot \frac{1}{2} = 3.125$

   This is an exponential relationship. The starting value is 100 and the decay factor is $\frac{1}{2}$.

18a. Pre-Golden Age: $\frac{21}{353} \approx 0.05949 \approx 5.9\%$
   (about 21.4°)

   Golden Age: $\frac{117}{353} \approx 0.33144 \approx 33.1\%$
   (about 119.3°)

   Post-Golden Age: $\frac{32}{353} \approx 0.09065 \approx 9.1\%$
   (about 32.6°)

   Pre-Silver Age: $\frac{93}{353} \approx 0.26345 \approx 26.3\%$
   (about 94.8°)

   Silver Age: $\frac{67}{353} \approx 0.18980 \approx 19.0\%$
   (about 68.3°)

   Post-Silver Age: $\frac{23}{353} \approx 0.06516 \approx 6.5\%$
   (about 23.5°)

Fran's Comic Book Collection

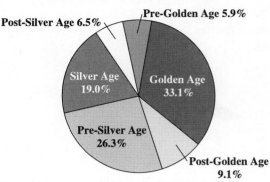

18b. Pre-Golden Age: $21 \div 42 = 0.5$

   Golden Age: $117 \div 8 = 14.625$

   Pre-Silver Age: $93 \div 6 = 15.5$

   Silver Age: $67 \div 14 = 4.79$

   Post-Silver Age: $23 \div 35 \approx 0.66$ (based on 2004)

   most: Pre-Silver Age, 15.5

   least: Pre-Golden Age, 0.5

18c. $5.9 + 33.1 + 9.1 + 26.3 + 19.0 + 6.5 = 99.9$

   No, because rounding introduces slight errors.

Page 350   In Your Own Words

Possible answer: symbolic rule for an equation: $y = 2x - 1$; symbolic rule for a transformation: $(x, y) \rightarrow (x - 1, y + 3)$; The symbolic rule for an equation describes a relationship between two variables algebraically: the product of two and x minus one is equal to y. The symbolic rule for a transformation describes how each coordinate of an object is transformed to another location: the x-coordinate is translated one unit to the left and the y-coordinate is translated three units up.

Review and Self-Assessment

Pages 353–355   Strategies and Applications

1a. rotation

1b.

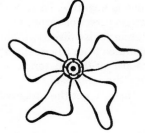

1c. $360° \div 5 = 72°$

2a. reflection and rotation symmetry

2b.

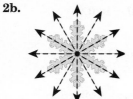

2c. $360° \div 6 = 60°$

3a. reflection

3b.

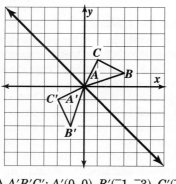

4. Answers will vary.

Possible answer: To reflect $\triangle ABC$ using the perpendicular bisector method, you would first reflect point A. Draw a segment perpendicular to the line with one endpoint at point A. Measure the distance from point A to the line, and mark point A' on the other side of the line so the distance from point A; to the line is the same as from point A to the line. Do the same with points B and C, making points B' and C'. Connect points A', and B', points B' and C', and points A' and C'.

5. Perform the reflection on a figure:
$\triangle ABC$: $A(0, 0)$, $B(3, 1)$, $C(1, 2)$

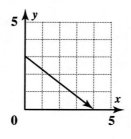

$\triangle A'B'C'$: $A'(0, 0)$, $B'(^-1, ^-3)$, $C'(^-2, ^-1)$

$y = ^-x$

6. Answers will vary.

Possible answer: To use a protractor and ruler, I would draw a line from each endpoint to the center of rotation. For each endpoint, I would draw another line from the center so that the angle it makes with the corresponding line is the given angle. If the angle is negative, I'd measure the angle in the clockwise direction; otherwise I'd measure in the counterclockwise direction. Then I would measure the distance from the endpoint to the centerpoint, and mark off that distance on the new line. That gives me the images of the endpoints. I'd connect them to get the image of the segment.

7. Perform the rotation on a figure:
$\triangle ABC$: $A(0, 0)$, $B(3, 1)$, $C(1, 2)$

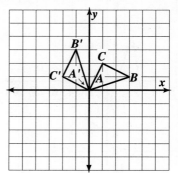

$\triangle A'B'C'$: $A'(0, 0)$, $B'(^-1, 3)$, $C'(^-2, 1)$

center: $(0, 0)$; angle: $90°$

8. Make an exact copy of the figure in the direction of the vector's arrow at a distance of the vector's length from the original figure.

9. Possible answer:

10. Answers will vary.

Possible answer: To dilate a figure using the projection method, first draw a point. Then draw segments from that point to every vertex of the figure. If the scale factor is greater than one, extend the segments. Make points at corresponding points on the segments, depending on the scale factor. Then connect the points to form the new figure.

11. $8 \cdot 1.5 = 12$

$6 \cdot 1.5 = 9$

1.5

Page 355   Demonstrating Skills

12a. The segments that form Figure Z are $\frac{1}{2}$ those of Figure A.

Figure Z is a rotation about the origin $180°$.

Dilate using $\frac{1}{2}$ as the scale factor, and rotate $180°$ about the origin.

12b. no

13.

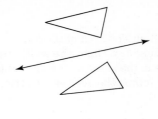

14.

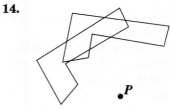

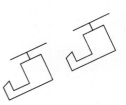

•*P*

15.

16. Figures should be the same shape and three times as large. Location of the dilated figure will vary.

Possible answer using the coordinate method: To find the new coordinates of each vertex, multiply the coordinates of the original vertices by 3.

$(3, 3) \cdot 3 = (9, 9)$

$(1.5, 1) \cdot 3 = (4.5, 3)$

$(1.5, {}^{-}2) \cdot 3 = (4.5, {}^{-}6)$

$(2, {}^{-}3) \cdot 3 = (6, {}^{-}9)$

$(0, {}^{-}3) \cdot 3 = (0, {}^{-}9)$

$(0.5, {}^{-}2) \cdot 3 = (1.5, {}^{-}6)$

$(0.5, 1) \cdot 3 = (1.5, 3)$

$({}^{-}1, 3) \cdot 3 = ({}^{-}3, 9)$

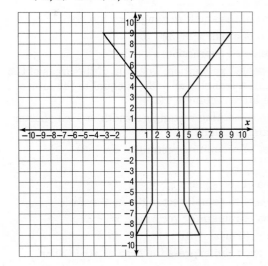

Chapter 6 Working with Expressions

6-1 | Rearranging Algebraic Expressions

Pages 359–360   Problem Set A

1a. The entire rectangle has area $x(x + 3)$.

1b. area of the square: $x \cdot x = x^2$

area of the small rectangle: $x \cdot 3 = 3x$

sum of areas: $x^2 + 3x$

expanded expression: $x^2 + 3x$

Possible explanation: The sum of the areas of the small rectangles, $x^2 + 3x$, is equal to the area of the large rectangle, $x(x + 3)$.

2a. The remaining rectangle's width is 3 cm shorter than it's height.

area of remaining rectangle: $x(x - 3)$

or

area of the square: $x \cdot x = x^2$

area of the small rectangle: $x \cdot 3 = 3x$

area of remaining rectangle: $x^2 - 3x$

$x(x - 3)$ or $x^2 - 3x$

2b. Yes; you can express the area as $x(x - 3)$ or $x^2 - 3x$.

3. Multiply the length and width of the square, to get a^2, and subtract the area of the shaded rectangle, which is $a \cdot 1$, to get $a^2 - a$. Or, multiply a by $a - 1$ to get $a(a - 1)$.

4a. $b^2 + 4b$

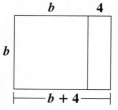

4b. $m^2 - 6m$

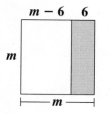

Pages 360–361   Problem Set B

1a. x

1b. $x + x + 1 = 2x + 1$

1c. $x(2x + 1)$

1d. area of each square $= x^2$

area of small rectangle $= x$

total area $= x^2 + x^2 + x = 2x^2 + x$

1e. $x(2x + 1) = 2x^2 + x$

$x(2x + 1) = x(2x) + x(1)$

$\qquad\qquad = 2x^2 + x$

2. Possible explanation: The area of the large rectangle is the height, x, times the width, $2x - 1$, or $x(2x - 1)$. This is the same as the area of the two squares, $2x^2$, minus the area of the strip, x, or $2x^2 - x$.

3a. $2x^2 + 2x$

3b. Possible explanation: $2x(x + 1)$ is the area of the large rectangle found by multiplying the two dimensions ($2x$ and $x + 1$), and $2x^2 + 2x$ is the area of the large rectangle found by adding the areas of its components (x^2, x^2, and $2x$).

4a. Possible expression: $2a^2 - 2a$

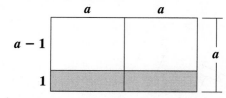

4b. $b(b - 3)$

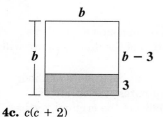

4c. $c(c + 2)$

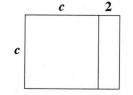

5a. $3a^2 + 12a$

5b. $6m^2 - 4m$

5c. $12x + 8x^2$

Page 361   Share and Summarize

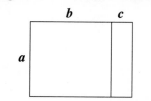

Possible answer: $a(b + c)$ means you are multiplying the sum of b and c by a. If a is the height of a rectangle and $b + c$ is the width, $a(b + c)$ represents the rectangle's area. Using the diagram, it is easy to see that the area of the large rectangle is the sum of the areas of the two smaller rectangles with height a and widths b and c. So, $a(b + c) = ab + ac$.

Pages 363–364   Problem Set C

1. $4p + 3$ and $2p + 3 + 2p$

2. $2y^2 + 3y - 5 + 2y - 2 + 3y^2 + 7 = 5y^2 + 5y$
   $2y^2 + 3y^2 + 5y$ and $5y^2 + 5y$

3. correct

4. He added the exponents instead of the terms; $2m^2 - 4$.

5. He added the exponents on b^1 and b^2; $2 + b + b^2$ can't be simplified further.

6. $3 - b^2 + b^2 + 2b^2 = 2b^2 + 3$
   correct

7a. $m(m + 4) + 5m + m(m + 4) + 0.5m(7 + m) =$
   $m^2 + 4m + 5m + m^2 + 4m + 3.5m + 0.5m^2 =$
   $2.5m^2 + 16.5m$

7b. $2.5(6)^2 + 16.5(6) = 189 \text{ ft}^2$

7c. the expression from Part a

8a. no; Possible explanations: Combining the a^2 terms gives $4a^2$. *Or*, if the expressions were equivalent, Keenan would have found the same result for $a = 2$.

8b. Possible answer: Just because one value works doesn't mean two expressions are equivalent. It's better to substitute two or three values so that you have more evidence to help you decide whether they are equivalent.

Pages 364–365   Problem Set D

1. $3x + 3 + 14 - 7x - 20x + 5 = {}^-24x + 22$

2. $3a + 2a - 12 + 4 - 2a = 3a - 8$

3. $3y + 9 - 2y + 9 - y = 18$

4. $x^2 - 7 - 2 + 2x - 2x^2 = {}^-x^2 + 2x - 9$

5. $(2a^2 - 9a) - 2a(a - 5) = 2a^2 - 9a - 2a^2 + 10a = a$

   $a^2 + 2a + 3 - a(a + 1) = a^2 + 2a + 3 - a^2 - a$
   $= a + 3$

   $a + a + 3 = 2a + 3$

   $a + a(2a + 1) = a + 2a^2 + a = 2a^2 + 2a$

   $a(a + 1) + 2a(a - 5) = a^2 + a + 2a^2 - 10a$
   $= 3a^2 - 9a$

   $a(a + 1) + a(2a + 1) = a^2 + a + 2a^2 + a$
   $= 3a^2 + 2a$

   $3a^2 + 5a - a(2a + 1) = 3a^2 + 5a - 2a^2 - a$
   $= a^2 + 4a$ or $a(a + 4)$

   $a^2 + 4a + a + 3 = a^2 + 5a + 3$

   $a^2 + 4a + 2a(a - 5) = a^2 + 4a + 2a^2 - 10a$
   $= 3a^2 - 6a$

$+$	$a + 3$	$2a(a - 5)$	$a(2a + 1)$
a	$2a + 3$	$2a^2 - 9a$	$2a^2 + 2a$
$a(a + 1)$	$a^2 + 2a + 3$	$3a^2 - 9a$	$3a^2 + 2a$
$a^2 + 4a$ or $a(a + 4)$	$a^2 + 5a + 3$	$3a^2 - 6a$	$3a^2 + 5a$

6. $3(x^2 + x - 2) + 2y = 4x - 3$
   $3x^2 + 3x - 6 + 2y = 4x - 3$
   $2y = {}^-3x^2 + x + 3$
   $y = -\dfrac{3}{2}x^2 + \dfrac{1}{2}x + \dfrac{3}{2}$

   Possible answer: $3(x^2 + x - 2) +$
   $2\left(-\dfrac{3}{2}x^2 + \dfrac{1}{2}x + \dfrac{3}{2}\right)$

7a. $y = 2x^2 + 5x + 4 - 2x^2 - 2 - 3x$
   $y = 2x + 2$

   The equation simplifies to $y = 2x + 2$, which is a linear equation whose graph is a line.
   linear

7b. $y = 2x^2 + 5x + 4 - 2x^2 - 2 - 3x$
   $y = 2x + 2$

   Expand the right side and then combine like terms. The equation is equivalent to $y = 2x + 2$, a linear equation.

Page 365   Share and Summarize

Answers will vary.

Pages 366–367   Lab

1.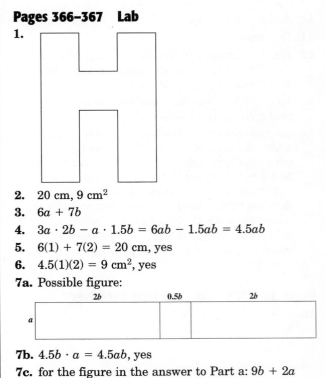

2. 20 cm, 9 cm²

3. $6a + 7b$

4. $3a \cdot 2b - a \cdot 1.5b = 6ab - 1.5ab = 4.5ab$

5. $6(1) + 7(2) = 20$ cm, yes

6. $4.5(1)(2) = 9$ cm², yes

7a. Possible figure:

	2b	0.5b	2b
a			

7b. $4.5b \cdot a = 4.5ab$, yes

7c. for the figure in the answer to Part a: $9b + 2a$

7d. $9(2) + 2(1) = 20$ cm
   Possible answer: For the figure in the answer to Part a, the perimeters will be the same when $a = 1$ and $b = 2$. This doesn't mean the perimeters are equivalent; just because they're equal for one set of values doesn't mean they're always equal.

8a. Possible figure:

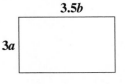

3.5b

3a

8b. $6a + 7b$, yes

8c. $3a \cdot 3.5b = 10.5ab$

for the figure in the answer to Part a: $10.5ab$

8d. $4.5ab \stackrel{?}{=} 10.5ab$

$$ab \stackrel{?}{=} 2\frac{1}{3}ab$$

$$\frac{ab}{ab} \stackrel{?}{=} 2\frac{1}{3}$$

$$1 \neq 2\frac{1}{3}$$

no

9. Possible rectangle:

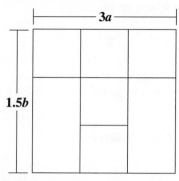

10. Answers will vary.

11. the same

12. For the rectangle in the answer to Question 9: $6a + 3b$. In this case the perimeters are different for all nonzero values of a and b.

13. $3a \cdot 1.5b = 4.5ab$; the areas are the same regardless of the values of a and b.

14. Jenny is incorrect. Students may cite examples in which the area stays the same when the perimeter increases, such as going from a 6-by-6 to a 3-by-12 rectangle; the area in each case is 36 but the perimeter increases from 24 to 30. Or they might find figures whose area actually decreases, such as going from a 6-by-6 to a 8.5-by-4 rectangle, in which the perimeter increases from 24 to 25 but the area decreases from 36 to 34.

Pages 368–372   On Your Own Exercises

1a. $x \cdot x = x^2, x \cdot 7 = 7x$

1b. $7x - x^2$

1c. $7 - x, x$

1d. $x(7 - x)$

1e. $x(7 - x) = 7x - x^2$

2. $3x^2 - 6x$; The dimensions of the entire unshaded region are $3x$ and $x - 2$, so its area is $3x(x - 2)$. The area of the unshaded region is also the sum of the areas of the three squares, $3x^2$, minus the sum of the areas of the three shaded rectangles, $3(2x) = 6x$. So $3x(x - 2) = 3x^2 - 6x$.

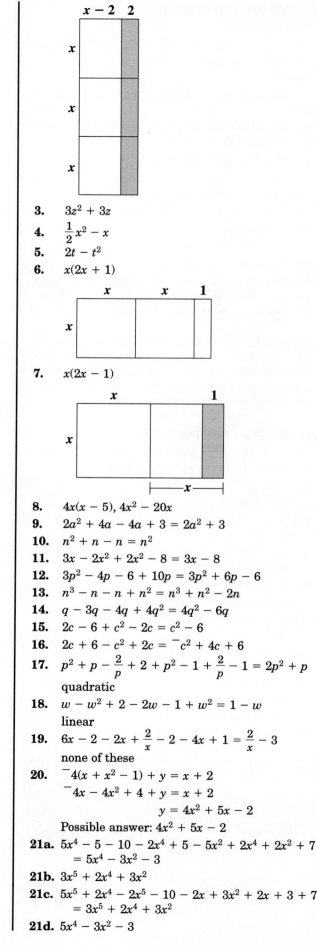

3. $3z^2 + 3z$

4. $\frac{1}{2}x^2 - x$

5. $2t - t^2$

6. $x(2x + 1)$

7. $x(2x - 1)$

8. $4x(x - 5), 4x^2 - 20x$

9. $2a^2 + 4a - 4a + 3 = 2a^2 + 3$

10. $n^2 + n - n = n^2$

11. $3x - 2x^2 + 2x^2 - 8 = 3x - 8$

12. $3p^2 - 4p - 6 + 10p = 3p^2 + 6p - 6$

13. $n^3 - n - n + n^2 = n^3 + n^2 - 2n$

14. $q - 3q - 4q + 4q^2 = 4q^2 - 6q$

15. $2c - 6 + c^2 - 2c = c^2 - 6$

16. $2c + 6 - c^2 + 2c = {}^-c^2 + 4c + 6$

17. $p^2 + p - \frac{2}{p} + 2 + p^2 - 1 + \frac{2}{p} - 1 = 2p^2 + p$

quadratic

18. $w - w^2 + 2 - 2w - 1 + w^2 = 1 - w$

linear

19. $6x - 2 - 2x + \frac{2}{x} - 2 - 4x + 1 = \frac{2}{x} - 3$

none of these

20. ${}^-4(x + x^2 - 1) + y = x + 2$

${}^-4x - 4x^2 + 4 + y = x + 2$

$\phantom{{}^-4x - 4x^2 + 4 + }y = 4x^2 + 5x - 2$

Possible answer: $4x^2 + 5x - 2$

21a. $5x^4 - 5 - 10 - 2x^4 + 5 - 5x^2 + 2x^4 + 2x^2 + 7$
$= 5x^4 - 3x^2 - 3$

21b. $3x^5 + 2x^4 + 3x^2$

21c. $5x^5 + 2x^4 - 2x^5 - 10 - 2x + 3x^2 + 2x + 3 + 7$
$= 3x^5 + 2x^4 + 3x^2$

21d. $5x^4 - 3x^2 - 3$

21e. $x + 4 + 5x + 5x^2 - 8 + 2x - 10x + 5 - 2x - 5x^2 = 1 - 4x$

21f. $3x^5 + 3x^2 + 2x^4 + 6x - 6x = 3x^5 + 2x^4 + 3x^2$
a and d; b, c, and f; e

22. $(2x)(2x) = 4x^2$
Shade four x-by-x squares.

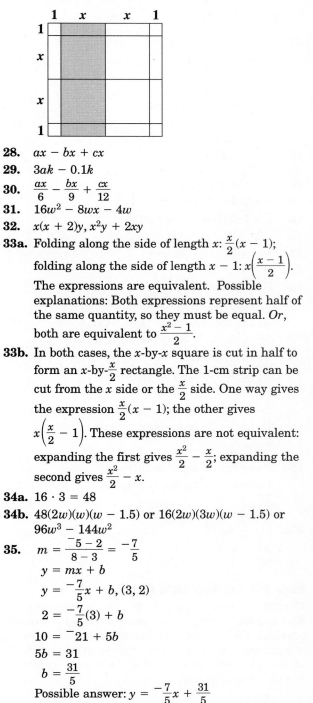

23. $2x^2$
Shade two x-by-x squares.
Possible answer:

24. $2x^2 + x$
Shade two x-by-x squares and one x-by-1 rectangle.
Possible answer:

25. Shade two x-by-1 rectangles and two 1-by-1 squares.
Possible answer:

26. $(2x + 2)(2x + 2) = 4x^2 + 8x + 4$
Shade four x-by-x squares, eight x-by-1 rectangles, and four 1-by-1 squares.

Possible answer:

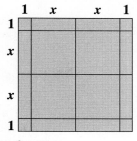

27. $2x^2 + 2x$
Shade two x-by-x squares and two x-by-1 rectangles.
Possible answer:

28. $ax - bx + cx$

29. $3ak - 0.1k$

30. $\dfrac{ax}{6} - \dfrac{bx}{9} + \dfrac{cx}{12}$

31. $16w^2 - 8wx - 4w$

32. $x(x + 2)y, x^2y + 2xy$

33a. Folding along the side of length x: $\dfrac{x}{2}(x - 1)$; folding along the side of length $x - 1$: $x\left(\dfrac{x - 1}{2}\right)$. The expressions are equivalent. Possible explanations: Both expressions represent half of the same quantity, so they must be equal. *Or*, both are equivalent to $\dfrac{x^2 - 1}{2}$.

33b. In both cases, the x-by-x square is cut in half to form an x-by-$\dfrac{x}{2}$ rectangle. The 1-cm strip can be cut from the x side or the $\dfrac{x}{2}$ side. One way gives the expression $\dfrac{x}{2}(x - 1)$; the other gives $x\left(\dfrac{x}{2} - 1\right)$. These expressions are not equivalent: expanding the first gives $\dfrac{x^2}{2} - \dfrac{x}{2}$; expanding the second gives $\dfrac{x^2}{2} - x$.

34a. $16 \cdot 3 = 48$

34b. $48(2w)(w)(w - 1.5)$ or $16(2w)(3w)(w - 1.5)$ or $96w^3 - 144w^2$

35. $m = \dfrac{-5 - 2}{8 - 3} = \dfrac{-7}{5}$
$y = mx + b$
$y = \dfrac{-7}{5}x + b, (3, 2)$
$2 = \dfrac{-7}{5}(3) + b$
$10 = {}^-21 + 5b$
$5b = 31$
$b = \dfrac{31}{5}$
Possible answer: $y = \dfrac{-7}{5}x + \dfrac{31}{5}$

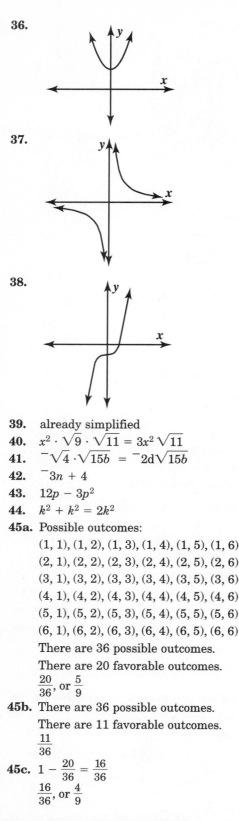

36.

37.

38.

39. already simplified

40. $x^2 \cdot \sqrt{9} \cdot \sqrt{11} = 3x^2\sqrt{11}$

41. $^-\sqrt{4} \cdot \sqrt{15b} = {}^-2d\sqrt{15b}$

42. $^-3n + 4$

43. $12p - 3p^2$

44. $k^2 + k^2 = 2k^2$

45a. Possible outcomes:

$(1, 1), (1, 2), (1, 3), (1, 4), (1, 5), (1, 6)$
$(2, 1), (2, 2), (2, 3), (2, 4), (2, 5), (2, 6)$
$(3, 1), (3, 2), (3, 3), (3, 4), (3, 5), (3, 6)$
$(4, 1), (4, 2), (4, 3), (4, 4), (4, 5), (4, 6)$
$(5, 1), (5, 2), (5, 3), (5, 4), (5, 5), (5, 6)$
$(6, 1), (6, 2), (6, 3), (6, 4), (6, 5), (6, 6)$

There are 36 possible outcomes.

There are 20 favorable outcomes.

$\frac{20}{36}$, or $\frac{5}{9}$

45b. There are 36 possible outcomes.

There are 11 favorable outcomes.

$\frac{11}{36}$

45c. $1 - \frac{20}{36} = \frac{16}{36}$

$\frac{16}{36}$, or $\frac{4}{9}$

Page 369   In Your Own Words

Possible answer: To simplify an algebraic expression, I first eliminate any parentheses to make an expanded expression. I then combine like terms by adding or subtracting. I know when an expression is simplified as much as possible when all of the remaining terms are unlike and can not be combined.

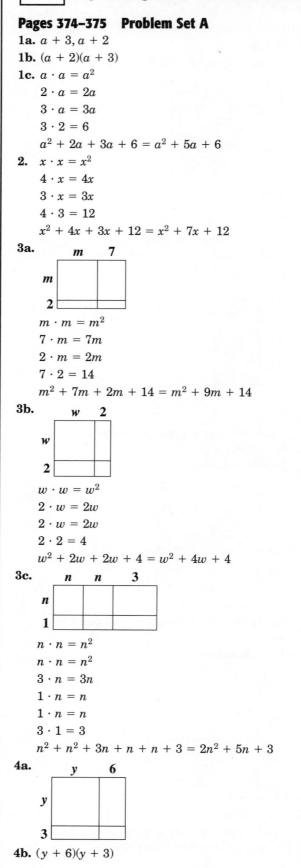

6-2 Expanding Products of Binomials

Pages 374–375   Problem Set A

1a. $a + 3, a + 2$

1b. $(a + 2)(a + 3)$

1c. $a \cdot a = a^2$

$2 \cdot a = 2a$

$3 \cdot a = 3a$

$3 \cdot 2 = 6$

$a^2 + 2a + 3a + 6 = a^2 + 5a + 6$

2. $x \cdot x = x^2$

$4 \cdot x = 4x$

$3 \cdot x = 3x$

$4 \cdot 3 = 12$

$x^2 + 4x + 3x + 12 = x^2 + 7x + 12$

3a.

$m \cdot m = m^2$

$7 \cdot m = 7m$

$2 \cdot m = 2m$

$7 \cdot 2 = 14$

$m^2 + 7m + 2m + 14 = m^2 + 9m + 14$

3b.

$w \cdot w = w^2$

$2 \cdot w = 2w$

$2 \cdot w = 2w$

$2 \cdot 2 = 4$

$w^2 + 2w + 2w + 4 = w^2 + 4w + 4$

3c.

$n \cdot n = n^2$

$n \cdot n = n^2$

$3 \cdot n = 3n$

$1 \cdot n = n$

$1 \cdot n = n$

$3 \cdot 1 = 3$

$n^2 + n^2 + 3n + n + n + 3 = 2n^2 + 5n + 3$

4a.

4b. $(y + 6)(y + 3)$

5a.

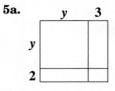

5b. $(y + 2)(y + 3)$

Page 375   Share and Summarize

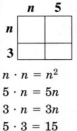

$n \cdot n = n^2$

$5 \cdot n = 5n$

$3 \cdot n = 3n$

$5 \cdot 3 = 15$

$n^2 + 5n + 3n + 15 = n^2 + 8n + 15$

So, $(n + 3)(n + 5) = n^2 + 8n + 15$.

Page 377   Problem Set B

1. $(x + 3)(x + 4) = (x + 3) \cdot x + (x + 3) \cdot 4$
$= x^2 + 3x + 4x + 12$
$= x^2 + 7x + 12$

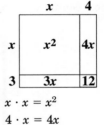

$x \cdot x = x^2$

$4 \cdot x = 4x$

$3 \cdot x = 3x$

$4 \cdot 3 = 12$

$x^2 + 4x + 3x + 12 = x^2 + 7x + 12$ ✓

2. $(k + 5)(k + 5) = (k + 5) \cdot k + (k + 5) \cdot 5$
$= k^2 + 5k + 5k + 25$
$= k^2 + 10k + 25$

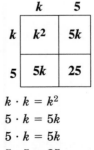

$k \cdot k = k^2$

$5 \cdot k = 5k$

$5 \cdot k = 5k$

$5 \cdot 5 = 25$

$k^2 + 5k + 5k + 25 = k^2 + 10k + 25$ ✓

3. $(x + a)(x + b) = (x + a) \cdot x + (x + a) \cdot b$
$= x^2 + ax + xb + ab$
$= x^2 + ax + bx + ab$

$x^2 + ax + bx + ab$ or $x^2 + (a + b)x + ab$

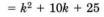

$x \cdot x = x^2$

$b \cdot x = bx$

$a \cdot x = ax$

$a \cdot b = ab$

$x^2 + bx + ax + ab$ ✓

Page 378   Problem Set C

1. $y = 0(0 + 1) - 3(0 + 1)(0 + 2) + 3(0 + 2)(0 + 3)$
    $\quad - (0 + 3)(0 + 4)$
$= 0 - 6 + 18 - 12$
$= 0$

$y = 1(1 + 1) - 3(1 + 1)(1 + 2) + 3(1 + 2)(1 + 3)$
    $\quad - (1 + 3)(1 + 4)$
$= 2 - 18 + 36 - 20$
$= 0$

$y = 2(2 + 1) - 3(2 + 1)(2 + 2) + 3(2 + 2)(2 + 3)$
    $\quad - (2 + 3)(2 + 4)$
$= 6 - 36 + 60 - 30$
$= 0$

$y = 3(3 + 1) - 3(3 + 1)(3 + 2) + 3(3 + 2)(3 + 3)$
    $\quad - (3 + 3)(3 + 4)$
$= 12 - 60 + 90 - 42$
$= 0$

$y = 4(4 + 1) - 3(4 + 1)(4 + 2) + 3(4 + 2)(4 + 3)$
    $\quad - (4 + 3)(4 + 4)$
$= 20 - 90 + 126 - 56$
$= 0$

$y = 5(5 + 1) - 3(5 + 1)(5 + 2) + 3(5 + 2)(5 + 3)$
    $\quad - (5 + 3)(5 + 4)$
$= 30 - 126 + 168 - 72$
$= 0$

x	0	1	2	3	4	5
y	0	0	0	0	0	0

2. y is always 0.

3. Expand the right-hand side of the equation:
$x^2 + x - 3x^2 - 9x - 6 + 3x^2 + 15x + 18 - x^2 - 7x$
$- 12$; simplifying by combining like terms gives 0.

Page 378   Share and Summarize

$ac + ad + bc + bd$; Possible explanation: The dimensions are $a + b$ and $c + d$. The areas of the four rectangles are ac, bc, ad, and bd. Adding these gives $ac + ad + bc + bd$.

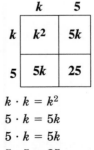

Page 379 Problem Set D

1. $(b - 2)(b + 3) = (b - 2) \cdot b + (b - 2) \cdot 3$
$$= b^2 - 2b + 3b - 6$$
$$= b^2 + b - 6$$

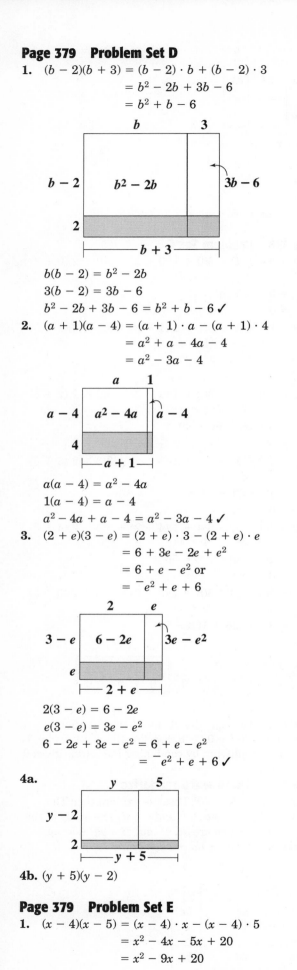

$b(b - 2) = b^2 - 2b$
$3(b - 2) = 3b - 6$
$b^2 - 2b + 3b - 6 = b^2 + b - 6 ✓$

2. $(a + 1)(a - 4) = (a + 1) \cdot a - (a + 1) \cdot 4$
$$= a^2 + a - 4a - 4$$
$$= a^2 - 3a - 4$$

$a(a - 4) = a^2 - 4a$
$1(a - 4) = a - 4$
$a^2 - 4a + a - 4 = a^2 - 3a - 4 ✓$

3. $(2 + e)(3 - e) = (2 + e) \cdot 3 - (2 + e) \cdot e$
$$= 6 + 3e - 2e + e^2$$
$$= 6 + e - e^2 \text{ or}$$
$$= {}^-e^2 + e + 6$$

$2(3 - e) = 6 - 2e$
$e(3 - e) = 3e - e^2$
$6 - 2e + 3e - e^2 = 6 + e - e^2$
$$= {}^-e^2 + e + 6 ✓$$

4a.

4b. $(y + 5)(y - 2)$

Page 379 Problem Set E

1. $(x - 4)(x - 5) = (x - 4) \cdot x - (x - 4) \cdot 5$
$$= x^2 - 4x - 5x + 20$$
$$= x^2 - 9x + 20$$

2. $(R - 2)(R - 2) = (R - 2) \cdot R - (R - 2) \cdot 2$
$$= R^2 - 2R - 2R + 4$$
$$= R^2 - 4R + 4$$

3. $(2 - f)(3 - f) = (2 - f) \cdot 3 - (2 - f) \cdot f$
$$= 6 - 3f - 2f + f^2$$
$$= 6 - 5f + f^2 \text{ or}$$
$$= f^2 - 5f + 6$$

4. $(a - 2b)(3a - b) = (a - 2b) \cdot 3a - (a - 2b) \cdot b$
$$= 3a^2 - 6ab - ab + 2b^2$$
$$= 3a^2 - 7ab + 2b^2$$

Page 380 Problem Set F

1. Let the integers be $x, x + 1, x + 2$, and $x + 3$.
$x(x + 3) = x^2 + 3x$
$(x + 1)(x + 2) = (x + 1) \cdot x + (x + 1) \cdot 2$
$$= x^2 + x + 2x + 2$$
$$= x^2 + 3x + 2$$
$(x^2 + 3x + 2) - (x^2 + 3x) = 2$
The trick works.

2. Let the integers be $x, x + 1$, and $x + 2$.
$x(x + 1)(x + 2) = x^3 + 3x^2 + 2x$
If $x = 1, 1^3 + 3(1)^2 + 2(1) = 6$, which is not divisible by 4.
The trick doesn't work. Possible counterexample: 1, 2 and 3, with a product of 6

3a. $2x + 2$

3b. $2x(2x + 2) + 1 = 4x^2 + 4x + 1$

3c.

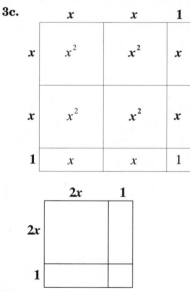

3d. $2x + 1$

3e. Yes; since $(2x + 1)^2$ is equivalent to $2x(2x + 2) + 1$, which represents Lydia's number trick and is a perfect square, the trick works.

Page 380 Share and Summarize

$(a - b)(c + d) = a(c + d) - b(c + d)$
$$= ac + ad - bc - bd$$

Possible diagram:

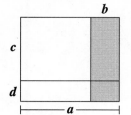

Page 381   Problem Set G
1. $y^2 - 3y + 6y - 18 = y^2 + 3y - 18$
2. $p^2 + 3p + 4p + 12 = p^2 + 7p + 12$
3. $t^2 - 3t - 11t + 33 = t^2 - 14t + 33$
4. $6x^2 + 4x + 3x + 2 = 6x^2 + 7x + 2$
5. $4n^2 - 6n + 6n - 9 = 4n^2 - 9$

Page 382   Problem Set H
1. $y^2 + 7y - 4y - 28 = y^2 + 3y - 28$
2. $p^2 + 1p - 5p - 5 = p^2 - 4p - 5$
3. $t^2 - 4t - 4t + 16 = t^2 - 8t + 16$
4. $2x^2 - 1x - 4x + 2 = 2x^2 - 5x + 2$
5. $6n^2 + 4n - 9n - 6 = 6n^2 - 5n - 6$

Page 383   Problem Set I
1a. when $x = 2$:
$$(2 - 2)(2 - 3) = 0$$
$$0 \cdot {}^{-}1 = 0$$
when $x = 3$:
$$(3 - 2)(3 - 3) = 0$$
$$1 \cdot 0 = 0$$
some values

1b. Possible answer: The equation has two solutions, 2 and 3.

2a. $(x + 3)(x + 2) = x^2 + 2x + 3x + 6$
$$= x^2 + 5x + 6$$
all values

2b. Possible answer: $(x + 3)(x + 2)$ expands to $x^2 + 5x + 6$, which is the right side of the equation, so it's always true.

3a. $(x - b)(x - b) = x^2 - xb - xb + b^2$
$$= x^2 - 2xb + b^2$$
all values

3b. Possible answer: $(x - b)^2$ expands to $x^2 - 2xb + b^2$, which is the right side of the equation, so it's always true.

4a. $(x + 3)(x - 1) = x^2 - x + 3x - 3$
$$= x^2 + 2x - 3$$
no values

4b. Possible answer: $(x + 3)(x - 1)$ expands to $x^2 + 2x - 3$, so the equation is the same as $x^2 + 2x - 3 = x^2 + 2x + 3$ or $^{-}3 = 3$, which is never true.

5a. $(x - 3)(x + 3) = x^2 + 3x - 3x - 9$
$$= x^2 - 9$$
some values

5b. Possible answer: $(x - 3)(x + 3)$ expands to $x^2 - 9$, so the equation is the same as $x^2 - 9 = x^2 - 6x - 9$, or $0 = {}^{-}6x$, which is true only when $x = 0$.

6a. $2 \cdot 10 = 20$
$3 \cdot 9 = 27$
$27 - 20 = 7$
$11 \cdot 19 = 209$
$12 \cdot 18 = 216$
$216 - 209 = 7$
$21 \cdot 29 = 609$
$22 \cdot 28 = 616$
$616 - 609 = 7$

This pattern works. Possible explanation: If x is the first number in the square, $x + 1$ is the second and $x + 7$ and $x + 8$ are the others. The products of the diagonals are $x(x + 8) = x^2 + 8x$ and $(x + 1)(x + 7) = x^2 + 8x + 7$. Their difference is 7.

6b. $2 \cdot 9 = 18$
$3 \cdot 10 = 30$
$30 - 18 = 12$
$11 \cdot 18 = 198$
$12 \cdot 19 = 228$
$228 - 198 = 30$

This pattern does not always work. Possible explanation: The square with 11, 12, 18, and 19 has products 198 and 228; their difference is 30.

6c. $2 \cdot 3 = 6$
$9 \cdot 10 = 90$
$90 - 6 = 84$
$11 \cdot 12 = 132$
$18 \cdot 19 = 342$
$342 - 132 = 210$
$21 \cdot 22 = 462$
$28 \cdot 29 = 812$
$812 - 462 = 350$

This pattern works. Possible explanation: The product of the top row is $x(x + 1) = x^2 + x$, and the product of the bottom row is $(x + 7)(x + 8) = x^2 + 15x + 56$. Their difference is $14x + 56$, or $2(7x + 28)$, which is always even.

Page 383   Share and Summarize
1. Possible answer: Multiply $2x$ and x to get $2x^2$ and write it down. Then multiply 3 and $^{-}1$ to get $^{-}3$; write it down with space between $2x^2$ and $^{-}3$. Finally, multiply $2x$ and $^{-}1$ and add it to the product of 3 and x; $^{-}2x + 3x$, or x. Write that between the two other terms (adding it): $2x^2 + x - 3$.

2. Possible answer: I don't have to write as much.

Pages 384–389   On Your Own Exercises
1a. $a \cdot a = a^2$
$2 \cdot a = 2a$
$10 \cdot a = 10a$
$10 \cdot 2 = 20$

1b. $a^2 + 2a + 10a + 20 = a^2 + 12a + 20$

2a. $y \cdot y = y^2$

$\quad\quad 9 \cdot y = 9y$

$\quad\quad 8 \cdot y = 8y$

$\quad\quad 9 \cdot 8 = 72$

2b. $y^2 + 9y + 8y + 72 = y^2 + 17y + 72$

3.

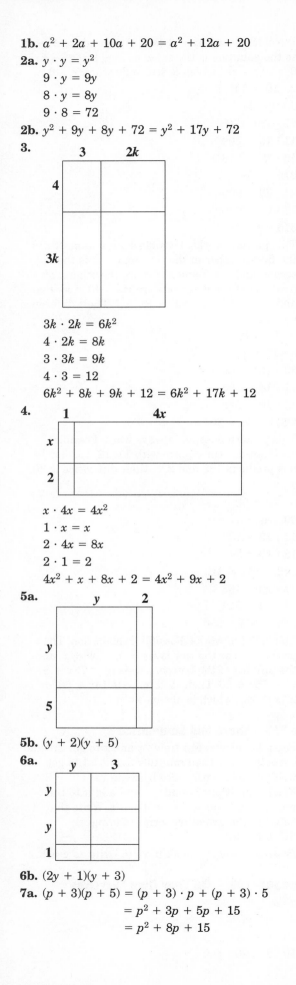

$3k \cdot 2k = 6k^2$

$4 \cdot 2k = 8k$

$3 \cdot 3k = 9k$

$4 \cdot 3 = 12$

$6k^2 + 8k + 9k + 12 = 6k^2 + 17k + 12$

4.

$x \cdot 4x = 4x^2$

$1 \cdot x = x$

$2 \cdot 4x = 8x$

$2 \cdot 1 = 2$

$4x^2 + x + 8x + 2 = 4x^2 + 9x + 2$

5a.

5b. $(y + 2)(y + 5)$

6a.

6b. $(2y + 1)(y + 3)$

7a. $(p + 3)(p + 5) = (p + 3) \cdot p + (p + 3) \cdot 5$

$\quad\quad\quad\quad\quad\quad = p^2 + 3p + 5p + 15$

$\quad\quad\quad\quad\quad\quad = p^2 + 8p + 15$

7b.

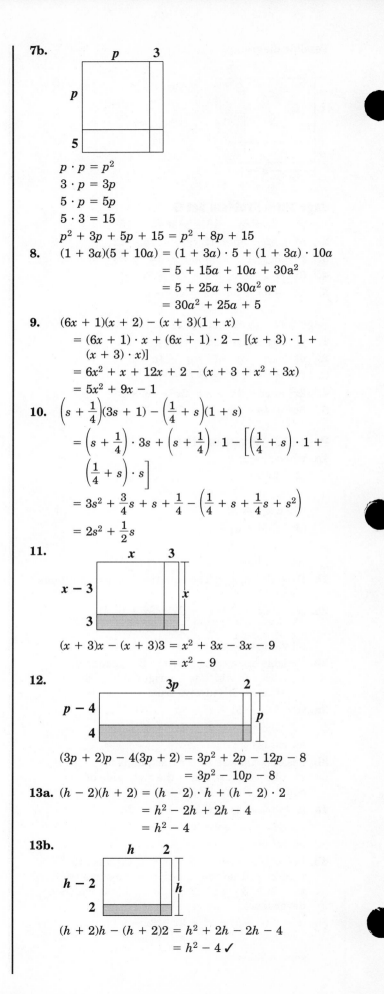

$p \cdot p = p^2$

$3 \cdot p = 3p$

$5 \cdot p = 5p$

$5 \cdot 3 = 15$

$p^2 + 3p + 5p + 15 = p^2 + 8p + 15$

8. $(1 + 3a)(5 + 10a) = (1 + 3a) \cdot 5 + (1 + 3a) \cdot 10a$

$\quad\quad\quad\quad\quad\quad\quad = 5 + 15a + 10a + 30a^2$

$\quad\quad\quad\quad\quad\quad\quad = 5 + 25a + 30a^2 \text{ or}$

$\quad\quad\quad\quad\quad\quad\quad = 30a^2 + 25a + 5$

9. $(6x + 1)(x + 2) - (x + 3)(1 + x)$

$\quad = (6x + 1) \cdot x + (6x + 1) \cdot 2 - [(x + 3) \cdot 1 +$

$\quad\quad (x + 3) \cdot x)]$

$\quad = 6x^2 + x + 12x + 2 - (x + 3 + x^2 + 3x)$

$\quad = 5x^2 + 9x - 1$

10. $\left(s + \dfrac{1}{4}\right)(3s + 1) - \left(\dfrac{1}{4} + s\right)(1 + s)$

$\quad = \left(s + \dfrac{1}{4}\right) \cdot 3s + \left(s + \dfrac{1}{4}\right) \cdot 1 - \left[\left(\dfrac{1}{4} + s\right) \cdot 1 + \right.$

$\quad\quad \left. \left(\dfrac{1}{4} + s\right) \cdot s\right]$

$\quad = 3s^2 + \dfrac{3}{4}s + s + \dfrac{1}{4} - \left(\dfrac{1}{4} + s + \dfrac{1}{4}s + s^2\right)$

$\quad = 2s^2 + \dfrac{1}{2}s$

11.

$(x + 3)x - (x + 3)3 = x^2 + 3x - 3x - 9$

$\quad\quad\quad\quad\quad\quad\quad = x^2 - 9$

12.

$(3p + 2)p - 4(3p + 2) = 3p^2 + 2p - 12p - 8$

$\quad\quad\quad\quad\quad\quad\quad\quad = 3p^2 - 10p - 8$

13a. $(h - 2)(h + 2) = (h - 2) \cdot h + (h - 2) \cdot 2$

$\quad\quad\quad\quad\quad\quad\quad = h^2 - 2h + 2h - 4$

$\quad\quad\quad\quad\quad\quad\quad = h^2 - 4$

13b.

$(h + 2)h - (h + 2)2 = h^2 + 2h - 2h - 4$

$\quad\quad\quad\quad\quad\quad\quad = h^2 - 4 \checkmark$

14. $(x - 7)(x - 2) = (x - 7) \cdot x - (x - 7) \cdot 2$
$\qquad\qquad = x^2 - 7x - 2x - 14$
$\qquad\qquad = x^2 - 9x + 14$

15. $(3 - g)(4 - g) = (3 - g) \cdot 4 - (3 - g)g$
$\qquad\qquad = 12 - 4g - 3g + g^2$
$\qquad\qquad = g^2 - 7g + 12$

16. $(4 - 2p)(4 - p) = (4 - 2p) \cdot 4 - (4 - 2p) \cdot p$
$\qquad\qquad = 16 - 8p - 4p + 2p^2$
$\qquad\qquad = 2p^2 - 12p + 16$

17. $(2w + 1)(w - 6) = (2w + 1) \cdot w - (2w + 1) \cdot 6$
$\qquad\qquad = 2w^2 + w - 12w - 6$
$\qquad\qquad = 2w^2 - 11w - 6$

18. $(1 - 5q)(2 + 2q) = (1 - 5q) \cdot 2 + (1 - 5q) \cdot 2q$
$\qquad\qquad = 2 - 10q + 2q - 10q^2$
$\qquad\qquad = {}^-10q^2 - 8q + 2$

19. $(3v - 5)(v + 1) = (3v - 5) \cdot v + (3v - 5) \cdot 1$
$\qquad\qquad = 3v^2 - 5v + 3v - 5$
$\qquad\qquad = 3v^2 - 2v - 5$

20a.

20b. $(y + 8)(y - 4)$

21a.

21b. $(2y - 3)(y + 2)$

22. Let the integers be x, $x + 1$, and $x + 2$.
$x(x + 2) = x^2 + 2x$
$(x + 1)^2 - 1 = x^2 + 2x + 1 - 1 = x^2 + 2x$
It works; $x(x + 2) = x^2 + 2x$ and $(x + 1)^2 - 1 = x^2 + 2x + 1 - 1$, and $(x + 1)^2 - 1 = x^2 + 2x + 1 - 1 = x^2 + 2x$.

23. Let the consecutive odd integers be $2x - 1$ and $2x + 1$.
$(2x - 1)^2 = 4x^2 - 4x + 1$
$(2x + 1)^2 = 4x^2 + 4x + 1$
$4x^2 + 4x + 1 - (4x^2 - 4x + 1) = 8x$
If $x = 2$ (and the consecutive odd integers are 3 and 5), $8x = 16$ (the difference of the squares of 3 and 5), which is not divisible by 6.
Doesn't work. Possible counterexample: 3 and 5 square to give 9 and 25, and $25 - 9 = 16$, which isn't divisible by 6.

24. $16x^2 - 4x + 4x - 1 = 16x^2 - 1$

25. $r^2 - 12r - 12r + 144 = r^2 - 24r + 144$

26. $2x^2 - 4x + 2x - 4 = 2x^2 - 2x - 4$

27. $(4x + 1)(4x + 1) = 16x^2 + 4x + 4x + 1$
$\qquad\qquad = 16x^2 + 8x + 1$

28. $(5M + 5)(5M + 5) = 25M^2 + 25M + 25M + 25$
$\qquad\qquad = 25M^2 + 50M + 25$

29. $(n + 1)(n + 1) + (n - 1)(n - 1)$
$\qquad = n^2 + n + n + 1 + n^2 - n - n + 1$
$\qquad = 2n^2 + 2$

30. $x^2 - 4x + 3x - 12 \overset{?}{=} x^2 + 7x - 12$
$\qquad x^2 - 1x - 12 \neq x^2 + 7x - 12$
for $x = 0$:
$0 - 0 - 12 = 0 + 0 - 12$
${}^-12 = {}^-12$
for one value only ($x = 0$)

31. $2x^2 - 2x + x - 1 \overset{?}{=} 2x^2 - x - 1$
$\qquad 2x^2 - x - 1 \overset{?}{=} 2x^2 - x - 1 ✓$
for all x

32. $(9x^2 - 3x + 3x - 1)x \overset{?}{=} 9x^3 - x - 1$
$\qquad (9x^2 - 1)x \overset{?}{=} 9x^3 - x - 1$
$\qquad 9x^3 - x \overset{?}{=} 9x^3 - x - 1$
$0 \neq {}^-1$
for no values of x

33. $9^2 = 81$
$2 \cdot 16 = 32$
$81 - 32 = 49$
$12^2 = 144$
$5 \cdot 19 = 95$
$144 - 95 = 49$
$21^2 = 441$
$14 \cdot 28 = 392$
$441 - 392 = 49$
Yes; if the first date is x, the others are $x + 7$ and $x + 14$. $(x + 7)^2 - x(x + 14) = x^2 + 14x + 49 - x^2 - 14x = 49$.

34a. xy

34b. $(x + 2)(y + 2) - xy$
$xy + 2x + 2y + 4 - xy$
$2x + 2y + 4$

35.

$(x + 5) - (x + 1) = 4$
$(y + 4) - (y + 2) = 2$
$(x + 5)(y + 4) - 4 \cdot 2 = xy + 4x + 5y + 20 - 8$
$\qquad\qquad = xy + 4x + 5y + 12$

36. $x + y + x^3 + x^2y + x + y + yx + y^2 - x^3 - x^2y - xy = 2x + 2y + y^2$

37. $2x + 2y + 3x^2 + 6x + x^2y + 2xy$
$\qquad = 8x + 2y + 3x^2 + x^2y + 2xy$

38. $x^2 + x + yx + y + x + 1$
$= x^2 + 2x + xy + y + 1$

39. $a^2 + 2a + ba + 2b + a + 2$
$= a^2 + 3a + ab + 2b + 2$

40. $x^2 + x + yx + y + 2x + 2$
$= x^2 + 3x + xy + y + 2$

41a. $2x^2 + 4xy + yx + 2y^2$
$= 2x^2 + 5xy + 2y^2$

41b.

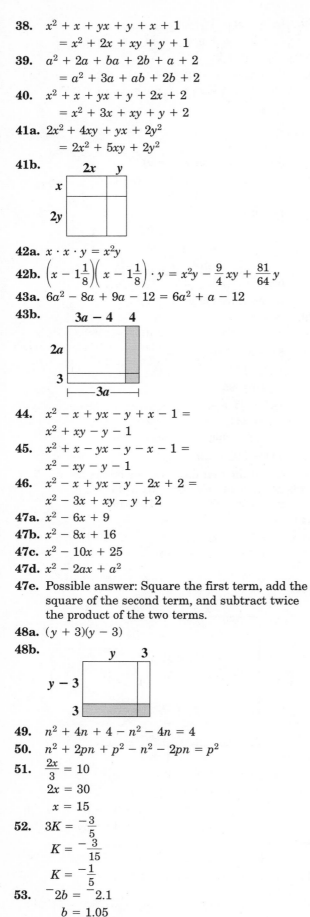

42a. $x \cdot x \cdot y = x^2y$

42b. $\left(x - 1\frac{1}{8}\right)\left(x - 1\frac{1}{8}\right) \cdot y = x^2y - \frac{9}{4}xy + \frac{81}{64}y$

43a. $6a^2 - 8a + 9a - 12 = 6a^2 + a - 12$

43b.

44. $x^2 - x + yx - y + x - 1 =$
$x^2 + xy - y - 1$

45. $x^2 + x - yx - y - x - 1 =$
$x^2 - xy - y - 1$

46. $x^2 - x + yx - y - 2x + 2 =$
$x^2 - 3x + xy - y + 2$

47a. $x^2 - 6x + 9$

47b. $x^2 - 8x + 16$

47c. $x^2 - 10x + 25$

47d. $x^2 - 2ax + a^2$

47e. Possible answer: Square the first term, add the square of the second term, and subtract twice the product of the two terms.

48a. $(y + 3)(y - 3)$

48b.

49. $n^2 + 4n + 4 - n^2 - 4n = 4$

50. $n^2 + 2pn + p^2 - n^2 - 2pn = p^2$

51. $\frac{2x}{3} = 10$
$2x = 30$
$x = 15$

52. $3K = \frac{-3}{5}$
$K = \frac{-\frac{3}{5}}{15}$
$K = \frac{-1}{5}$

53. $^-2b = {}^-2.1$
$b = 1.05$

54.

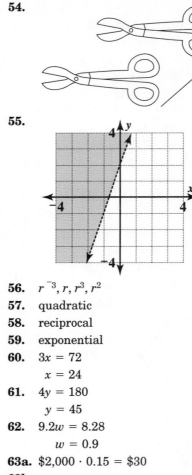

55.

56. r^{-3}, r, r^3, r^2

57. quadratic

58. reciprocal

59. exponential

60. $3x = 72$
$x = 24$

61. $4y = 180$
$y = 45$

62. $9.2w = 8.28$
$w = 0.9$

63a. $\$2,000 \cdot 0.15 = \$30$

63b.

Month	Balance	Interest Added	Amount Paid	New Balance
1	$2,000.00	—	$100.00	$1,900.00
2	1,900.00	$28.50	100.00	1,828.50
3	1,828.50	27.43	100.00	1,755.93
4	1,755.93	26.34	100.00	1,682.27
5	1,682.27	25.23	100.00	1,607.50
6	1,607.50	24.11	100.00	1,531.61

63c. $\$100 \cdot 6 = \$600$

63d. $\$2,000 - \$1,531.61 = \$468.39$

63e. $\$131.61$

Page 387   In Your Own Words

Possible answer:

Rectangle diagram

	x	a
x	x^2	ax
b	bx	ab

Area of rectangle: $x^2 + ax + bx + ab \neq x^2 + ab$

By applying the distributive property: $(x + a)(x + b)$
$= x^2 + ax + bx + ab \neq x^2 + ab$

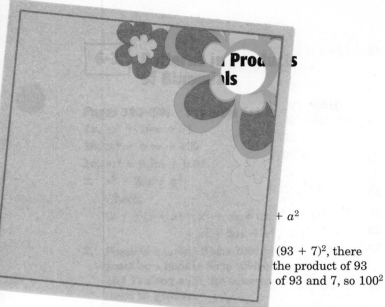

Proc s
ls

$+ a^2$

$(93 + 7)^2$, there
the product of 93
of 93 and 7, so 100^2

4. If they were equal to each other, $2ax$ must be 0, which means either x or a would be 0.

Page 391 Problem Set B

1a. $x^2 + {}^-2x + 1$ or $x^2 - 2x + 1$

1b. $(x + {}^-1)(x + {}^-1) = x^2 - x - x + 1 = x^2 - 2x + 1$

2a. $m^2 - 18m + 81$

2b. $m^2 - 40m + 400$

2c. $m^2 - 0.2m + 0.01$

3. $x^2 - 2a + a^2$

4.

$$
\begin{array}{cc}
x - a & a
\end{array}
$$

Possible explanations: If you start with an x-by-x square, you can subtract the rectangle with area ax along the right side and then subtract the rectangle with area ax along the bottom. However, both of those strips include the square in the lower-right corner, with area a^2, so you have to add that area back once, giving $x^2 - ax - ax + a^2$, or $x^2 - 2ax + a^2$. Or, the areas of the four rectangles are $(x - a)^2$, $a(x - a)$, $a(x - a)$, and a^2. So $(x - a)^2$ is the area of the big square, x^2, minus the area of the three others: $x^2 - a(x - a) - a(x - a) - a^2$, or $x^2 - ax + a^2 - ax + a^2 - a^2$, or $x^2 - 2ax + a^2$.

Pages 391–392 Problem Set C

1. $9m^2 + 12m + 4$

2. $4x^2 - 4xy + y^2$

3. $4m^2 - 16mn + 16n^2$

4. $g^4 - 2g^2a^4 + a^8$

5a. $(n + 2)^2$ or $n^2 + 4n + 4$

5b. $(n + 2)^2 - n^2$ or $4n + 4$

6. Possible answer: If you take the difference of the squares of any two consecutive numbers, $(n + 1)^2 - n^2$, you get $n^2 + 2n + 1 - n^2$, or $2n + 1$, which is an odd number.

Page 392 Share and Summarize

Possible letter: When you square a binomial, you have to multiply it by itself: $(a + b)^2 = (a + b)(a + b)$. Using the distributive property twice, this is $a^2 + 2ab + b^2$. And $(a - b)^2 = (a - b)(a - b) = a^2 - 2ab + b^2$.

Page 393 Problem Set D

1a. $x^2 - 10x + 10x - 100 = x^2 - 100$

1b. $k^2 - 3k + 3k - 9 = k^2 - 9$

1c. $S^2 - S + S - 1 = S^2 - 1$

1d. $x^2 - 5x + 5x - 25 = x^2 - 25$

1e. $4t^2 - 10t + 10t - 25 = 4t^2 - 25$

1f. $9y^2 + 21y - 21y - 49 = 9y^2 - 49$

2. Possible answers: The second terms in the factors of each product are opposites. *Or,* the second terms are the same, but one is added and one subtracted. *Or,* the products look like $(a + b)(a - b)$.

3. Possible answers: They have no middle term; they're all the first term from one of the binomials squared minus the second term from one of the binomials squared.

4. $x^2 - ax + ax - a^2 = x^2 - a^2$, which is the square of the first term minus the square of the second term.

5a. $x^2 - 400$

5b. $b^2 - 1$

5c. does not fit the pattern

5d. does not fit the pattern

5e. $j^2 - 0.04$

5f. does not fit the pattern

5g. $4n^2 - \dfrac{1}{9}$

5h. $9 - p^2$

6. $(x + 7)(x - 7)$

7. The expanded product is the difference between two squares.

Pages 394–395 Problem Set E

1. $99 \cdot 101 = (100 - 1)(100 + 1) = 10,000 - 1 = 9,999$

2. $(50 - 1)(50 + 1) = 2,499$

3. $(30 - 2)(30 + 2) = 896$

4. $(40 + 3)(40 - 3) = 1,591$

5. $(30 + 5)(30 - 5) = 875$

6. $(4 + 0.1)(4 - 0.1) = 15.99$

7. ${}^-(15 - 1)(15 + 1) = {}^-224$ or $(1 - 15)(1 + 15) = {}^-224$

8. $(39.5 + 1.5)(39.5 - 1.5)$ is not reasonable to use as a shortcut.

9. ${}^-(100 + 1)(100 - 1) = {}^-(10,000 - 1) = {}^-9,999$

10. $\left(10 + \dfrac{1}{4}\right)\left(10 - \dfrac{1}{4}\right) = 100 - \dfrac{1}{16} = 99\dfrac{15}{16}$

11. ${}^-(0.95 + 0.25)(0.95 - 0.25)$ is not reasonable to use as a shortcut.

12a. Possible problems:

$64 \cdot 56 = 3,584$

$83 \cdot 97 = 8,051$

$^-12.5 \cdot 13.5 = 168.5$

12b. See students' work.

13a. **i.** 32 is $31 + 1$, so $(32)29 = (31 + 1)29$. Using the distributive property, $(31 + 1)29 = 31 \cdot 29 + 29$.

ii. $(30 + 1)(30 - 1) = 900 - 1 = 899$

iii. $899 + 29 = 928$

13b. $21 \cdot 18 = 22 \cdot 18 - 18$

$= (20 + 2)(20 - 2) - 18$

$= 400 - 4 - 18$

$= 378$

13c. Possible answers: $22 \cdot 18 - 18 = (20 + 2)(20 - 2) - 18 = 396 - 18$, *or* $21 \cdot 19 - 21 = (20 + 1)(20 - 1) - 21 = 399 - 21$

Page 395 Share and Summarize

1a. Possible answer: You can use it if the product is in the form $(a + b)(a - b)$. For example, $(x + 7)(x - 7)$.

1b. Square the first term and subtract the square of the second term.

2a. Possible answer: $(x - 4)(x + 4)$

2b. Possible answer: $(2x + 1)(x - 5)$

Pages 396–399 On Your Own Exercises

1. $a^2 + 10a + 25$

2. $m^2 + 22m + 121$

3. $x^2 + 5x + 6.25$

4. $t^2 - 22t + 121$

5. $p^2 - 5p + 6.25$

6. $6.25 - 5k + k^2$

7. $q^2 - \frac{1}{2}q + \frac{1}{16}$

8. $g^4 - 2g^2 + 1$

9. $s^4 - 2s^2y^2 + y^4$

10. $9f^2 + 12f + 4$

11. $9x^2 + 6xy + y^2$

12. $9m^2 - 12mn + 4n^2$

13a. $n(n + 25)$

13b. $(n + 2)(n + 27)$

14. $100 - k^2$

15. $9h^2 - 25$

16. $0.16 - 4x^2$

17. $\frac{1}{25} - k^2$

18. $(2x - 1)(2x + 1)$

19. $(4 - 5x)(4 + 5x)$

20. $(x - y)(x + y)$

21. $(40 - 5)(40 + 5) = 1,600 - 25 = 1,575$

22. $(30 - 3)(30 + 3) = 900 - 9 = 891$

23. $(200 + 7)(200 - 7) = 40,000 - 49 = 39,951$

24. $(100 + 11)(100 - 11) = 10,000 - 121 = 9,879$

25. $12 \cdot 9 = 11 \cdot 9 + 9$

$= (10 + 1)(10 - 1) + 9$

$= 100 - 1 + 9$

$= 108$

26. $37 \cdot 25 = 35 \cdot 25 + 25 + 25$

$= (30 + 5)(30 - 5) + 50$

$= 900 - 25 + 50$

$= 925$

27. $\frac{x^2}{4} + \frac{xy}{2} + \frac{y^2}{4}$

28. $9 - 6xy + x^2y^2$

29. $x^2y^2 - 2x^2y + x^2$

30. $4x^2y^2 - 4xy + 1 + 4x^2y^2 - 4xy^2 + y^2$

$= 8x^2y^2 - 4xy^2 + y^2 - 4xy + 1$

31. $\frac{1}{2}(a + 2)(a + 2) = \frac{1}{2}(a^2 + 4a + 4)$

$= \frac{1}{2}a^2 + 2a + 2$

32. $(x + a)^2 = x^2 + 2ax + a^2$, and $(x + a)^2 > x^2 + a^2$, when x and a are both positive or both negative, since the middle term $(2ax)$ will be positive in both cases.

33. $x^4 - y^4$

34. $1 - y^6$

35. $x^2y^2 - x^2$

36. $3a + ax + 3bx + bx^2 = bx^2 + (a + 3b)x + 3a$

$2x^2 + (1 + 3 \cdot 2)x + 3(1) = 2x^2 + 7x + 3$

$a = 1, b = 2$

37. $ab - ax + bx - x^2 = {}^-x^2 + (b - a)x + ab$

$^-x^2 + (4 - 5)x + 5 \cdot 4 = {}^-x^2 - x + 20$

$a = 5, b = 4$

38. $21 - 3bx - 7ax + abx^2$

$= abx^2 - (3b + 7a)x + 21$

$2 \cdot 3 \cdot x^2 - (3 \cdot 3 + 7 \cdot 2)x + 21$

$= 6x^2 + 23x + 21$

$a = 2, b = 3$

39a. $2a + 2bt - ta - bt^2 = 2a + (2b - a)t - bt^2$

$2(2) + (2 \cdot 16 - 2)t - 16t^2 = 30t - 16t^2 + 4$

$a = 2, b = 16$

39b. $(2 - t)(2 + 16t)$

$(2 - 2) = 0, t = 2$

$\left(2 + 16 \cdot \frac{^-1}{8}\right) = 0, t = \frac{^-1}{8}$

$2, \frac{^-1}{8}$

39c. 2; The other solution is negative, indicating a time before the object was thrown.

40. Region a: $\frac{1}{2} \cdot 1 \cdot (x - 2) = \frac{x}{2} - 1$

Region b: $h = x + 2 - 1 = x + 1$

$\frac{1}{2}(x - 2)(x + 1) = \frac{x^2}{2} - \frac{x}{2} - 1$

Region c: $\frac{1}{2}(x + 2)(x - 2) = \frac{x^2}{2} - 2$

41a. Possible answer: The area of the original rectangle is the same as the area of the final rectangles. The original rectangle has area $(a - b)(a + b)$; the final shape is a square with area $a(a - b + b)$ or a^2 minus a piece with area $[a - (a - b)]b$ or b^2, so the area of the shape is $a^2 - b^2$.

41b. Possible answer: The area of the original square is the same as the area of the final rectangles. The area of the final rectangles is easier to see if you add a line:

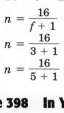

The square at the bottom has dimensions b and b (since the left rectangle has a vertical length of $a - b$ and the right rectangle has a vertical length of a). The rest of the shape has dimensions $a - b$ and $a + b$. So $a^2 = (a - b)(a + b) + b^2$, or $a^2 - b^2 = (a - b)(a + b)$.

42. input x:

$ax^2 + bx + c$

input $(x + 1)$:

$a(x + 1)^2 + b(x + 1) + c$
$= ax^2 + 2ax + a + bx + b + c$

input $(x + 2)$:

$a(x + 2)^2 + b(x + 2) + c$
$= ax^2 + 4ax + 4a + bx + 2b + c$

input $(x + 3)$:

$a(x + 3)^2 + b(x + 3) + c$
$= ax^2 + 6ax + 9a + bx + 3b + c$

first differences:

$ax^2 + 2ax + a + bx + b + c - (ax^2 + bx + c)$
$= 2ax + a + b$

$ax^2 + 4ax + 4a + bx + 2b + c - (ax^2 + 2ax + a + bx + b + c) = 2ax + 3a + b$

$ax^2 + 6ax + 9a + bx + 3b + c - (ax^2 + 4ax + 4a + bx + 2b + c) = 2ax + 5a + b$

second differences:

$2ax + 3a + b - (2ax + a + b) = 2a$

$2ax + 5a + b - (2ax + 3a + b) = 2a$

Possible answer: The outputs are $ax^2 + bx + c$, $a(x + 1)^2 + b(x + 1) + c$, $a(x + 2)^2 + b(x + 2) + c$, $a(x + 3)^2 + b(x + 3) + c$, and so on. Expanding gives $ax^2 + bx + c$, $ax^2 + 2ax + a + bx + b + c$, $ax^2 + 4ax + 4a + bx + 2b + c$, $ax^2 + 6ax + 9a + bx + 3b + c$, and so on. The first differences are $2ax + a + b$, $2ax + 3a + b$, $2ax + 5a + b$, and so on. The second differences are all $2a$, a constant.

43. $\dfrac{7}{33}$

44. $\dfrac{1}{5}$

45. $\dfrac{3}{10}$

46. $y = 80(0.4)^x$

47. $xy = 24$ or $y = \dfrac{24}{x}$

48. $y = {}^-7x - 18$

49.

50a. $16 \div 4 = 4$

50b. $16 \div 6 = 2\dfrac{2}{3}$

50c. $n = \dfrac{16}{f + 1}$

50d. $n = \dfrac{16}{3 + 1} = \dfrac{16}{4} = 4$

$n = \dfrac{16}{5 + 1} = \dfrac{16}{6} = 2\dfrac{2}{3}$

Page 398   In Your Own Words

Possible answer: $67 \cdot 73 = (70 - 3)(70 + 3) = 4{,}900 - 9 = 4{,}891$; $9.8 \cdot 10.2 = (10 - 0.2)(10 + 0.2) = 100 - 0.04 = 99.96$; Finding products using the difference of squares is a shortcut that makes it easier to solve harder types of problems. If you can get the factors in the form of $(a + b)(a - b)$, you can then use $a^2 - b^2$, where a and b are numbers that are easy to square to solve the multiplication problem.

6-4   Working with Algebraic Fractions

Page 401   Problem Set A

1. $\dfrac{24}{4 \cdot 3 \cdot 2 \cdot 1} = \dfrac{24}{24} = 1$

$\dfrac{24}{5 \cdot 4 \cdot 3 \cdot 2} = \dfrac{24}{120} = \dfrac{1}{5}$

2. $\dfrac{24}{0 \cdot {}^-1 \cdot {}^-2 \cdot {}^-3} = \dfrac{24}{0}$ undefined

$\dfrac{24}{1 \cdot 0 \cdot {}^-1 \cdot {}^-2} = \dfrac{24}{0}$ undefined

There is no value for y because you can't divide a number by 0; 3 and 4.

3. Possible answers:

$x = 1.5, y = {}^-25.6$

$x = {}^-2, y = \dfrac{1}{15}$

4a.

x	y
0	1
0.25	1.7732
0.5	3.6571
0.75	10.503
1	ERROR
1.25	−26.6
1.5	−25.6
1.75	−45.51
2	ERROR
2.25	58.514
2.5	42.667
2.75	58.514
3	ERROR
3.25	−45.51
3.5	−25.6
3.75	−26.6
4	ERROR
4.25	10.503
4.5	3.6571
4.75	1.7732
5	1

The table says "error" at $x = 1, 2, 3,$ and 4.

4b.

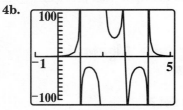

There's either a vertical line or a gap at those values.

Pages 402–403 Problem Set B

1a. the amount of money the friends intended to spend for each comic book

1b. the amount Ling spent on each comic book, or $5 more than her intended maximum

1c. the amount Carlota spent on each comic book, or $5 less than her intended maximum

2. Ling: $\frac{100}{x + 5}$; Carlota: $\frac{120}{x - 5}$

3a. correct

3b. incorrect; Possible explanation: Just because the expression doesn't make sense for certain values doesn't mean it makes no sense at all.

3c. correct

3d. Incorrect; x can't be less than 5, or Carlota would have paid less than $0 per comic.

3e. correct

3f. correct

4. 15, 20, or 45

5.

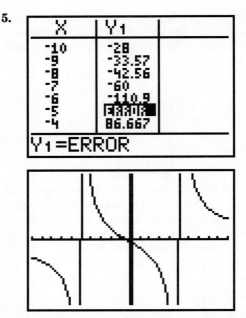

Possible answer: The table gives an error at those values. The graph has vertical (or nearly vertical) lines at $x = {}^-5$ and $x = 5$.

Page 403 Share and Summarize

1. Possible answer: Mathematical sense involves only whether values will work in the expression, not whether they make sense in the situation. For example, if a pack of gum costs 55 cents, I can buy x packs of gum for $55x$ cents. Since any number for x will give a value for the expression, it makes mathematical sense. However, in the context of the given situation, only whole numbers make sense.

2a. what values would make a denominator equal to 0 (those values would not make mathematical sense)

2b. Possible answer: What the variables and the expression represented: x is the number of comic books, so it must be positive and an integer. The expression stood for the total amount of money paid, so it had to be positive; since the friends paid $220 altogether, it also had to be equal to $220.

Page 405 Problem Set C

1. $\frac{xy}{3}$

2. $\frac{2}{2(a + 2)} = \frac{1}{a + 2}$

3. $\frac{x}{x(x + 2)} = \frac{1}{x + 2}$

4. Possible answer: $\frac{2}{6 + 2a}$ and $\frac{5a}{15a + 5a^2}$

5. Possible answer: $\frac{x^2}{2x}$ and $\frac{4x}{8}$

6. Possible answer: $\frac{10y^2z}{2yz^2}$ and $\frac{20y}{4z}$

7. $\frac{4}{6d} = \frac{2}{3d}$

8. $\frac{{}^-2}{2(d - 5)} = \frac{-1}{d - 5}$

9. $\frac{4(d - 1)}{6d} = \frac{2(d - 1)}{3d}$ or $\frac{2d - 2}{3d}$

10. $\dfrac{1}{3(a-4)} \cdot \dfrac{5}{3a} = \dfrac{5}{9a(a-4)}$ or $\dfrac{5}{9a^2-36a}$

11. $\dfrac{a}{7} \cdot \dfrac{5}{3a} = \dfrac{5a}{21a} = \dfrac{5}{21}$

12. $\dfrac{1}{a} \cdot \dfrac{a+1}{1} = \dfrac{a+1}{a}$

Pages 405–406   Problem Set D

1. $\dfrac{(2x)^2+12}{4} - x^2 = \dfrac{4x^2+12}{4} - x^2 = \dfrac{4(x^2+3)}{4} - x^2$
$= x^2 + 3 - x^2 = 3$

It always works. If you choose x, you get the expression $\dfrac{(2x)^2+12}{4} - x^2$, which simplifies to $x^2 + 3 - x^2$, or 3, for any value of x.

2. $\dfrac{6(x+2)^2-24}{6x} - 4 = \dfrac{6x^2+24x}{6x} - 4 = \dfrac{6x(x+4)}{6x} - 4 = x + 4 - 4 = x$

It works for all numbers except 0. If you choose x, you get the expression $\dfrac{6(x+2)^2-24}{6x} - 4$, which simplifies to $\dfrac{6x^2+24x}{6x} - 4 = x + 4 - 4 = x$. It doesn't work for 0 because you can't divide by 0.

3. $\dfrac{3x-4}{2} + 5 = 6$

$\quad\quad \dfrac{3x-4}{2} = 1$

$\quad\quad 3x - 4 = 2$

$\quad\quad\quad 3x = 6$

$\quad\quad\quad\quad x = 2$

It doesn't work in general. If you choose x, you get $\dfrac{3x-4}{2} + 5$. Solving $\dfrac{3x-4}{2} + 5 = 6$ gives $x = 2$, so the only number this works for is 2.

4. $\dfrac{(x+6)x+9}{x+3} - x = \dfrac{x^2+6x+9}{x+3} - x = \dfrac{(x+3)^2}{x+3} - x$
$= x + 3 - x = 3$

It works for all numbers except -3. If you choose x, you get the expression $\dfrac{(x+6)x+9}{x+3} - x$, which simplifies to $\dfrac{x^2+6x+9}{x+3} - x = \dfrac{(x+3)^2}{x+3} - x = x + 3 - x = 3$. You can't use $^-3$ because that would mean you are dividing by 0.

Page 406   Share and Summarize

1. Incorrect; $\dfrac{3}{x+3}$ can't be simplified because you can't factor a 3 out of $x + 3$.

2. Incorrect; $\dfrac{a}{a+4}$ can't be simplified because you can't factor an a out of $a + 4$.

3. correct

4. correct

Pages 407–410   On Your Own Exercises

1a. $2, ^-1$

1b. Possible answer: The graph will approach the lines $x = 2$ and $x = {}^-1$ but never touch them.

2a. $\dfrac{300}{d}$

2b. $\dfrac{300}{d+2}$

2c. $\dfrac{300}{d} + \dfrac{300}{d+2}$

2d. $0, ^-2$

2e. Possible answer: $d \le 0$, very large values, and values that could not represent dollars and cents

3a. $\dfrac{120}{s}$

3b. $\dfrac{120}{s-15}$

3c. $\dfrac{120}{s} + \dfrac{120}{s-15}$

3d. $0, 15$

3e. Possible answer: $s \le 0$, values that are too large or small for a speed limit, such as $s < 10$ and $s > 80$, or that are not whole numbers.

4. 6

5. $\dfrac{1}{2y}$

6. $\dfrac{5a}{4b}$

7. $\dfrac{3k}{k(k-6)} = \dfrac{3}{k-6}$

8. $\dfrac{1}{a}$

9. $\dfrac{x+1}{2}$

10. $\dfrac{nm}{m(m+2)} = \dfrac{n}{m+2}$

11. $\dfrac{3ab}{ab(ab-3)} = \dfrac{3}{ab-3}$

12. $\dfrac{1}{3a}$

13. $\dfrac{4d}{6} = \dfrac{2d}{3}$

14. $\dfrac{3a^2}{10a} = \dfrac{3a}{10}$

15. $\dfrac{1}{a} \cdot \dfrac{a}{1} = \dfrac{a}{a} = 1$

16. $\dfrac{m}{4} \cdot \dfrac{m}{4} = \dfrac{m^2}{16}$

17. $\dfrac{(2-x)}{3(2-x)} = \dfrac{1}{3}$

18. $\dfrac{(n-1)^2-1}{n} + 2 = \dfrac{n^2-2n+1-1}{n} + 2 = \dfrac{n^2-2n}{n} + 2 = \dfrac{n(n-2)}{n} + 2 = n - 2 + 2 = n$

It works for all numbers but 0. If you choose n, you get the expression $\dfrac{(n-1)^2-1}{n} + 2$, which simplifies to $\dfrac{n^2-2n+1-1}{n} + 2 = n - 2 + 2 = n$. It doesn't work for 0 because you can't divide by 0.

19. $\dfrac{(n+3)^2-4}{n+1} - 5 = \dfrac{n^2+6n+9-4}{n+1} - 5 = \dfrac{(n+1)(n+5)}{n+1} - 5 = n + 5 - 5 = n$

It works for all numbers but $^-1$. If you choose n, you get the expression $\dfrac{(n+3)^2-4}{n+1} - 5$, which simplifies to $\dfrac{n^2+6n+9-4}{n+1} - 5 = \dfrac{(n+1)(n+5)}{n+1} - 5 = n + 5 - 5 = n$. It doesn't work for $^-1$ because that would mean you are dividing by 0.

20a. $k^2 - k = k(k-1)$
$0, 1$

20b. Possible answer: The graph will approach $x = 0$ and $x = 1$ but never touch or cross these x-values.

21a. It doubles. It triples.

21b. It is divided by 4. It is divided by 9.

21c. $\dfrac{2M \cdot 2m}{(2r)^2} = \dfrac{4Mm}{4r^2} = \dfrac{Mm}{r^2}$

It doesn't. The gravitational force is the same.

22. $\dfrac{2(2k-1)}{2(k^2 + 2k - 2)} = \dfrac{2k-1}{k^2 + 2k - 1}$

23. $\dfrac{(u-3)(u+2)(u-1)}{{}^-1(u-3)(u-1)} = {}^-u - 2$

24a. $2 - 5x = 0$

$\qquad {}^-5x = {}^-2$

$\qquad x = \dfrac{2}{5}$

This value would make the denominator 0.

24b. $2 - 5x > 0$

$\qquad {}^-5x > {}^-2$

$\qquad x < \dfrac{2}{5}$

The expression will be positive only when the denominator is positive; that is, when $2 - 5x > 0$, or $x < \dfrac{2}{5}$.

24c. $2 - 5x < 0$

$\qquad {}^-5x < {}^-2$

$\qquad x > \dfrac{2}{5}$

The expression will be negative only when the denominator is negative; that is, when $2 - 5x < 0$, or $x > \dfrac{2}{5}$.

24d. none; Possible explanation: A fraction $\dfrac{a}{b}$ can equal 0 only if $a = 0$.

25a. $\dfrac{4x^3}{2x} = 2x^2$

The graph of $y = \dfrac{4x^3}{2x}$ looks like the graph of $y = 2x^2$, but with an open circle at the point where $x = 0$.

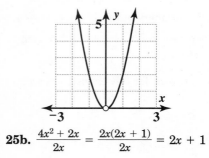

25b. $\dfrac{4x^2 + 2x}{2x} = \dfrac{2x(2x+1)}{2x} = 2x + 1$

The graph of $y = \dfrac{4x^2 + 2x}{2x}$ looks like the graph of $y = 2x + 1$, but with an open circle at the point where $x = 0$.

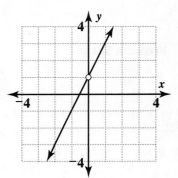

26. All values except 0 and ${}^-1$. $\dfrac{1}{m} > \dfrac{1}{m+1}$ when $m < m + 1$ for all values of m. However, $\dfrac{1}{m}$ has no value when $m = 0$, and $\dfrac{1}{m+1}$ has no value when $m = {}^-1$.

27. $\dfrac{16}{24} + \dfrac{15}{24} = \dfrac{31}{24}$, or $1\dfrac{7}{24}$

28. $\dfrac{6}{20} - \dfrac{5}{20} = \dfrac{1}{20}$

29. $\dfrac{9}{21} - \dfrac{56}{21} = \dfrac{-47}{21}$, or ${}^-2\dfrac{5}{21}$

30. $\dfrac{5}{12}$

31. $\dfrac{3}{10} \cdot 4 = \dfrac{6}{5}$, or $1\dfrac{1}{5}$

32. $\dfrac{8}{7}$, or $1\dfrac{1}{7}$

33. $(3x)^3$

34. $a^{12} \cdot a^{-14} = a^{12-14} = a^{-2}$ or $\left(\dfrac{1}{a}\right)^2$

35. $\left(\dfrac{2}{c}\right)^5$

36a. 19

36b. Possible Answer: 475; the middle data point is the highest of the four points in the 400–499 range.

36c. Possible Answer: The least number of calories is between 200 and 300, and there are only two sandwiches in this category. One of the sandwiches has between 900 and 1,000 calories. However, most are around 500 calories.

Page 409   In Your Own Words

Possible answer: Tim stores his baseball cards in a shoebox. Last month, he bought 15 special edition cards to add to his collection of x regular cards. The expression for the fraction of special edition cards in his collection is $\dfrac{15}{x+15}$. The value for x that does not make mathematical sense is ${}^-15$, because when the expression is evaluated for ${}^-15$, the result is $\dfrac{15}{0}$ which is undefined. The values that do not make sense in the context of the problem are numbers less than or equal to 0, since at least 1 baseball card is required to have a collection.

6-5 | Adding and Subtracting Algebraic Fractions

Pages 411–412 Problem Set A

1. Row 1, Column 3: $2 - \frac{1}{2} = \frac{3}{2}$

   Row 4, Column 3: $\frac{3}{5} + \frac{3}{2} = \frac{21}{10}$

   Row 2, Column 4: $\frac{1}{2} + \frac{3}{4} = \frac{5}{4}$

   Row 1, Column 2: $\frac{11}{5} - \frac{3}{5} = \frac{8}{5}$

   Row 2, Column 2: $\frac{8}{5} + \frac{1}{2} = \frac{21}{10}$

   Row 3, Column 1: $1 - \frac{3}{4} = \frac{1}{4}$

   Row 3, Column 2: $\frac{1}{4} + \frac{8}{5} = \frac{37}{20}$

   Row 3, Column 3: $\frac{1}{4} + \frac{3}{2} = \frac{7}{4}$

   Row 4, Column 4: $\frac{3}{5} + \frac{3}{4} = \frac{27}{20}$

$+$	$\frac{8}{5}$	$\frac{3}{2}$	$\frac{3}{4}$
$\frac{1}{2}$	$\frac{21}{10}$	2	$\frac{5}{4}$
$\frac{1}{4}$	$\frac{37}{20}$	$\frac{7}{4}$	1
$\frac{3}{5}$	$\frac{11}{5}$	$\frac{21}{10}$	$\frac{27}{20}$

2. $\frac{100 + 100}{w} = \frac{200}{w}$

3. $\frac{100 - 100}{w} = \frac{0}{w} = 0$

4. $\frac{100 + 100 + 100}{w} = \frac{300}{w}$

5. $\frac{3}{6x} + \frac{4}{6x} = \frac{3 + 4}{6x} = \frac{7}{6x}$

6. $\frac{2m}{6} + \frac{m}{6} = \frac{3m}{6} = \frac{m}{2}$

7. $\frac{2y}{2p} + \frac{1}{2p} = \frac{2y + 1}{2p}$

8. $\frac{30}{48} - \frac{40}{48} = \frac{-10}{12} = -\frac{5}{24}$

9. $\frac{3y}{2xy} - \frac{3x}{2xy} = \frac{3y - 3x}{2xy}$

10a. $\frac{400}{n}$

10b. $\frac{200}{n}$

10c. $\frac{1{,}000}{n}$

10d. $\frac{400 + 200 + 1{,}000}{n} = \frac{1{,}600}{n}$; the time it takes Dave to type 1,600 words

Page 413 Problem Set B

1. Row 1, Column 3: $\frac{2}{x} - \frac{1}{3x} = \frac{6}{3x} - \frac{1}{3x} = \frac{6 - 1}{3x} = \frac{5}{3x}$

   Row 2, Column 4: $\frac{1}{3x} + \frac{8}{15x} = \frac{5}{15x} + \frac{8}{15x} = \frac{13}{15x}$

   Row 4, Column 1: $\frac{53}{30x} - \frac{5}{3x} = \frac{53}{30x} - \frac{50}{30x} =$

   $\frac{53 - 50}{30x} = \frac{3}{30x} = \frac{1}{10x}$

Row 4, Column 4: $\frac{1}{10x} + \frac{8}{15x} = \frac{3}{30x} + \frac{16}{30x}$

$= \frac{3 + 16}{30x} = \frac{19}{30x}$

Row 1, Column 2: $\frac{3}{5x} - \frac{1}{10x} = \frac{6}{10x} - \frac{1}{10x}$

$= \frac{6 - 1}{10x} = \frac{5}{10x} = \frac{1}{2x}$

Row 2, Column 2: $\frac{1}{2x} + \frac{1}{3x} = \frac{3}{6x} + \frac{2}{6x} = \frac{3 + 2}{6x}$

$= \frac{5}{6x}$

Row 3, Column 1: $\frac{5}{4x} - \frac{1}{2x} = \frac{5}{4x} - \frac{2}{4x} = \frac{5 - 2}{4x}$

$= \frac{3}{4x}$

Row 3, Column 3: $\frac{3}{4x} + \frac{5}{3x} = \frac{9}{12x} + \frac{20}{12x}$

$= \frac{9 + 20}{12x} = \frac{29}{12x}$

Row 3, Column 4: $\frac{3}{4x} + \frac{8}{15x} = \frac{45}{60x} + \frac{32}{60x}$

$= \frac{45 + 32}{60x} = \frac{77}{60x}$

$+$	$\frac{1}{2x}$	$\frac{5}{3x}$	$\frac{8}{15x}$
$\frac{1}{3x}$	$\frac{5}{6x}$	$\frac{2}{x}$	$\frac{13}{15x}$
$\frac{3}{4x}$	$\frac{5}{4x}$	$\frac{29}{12x}$	$\frac{77}{60x}$
$\frac{1}{10x}$	$\frac{3}{5x}$	$\frac{53}{30x}$	$\frac{19}{30x}$

2. $\frac{12}{6x^2} - \frac{6}{6x^2} = \frac{12 - 6}{6x^2} = \frac{6}{6x^2} = \frac{1}{x^2}$

3. $\frac{6}{12t} - \frac{8t^2}{12t} = \frac{6 - 8t^2}{12t} = \frac{2(3 - 4t^2)}{12t} = \frac{3 - 4t^2}{6t}$

4. $\frac{12m}{24m^2} + \frac{12m}{24m^2} = \frac{12m + 12m}{24m^2} = \frac{24m}{24m^2} = \frac{1}{m}$

5a. $\frac{1}{2n}, \frac{1}{3n}$

5b. $\frac{1}{2n} + \frac{1}{3n} = \frac{3}{6n} + \frac{2}{6n} = \frac{3 + 2}{6n} = \frac{5}{6n}$

5c. $40 \div \frac{5}{6n} = 40 \cdot \frac{6n}{5} = 48n$ min

Page 413 Share and Summarize

1. Possible problems:

   $\frac{3}{c} + \frac{3c^2}{2} = \frac{6 + 3c^3}{2c}$

   $\frac{3}{2} + \frac{3c^2}{2c^2} = 3$

   $\frac{c}{2} - \frac{3}{2c^2} = \frac{c^3 - 3}{2c^2}$

   $\frac{3c^2}{3} - \frac{2}{c} = \frac{c^3 - 2}{c}$

2. Possible answer: $\frac{3}{2} + \frac{3c^2}{2c^2}$

Page 414 Problem Set C

1a. $\frac{2}{2} + \frac{1}{2} = \frac{3}{2}$

1b. $\frac{3}{6} + \frac{2}{6} = \frac{5}{6}$

1c. $\frac{4}{12} + \frac{3}{12} = \frac{7}{12}$

1d. $\frac{5}{20} + \frac{4}{20} = \frac{9}{20}$

2. The numerator is the sum of the denominators ($5 + 6 = 11$). The denominator is the product of the denominators ($5 \cdot 6 = 30$).

   $\frac{11}{30}$

3. The denominator of the sum is the product of the denominators of the addends.

4. The numerator of the sum is the sum of the denominators of the addends.

5. Possible answer: It's equal to $\dfrac{m + 1 + m}{m(m + 1)}$.

6a. 5

6b. Possible answer: $\dfrac{5 + 1 + 5}{5(6)} = \dfrac{11}{30}$, yes

6c. $\dfrac{6}{30} + \dfrac{5}{30} = \dfrac{11}{30}$

7. Possible answer: $\dfrac{1}{m}$ and $\dfrac{1}{m + 1}$ have a common denominator of $m(m + 1)$, so the sum is $\dfrac{m + 1}{m(m + 1)} + \dfrac{m}{m(m + 1)} = \dfrac{m + 1 + m}{m(m + 1)}$.

Page 415   Problem Set D

1. to get a common denominator of $m(m + 1)$

2. to get a common denominator of $m(m + 1)$

3. No; he didn't find a common denominator correctly. He added 1 to the numerator and denominator of the first fraction, which changes the value of the fraction.

Pages 416–417   Problem Set E

1. $\dfrac{m + 1}{m(m + 1)} + \dfrac{2m}{m(m + 1)} = \dfrac{3m + 1}{m(m + 1)}$

2. $\dfrac{4(m - 1)}{m(m - 1)} - \dfrac{m}{m - 1} = \dfrac{4m - 4 - m}{m(m - 1)} = \dfrac{3m - 4}{m(m - 1)}$

3. $\dfrac{4(b + 3)}{(b + 2)(b + 3)} + \dfrac{b(b + 2)}{(b + 2)(b + 3)}$

    $= \dfrac{4b + 12 + b^2 + 2b}{(b + 2)(b + 3)} = \dfrac{b^2 + 6b + 12}{(b + 2)(b + 3)}$

4. $\dfrac{2}{x} - \dfrac{1}{x - 3} = \dfrac{2(x - 3)}{x(x - 3)} - \dfrac{x}{x(x - 3)} = \dfrac{2x - 6 - x}{x(x - 3)}$

    $= \dfrac{x - 6}{x(x - 3)}$

5. $\dfrac{10}{x + 4} + \dfrac{1}{3x} = \dfrac{30x}{3x(x + 4)} + \dfrac{x + 4}{3x(x + 4)}$

    $= \dfrac{30x + x + 4}{3x(x + 4)} = \dfrac{31x + 4}{3x(x + 4)}$

6. $\dfrac{2x(x + 3)}{(x - 1)(x + 3)} - \dfrac{(x - 1)(x + 1)}{(x - 1)(x + 3)} = \dfrac{2x^2 + 6x - x^2 + 1}{(x - 1)(x + 3)}$

    $= \dfrac{x^2 + 6x + 1}{(x - 1)(x + 3)}$

7a. $\dfrac{3}{6} - \dfrac{2}{6} = \dfrac{1}{6}$

    $\dfrac{4}{12} - \dfrac{3}{12} = \dfrac{1}{12}$

    $\dfrac{5}{20} - \dfrac{4}{20} = \dfrac{1}{20}$

7b. $\dfrac{1}{30}$; The numerator is the difference of the denominators $(6 - 5 = 1)$. The denominator is the product of the denominators $(5 \cdot 6 = 30)$.

7c. $\dfrac{m + 1 - m}{m(m + 1)} = \dfrac{1}{m(m + 1)}$ or $\dfrac{1}{m^2 + m}$

Page 417   Share and Summarize

$\dfrac{2x}{2x(x + 1)} - \dfrac{x + 1}{2x(x + 1)} = \dfrac{x - 1}{2x(x + 1)}$

Explanations will vary.

Page 418   Problem Set F

1. $3x - 6 = 4(x - 8)$
    $3x - 6 = 4x - 32$
    $26 = x$

2. $3t + 2t = {}^-6$
    $5t = {}^-6$
    $t = \dfrac{{}^-6}{5}$, or $-1\dfrac{1}{5}$

3. $16a - 5(2 - a) = 600$
    $16a - 10 + 5a = 600$
    $21a = 610$
    $a = \dfrac{610}{21}$, or $29\dfrac{1}{21}$

4. $\dfrac{p}{5} = p - 0.4$
    $p = 5p - 2$
    $2 = 4p$
    $0.5 = p$

5. $\dfrac{x^2 - 4}{4} - \dfrac{2x - 1}{4} = \dfrac{x^2 - 4 - 2x + 1}{4} = \dfrac{x^2 - 2x - 3}{4}$

6. $\dfrac{k + 3}{5} - \dfrac{k - 3}{15} = \dfrac{3(k + 3)}{15} - \dfrac{k - 3}{15}$
    $= \dfrac{3k + 9 - k + 3}{15} = \dfrac{2k + 12}{15}$

7a. Possible answer: The intersection includes all the points where $y = \dfrac{n + 7}{2} + \dfrac{n}{3}$ and $y = 10$. So for every intersection point, $\dfrac{n + 7}{2} + \dfrac{n}{3} = 10$.

7b. Possible calculator screen:

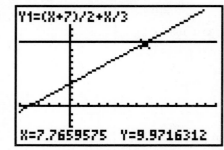

Estimates should be about 7.8.

7c. $3(n + 7) + 2n = 60$
    $3n + 21 + 2n = 60$
    $5n = 39$
    $n = 7.8$

Page 420   Problem Set G

1. $10(k - 3) = 7(k + 1)$
    $10k - 30 = 7k + 7$
    $3k = 37$
    $k = \dfrac{37}{3}$

2. $6 - 2x = 8(x - 3)$
    $6 - 2x = 8x - 24$
    $30 = 10x$
    $3 = x$
    Check: $\dfrac{6 - 2(3)}{3 - 3} = 8$
    $\dfrac{0}{0} = 8$
    no solution (The only apparent solution, 3, makes the denominator 0.)

3. $2(g-1) - 2(g+1) = 4(g+1)(g-1)$

$2g - 2 - 2g - 2 = 4g^2 - 4$

$0 = 4g^2$

$0 = g$

4. $\dfrac{20-a}{a^2-4} = \dfrac{5(a+2)}{(a-2)(a+2)} + \dfrac{3(a-2)}{(a-2)(a+2)}$

$\dfrac{20-a}{a^2-4} = \dfrac{5a+10}{a^2-4} + \dfrac{3a-6}{a^2-4}$

$20 - a = 5a + 10 + 3a - 6$

$16 = 9a$

$\dfrac{16}{9} = a$

5. $0 = \dfrac{2(s+2)}{(s+3)(s+2)} + \dfrac{s(s+3)}{(s+3)(s+2)}$

$0 = 2s + 4 + s^2 + 3s$

$0 = s^2 + 5s + 4$

Possible calculator screen:

$^-1, ^-4$

6. $^-60 - 12z = ^-120(z+5)$

$^-60 - 12z = ^-120z - 600$

$108z = ^-540$

$z = ^-5$

Check: $\dfrac{^-60 - 12(^-5)}{^-5 + 5} = ^-120$

$\dfrac{0}{0} = ^-120$

no solution (The only apparent solution, $^-5$, makes the denominator 0.)

Page 420   Share and Summarize

Possible answer: For Problem 6, I multiplied both sides by $z + 5$ to eliminate the fractions. That gave me $^-60 - 12z = ^-120z - 600$. I added $120z$ and 60 to both sides to get $108z = ^-540$. I then divided both sides by 108 to get $z = ^-5$. Then I substituted $^-5$ into the original equation, which gave a denominator of 0, so there isn't a solution.

Pages 421–425   On Your Own Exercises

1. $\dfrac{81}{72} - \dfrac{64}{72} = \dfrac{17}{72}$

2. $\dfrac{x}{4} + \dfrac{2y}{4} = \dfrac{x+2y}{4}$

3. $\dfrac{4xy}{6} - \dfrac{1}{6} = \dfrac{4xy-1}{6}$

4. $\dfrac{x}{x^2} + \dfrac{2}{x^2} = \dfrac{x+2}{x^2}$

5. $\dfrac{c^2}{ac} - \dfrac{a^2}{ac} = \dfrac{c^2-a^2}{ac}$

6a. $\dfrac{500}{2z}$ or $\dfrac{250}{z}$

6b. $\dfrac{500}{z}$

6c. $\dfrac{250}{z} + \dfrac{500}{z} = \dfrac{750}{z}$

6d. z minutes

7a. $\dfrac{300}{1.5n}$, or $\dfrac{200}{n}$

7b. $\dfrac{300}{n} - \dfrac{300}{1.5n}$, or $\dfrac{300}{n} - \dfrac{200}{n}$, or $\dfrac{100}{n}$

7c. $\dfrac{200}{n} + \dfrac{300}{n}$, or $\dfrac{500}{n}$

8. $\dfrac{1}{4x} + \dfrac{5}{2x} = \dfrac{1}{4x} + \dfrac{10}{4x} = \dfrac{11}{4x}$

$\dfrac{1}{4x} + \dfrac{4}{x} = \dfrac{1}{4x} + \dfrac{16}{4x} = \dfrac{17}{4x}$

$\dfrac{1}{4x} + 2x = \dfrac{1}{4x} + \dfrac{8x^2}{4x} = \dfrac{8x^2+1}{4x}$

$\dfrac{-2}{3x} + \dfrac{5}{2x} = \dfrac{-4}{6x} + \dfrac{15}{6x} = \dfrac{11}{6x}$

$\dfrac{-2}{3x} + \dfrac{4}{x} = \dfrac{-2}{3x} + \dfrac{12}{3x} = \dfrac{10}{3x}$

$\dfrac{-2}{3x} + 2x = \dfrac{-2}{3x} + \dfrac{6x^2}{3x} = \dfrac{-2+6x^2}{3x}$

$\dfrac{3+x}{2} + \dfrac{5}{2x} = \dfrac{x(3+x)}{2x} + \dfrac{5}{2x} = \dfrac{x^2+3x+5}{2x}$

$\dfrac{3+x}{2} + \dfrac{4}{x} = \dfrac{x(3+x)}{2x} + \dfrac{8}{2x} = \dfrac{x^2+3x+8}{2x}$

$\dfrac{3+x}{2} + 2x = \dfrac{3+x}{2} + \dfrac{4x}{2} = \dfrac{5x+3}{2}$

$+$	$\dfrac{5}{2x}$	$\dfrac{4}{x}$	$2x$
$\dfrac{1}{4x}$	$\dfrac{11}{4x}$	$\dfrac{17}{4x}$	$\dfrac{8x^2+1}{4x}$
$\dfrac{-2}{3x}$	$\dfrac{11}{6x}$	$\dfrac{10}{3x}$	$\dfrac{-2+6x^2}{3x}$
$\dfrac{3+x}{2}$	$\dfrac{x^2+3x+5}{2x}$	$\dfrac{x^2+3x+8}{2x}$	$\dfrac{5x+3}{2}$

9. $\dfrac{1(m+1)}{m(m+1)} - \dfrac{2m}{m(m+1)} = \dfrac{1m+1-2m}{m(m+1)} = \dfrac{1-m}{m(m+1)}$

10. $\dfrac{4(m+1)}{m(m+1)} + \dfrac{m}{m(m+1)} = \dfrac{4m+4+m}{m(m+1)} = \dfrac{5m+4}{m(m+1)}$

11. $\dfrac{3(d+1)}{d(d+1)} + \dfrac{4d}{d(d+1)} = \dfrac{3d+3+4d}{d(d+1)} = \dfrac{7d+3}{d(d+1)}$

12. $\dfrac{3(c-1)}{c(c-1)} - \dfrac{4c}{c(c-1)} = \dfrac{3c-3-4c}{c(c-1)} = \dfrac{-c-3}{c(c-1)}$

13. $\dfrac{5a}{5(a+4)} + \dfrac{3a(a+4)}{5(a+4)} = \dfrac{5a+3a^2+12a}{5(a+4)} = \dfrac{3a^2+17a}{5(a+4)}$

14. $\dfrac{x^2-1}{x^2-1} = 1$

15. $\dfrac{5(k+1)}{k(k+1)} - \dfrac{5k}{k(k+1)} = \dfrac{5k+5-5k}{k(k+1)} = \dfrac{5}{k(k+1)}$

16. $\dfrac{2y-1}{4} - \dfrac{2y}{4} = \dfrac{-1}{4}$

17. $8x + 3 = 12(x-1)$

$8x + 3 = 12x - 12$

$15 = 4x$

$\dfrac{15}{4} = x$

18. $2(v-2) + 3v = 60$

$2v - 4 + 3v = 60$

$5v = 64$

$v = \dfrac{64}{5}$

19. $n + 1 = 3(n-1)$

$n + 1 = 3n - 3$

$4 = 2n$

$2 = n$

20. $2 - u = 5(u + 1)$
$2 - u = 5u + 5$
$^-3 = 6u$
$-\dfrac{1}{2} = u$

21. $8w - 2w = 2(w + 5) + w$
$6w = 2w + 10 + w$
$3w = 10$
$w = \dfrac{10}{3}$

22. $3(c + 1) + 3(c - 1) = 21 - c$
$3c + 3 + 3c - 3 = 21 - c$
$7c = 21$
$c = 3$

23. $1 - \dfrac{r + 1}{r} = \dfrac{r}{r} - \dfrac{r + 1}{r} = \dfrac{r - r - 1}{r} = \dfrac{-1}{r}$

24. $\dfrac{2 - x}{7} - \dfrac{x}{14} = \dfrac{2(2 - x)}{14} - \dfrac{x}{14} = \dfrac{4 - 2x - x}{14} = \dfrac{4 - 3x}{14}$

25. $\dfrac{1}{v} - \dfrac{3v}{2} = \dfrac{2}{2v} - \dfrac{3v^2}{2v} = \dfrac{2 - 3v^2}{2v}$

26a. Meg's hourly pay rate

26b. Rashid's hourly pay rate

26c. their hourly pay rate if they work together

26d. their hourly pay rate if they work together

26e. total hours it takes both working together to earn \$1,000

26f. total hours it takes Meg working alone to earn \$1,000

26g. total hours it takes Rashid working alone to earn \$1,000

27. $\dfrac{c^2}{abc} - \dfrac{a^2}{abc} = \dfrac{c^2 - a^2}{abc}$

28. $\dfrac{2x^2}{2xy} + \dfrac{2y^2}{2xy} = \dfrac{2x^2 + 2y^2}{2xy} = \dfrac{2(x^2 + y^2)}{2xy} = \dfrac{x^2 + y^2}{xy}$

29. $\dfrac{(G + 1)(G + 1)}{(G - 1)(G + 1)} - \dfrac{2(G - 1)}{(G - 1)(G + 1)} =$
$\dfrac{G^2 + 2G + 1 - 2G + 2}{G^2 - 1} = \dfrac{G^2 + 3}{G^2 - 1}$

30. $\dfrac{2(4 - 2y)}{12} + \dfrac{3y}{12} = \dfrac{8 - 4y + 3y}{12} = \dfrac{8 - y}{12}$

31. $\dfrac{1}{x^2 y} + \dfrac{x}{x^2 y} = \dfrac{1 + x}{x^2 y}$

32. $\dfrac{py}{p^2 y} + \dfrac{y}{p^2 y} + \dfrac{p^2}{p^2 y} = \dfrac{py + y + p^2}{p^2 y}$

33. $\dfrac{1}{xc} + \dfrac{xc}{xc} - \dfrac{x}{xc} = \dfrac{1 + xc - x}{xc}$

34. $\dfrac{(a + 1)(a - 1)}{a - 1} + \dfrac{1}{a - 1} = \dfrac{a^2 - 1 + 1}{a - 1} = \dfrac{a^2}{a - 1}$

35. $\dfrac{2(s + 1)}{s + 1} - \dfrac{2}{s + 1} - \dfrac{s}{s + 1} = \dfrac{2s + 2 - 2 - s}{s + 1} = \dfrac{s}{s + 1}$

36. $\dfrac{(m + 1)(m + 2)}{m(m + 1)(m + 2)} + \dfrac{m(m + 2)}{m(m + 1)(m + 2)} +$
$\dfrac{m(m + 1)}{m(m + 1)(m + 2)}$
$= \dfrac{m^2 + 3m + 2 + m^2 + 2m + m^2 + m}{m(m + 1)(m + 2)}$
$= \dfrac{3m^2 + 6m + 2}{m(m + 1)(m + 2)}$

37. $\dfrac{(m + 1)(m + 2)}{m(m + 1)(m + 2)} - \dfrac{m(m + 2)}{m(m + 1)(m + 2)} -$
$\dfrac{m(m + 1)}{m(m + 1)(m + 2)}$
$= \dfrac{m^2 + 3m + 2 - m^2 - 2m - m^2 - m}{m(m + 1)(m + 2)}$
$= \dfrac{2 - m^2}{m(m + 1)(m + 2)}$

38a. $\dfrac{75}{x}$

38b. $\dfrac{60}{x + 10}$

38c. $\dfrac{75}{x} + \dfrac{60}{x + 10} = \dfrac{75(x + 10) + 60x}{x(x + 10)}$
$= \dfrac{75x + 750 + 60x}{x(x + 10)} = \dfrac{135x + 750}{x(x + 10)}$

39. $5(p + 2) + 2(p - 1) = 10(p + 1)$
$5p + 10 + 2p - 2 = 10p + 10$
$7p + 8 = 10p + 10$
$^-2 = 3p$
$-\dfrac{2}{3} = p$

40. $2(r - 8) + 3(r - 5) = 6(r - 5)$
$2r - 16 + 3r - 15 = 6r - 30$
$5r - 31 = 6r - 30$
$^-1 = r$

41. $3(T - 1) + 4(2 - T) + 6(T + 1) = 36$
$3T - 3 + 8 - 4T + 6T + 6 = 36$
$5T + 11 = 36$
$5T = 25$
$T = 5$

42. $\dfrac{v - 2}{4} + \dfrac{2}{v - 1} + \dfrac{1}{2} = \dfrac{v^2 - 9}{4(v - 1)}$
$(v - 1)(v - 2) + 8 + 2(v - 1) = v^2 - 9$
$v^2 - 3v + 2 + 8 + 2v - 2 = v^2 - 9$
$v^2 - v + 8 = v^2 - 9$
$^-v = ^-17$
$v = 17$

43. $\dfrac{Z - 5}{2} - \dfrac{3}{Z + 5} = \dfrac{(Z + 1)(Z - 3)}{2(Z + 5)}$
$(Z - 5)(Z + 5) - 6 = (Z + 1)(Z - 3)$
$Z^2 - 25 - 6 = Z^2 - 2Z - 3$
$^-31 = ^-2Z - 3$
$^-28 = ^-2Z$
$14 = Z$

44. $\dfrac{3}{x - 3} + \dfrac{4}{x + 3} = \dfrac{21 - x}{(x + 3)(x - 3)}$
$3(x + 3) + 4(x - 3) = 21 - x$
$3x + 9 + 4x - 12 = 21 - x$
$7x - 3 = 21 - x$
$8x = 24$
$x = 3$
Check: $\dfrac{3}{3 - 3} + \dfrac{4}{3 + 3} = \dfrac{21 - 3}{(3 + 3)(3 - 3)}$
$\dfrac{3}{0} + \dfrac{4}{6} = \dfrac{18}{0}$

no solution (The only apparent solution, 3, makes denominators 0.)

45.
$$\frac{51.75}{x} + \frac{40.5}{2x + 2} = \frac{162}{2x + 2}$$
$$51.75(2x + 2) + 40.5x = 162x$$
$$103.5x + 103.5 + 40.5x = 162x$$
$$144x + 103.5 = 162x$$
$$103.5 = 18x$$
$$5.75 = x$$

$5.75 per hour at the market, $13.50 tutoring

46a. $(x + 1)(x - 1) = x^2 - 1$

46b. $\dfrac{A(x - 1) + B(x + 1)}{x^2 - 1} = \dfrac{Ax - A + Bx + B}{x^2 - 1}$

46c. The numerators on both sides of the original equation must be equal, so $Ax + Bx = 5x$ and $^-A + B = 1$.

46d. $A + B = 5$
$^-A + B = 1$
$A + {}^-A + B + B = 5 + 1$
$2B = 6$
$B = 3$
$A + 3 = 5$
$A = 2$
$A = 2, B = 3$

47. $\sqrt{324} = 18$

48. $^-\sqrt{49} = {}^-7$

49. $^-8^2 = {}^-64$

50. $(^-7)^2 = 49$

51. $12^{-1} = \dfrac{1}{12}$

$4\sqrt{\dfrac{1}{9}} = 4 \cdot \dfrac{1}{3} = \dfrac{4}{3}$

$4\left(\dfrac{1}{3}\right)^{-1} = 4 \cdot 3 = 12$

$\sqrt{\dfrac{4}{9}} = \dfrac{2}{3}$

The reciprocal of 12 is $\dfrac{1}{12}$.

a and d, b and f

52a. 5

52b. $360° \div 5 = 72°$

53. $af^2 \text{ cm}^2$

54. $2y + 2x + 1 = 3x - 2y + 3$
$4y = x + 2$
$y = \dfrac{1}{4}x + \dfrac{1}{2}$

55. $6y = \dfrac{-3}{7}x + 2$
$y = \dfrac{-1}{14}x + \dfrac{1}{3}$

56. $8 = {}^-3x - 4 + 4 - y - 2y - 10$
$8 = {}^-3x - 3y - 10$
$3y = {}^-3x - 18$
$y = {}^-x - 6$

57a. Pennsylvania: p; Delaware: $3p$; New Jersey: $1.5p + 7$

57b. $0.25(p + 3p + 1.5p + 7) = 12.75$
$0.25p + 0.75p + 0.375p + 1.75 = 12.75$
$1.375p = 11$
$p = 8$

8 Pennsylvania quarters
$3 \cdot 8 = 24$ Delaware quarters
$1.5 \cdot 8 + 7 = 19$ New Jersey quarters

Page 424 In Your Own Words

Possible answer:

$\dfrac{5}{x + 3} + \dfrac{^-4}{x - 3}$

$= \dfrac{5(x - 3)}{(x + 3)(x - 3)} + \dfrac{^-4(x + 3)}{(x - 3)(x + 3)}$

The common denominator is $(x - 3)(x + 3)$.

$= \dfrac{5(x - 3) + {}^-4(x + 3)}{(x + 3)(x - 3)}$

Combine the numerators.

$= \dfrac{5x - 15 + {}^-4x - 12}{(x + 3)(x - 3)}$

Multiply using the Distributive Property.

$= \dfrac{x - 27}{(x + 3)(x - 3)}$

Simplify.

Review and Self-Assessment

Pages 426–428 Strategies and Applications

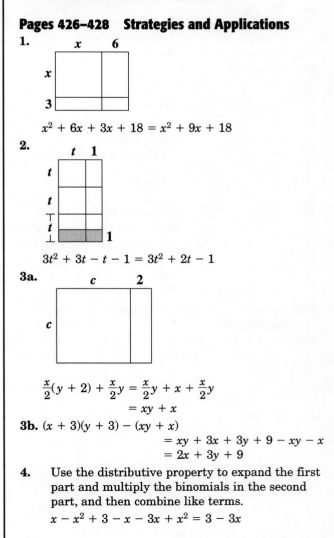

1.
$x^2 + 6x + 3x + 18 = x^2 + 9x + 18$

2.
$3t^2 + 3t - t - 1 = 3t^2 + 2t - 1$

3a.
$\dfrac{x}{2}(y + 2) + \dfrac{x}{2}y = \dfrac{x}{2}y + x + \dfrac{x}{2}y$
$= xy + x$

3b. $(x + 3)(y + 3) - (xy + x)$
$= xy + 3x + 3y + 9 - xy - x$
$= 2x + 3y + 9$

4. Use the distributive property to expand the first part and multiply the binomials in the second part, and then combine like terms.
$x - x^2 + 3 - x - 3x + x^2 = 3 - 3x$

5. $x^2y^2 - x^2 - y^2 + 1 - 1 - 2xy - x^2y^2$
$= {}^-2xy - x^2 - y^2$

6a. $x(x + 20) + x(x + 50) = x^2 + 20x + x^2 + 50x$
$= 2x^2 + 70x \text{ in}^2$

6b. $x(x + 18) + (x - 2)(x + 48)$
$= x^2 + 18x + x^2 + 46x - 96$
$= 2x^2 + 64x - 96 \text{ in}^2$

7a. The expanded expression is $a^2x^2 + 2abx + b^2$. You can show this works by applying the distributive property twice: $(ax + b)(ax + b) = ax(ax + b) + b(ax + b) = a^2x^2 + abx + abx + b^2 = a^2x^2 + 2abx + b^2$.

7b. $a = 1, b = 13$
$1^2x^2 + (2)(1)(13)x + 13^2 = x^2 + 26x + 169$

8a. The expanded expression is $a^2x^2 - 2abx + b^2$. You can show this works by applying the distributive property twice: $(ax - b)(ax - b) = ax(ax - b) - b(ax - b) = a^2x^2 - abx - abx + b^2 = a^2x^2 - 2abx + b^2$.

8b. $a = \frac{1}{2}, b = 1.5$
$\left(\frac{1}{2}\right)^2 x^2 - (2)\left(\frac{1}{2}\right)(1.5)x + 1.5^2$
$= \frac{x^2}{4} - 1.5x + 2.25$

9a. The expanded expression is $a^2x^2 - b^2$. You can show this works by applying the distributive property twice: $(ax + b)(ax - b) = ax(ax - b) + b(ax - b) = a^2x^2 - abx + abx - b^2 = a^2x^2 - b^2$.

9b. $a = y, b = 3$
$y^2x^2 - 3^2 = x^2y^2 - 9$

10. $(25 - 1)(25 + 1) = 625 - 1 = 624$

11. $\dfrac{-3x}{9 - 6x} = \dfrac{-3x}{3(3 - 2x)}$ Factor out 3 from the denominator.
$= \dfrac{3}{3} \cdot \dfrac{-x}{3 - 2x}$ Factor out 1 in the form $\frac{3}{3}$.
$= \dfrac{-x}{3 - 2x}$ Simplify.

12. $\dfrac{15xy}{3x^3y^3} = \dfrac{3xy(5)}{3xy(x^2y^2)}$ Factor out $3xy$ from the numerator and denominator.
$= \dfrac{3xy}{3xy} \cdot \dfrac{5}{x^2y^2}$ Factor out 1 in the form of $\dfrac{3xy}{3xy}$.
$= \dfrac{5}{x^2y^2}$ Simplify.

13a. Possible Answer: Multiply both sides by the common denominator $(x + 1)(x - 1) = x^2 - 1$.

13b. $x - 1 + 2(x + 1) = 8$
$x - 1 + 2x + 2 = 8$
$3x = 7$
$x = \dfrac{7}{3}$

14a. $2k - 5(k - 1) = 2$
$2k - 5k + 5 = 2$
${}^-3k = {}^-3$
$k = 1$
Check: $\dfrac{1}{1 - 1} - \dfrac{5}{2} = \dfrac{1}{1 - 1}$
$\dfrac{1}{0} - \dfrac{5}{2} = \dfrac{1}{0}$
There is no solution.

14b. There is the possibility that a value or values can't be permitted since they would make a denominator 0.

15a. $\dfrac{156}{s}$

15b. $\dfrac{156}{s + 16}$

15c. $\dfrac{156}{s} + \dfrac{156}{s + 16} = 10.4$
$156(s + 16) + 156s = 10.4s(s + 16)$
$156s + 2,496 + 156s = 10.4s^2 + 166.4s$
$0 = 10.4s^2 - 145.6s - 2,496$
$s = 24$

Possible calculator screens:

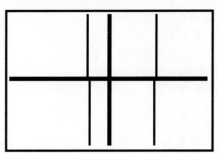

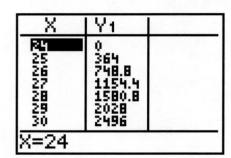

Page 429   Demonstrating Skills

16. ${}^-6x - 6 + 10 - 2x - 9 + 9x = x - 5$

17. ${}^-a + 3a^2 - 2a^2 + 5a = a^2 + 4a$

18. $8b + 2b^2 + 4 + b = 2b^2 + 9b + 4$

19. $5x - x^2 + 5 - x = 5 + 4x - x^2$

20. $2c^2 - 4c - 8c + 16 = 2c^2 - 12c + 16$

21. $2xy - 2x^2y + y^2 - xy^2$

22. $L^2 - 16L + 64$

23. $x^2 - x^2y^2$

24. $7xy$

25. $5xy - 10x^2y + 4x - 2$

26. $d - d^2 + 2 - 2d + 3 - d - 6d + 2d^2$
$= d^2 - 8d + 5$

27. $\dfrac{5n}{n - 1} + \dfrac{3n}{2(n - 1)} = \dfrac{10n}{2(n - 1)} + \dfrac{3n}{2(n - 1)} = \dfrac{13n}{2n - 2}$

28. $\dfrac{b}{3} + \dfrac{b-1}{b+1} - \dfrac{b}{2(b+1)}$

$= \dfrac{2b(b+1)}{6(b+1)} + \dfrac{6(b-1)}{6(b+1)} - \dfrac{3b}{6(b+1)}$

$= \dfrac{2b^2 + 2b + 6b - 6 - 3b}{6(b+1)}$

$= \dfrac{2b^2 + 5b - 6}{6(b+1)}$

29. $\dfrac{k+2}{(k-1)(k+2)} - \dfrac{k-1}{(k-1)(k+2)} = \dfrac{k+2-k+1}{(k-1)(k+2)}$

$= \dfrac{3}{(k-1)(k+2)}$

30. $3(x-4) = 2(x+4)$

$3x - 12 = 2x + 8$

$x = 20$

31. $^-2x + 2 = {}^-3(x-1)$

${}^-2x + 2 = {}^-3x + 3$

$x = 1$

Check: $\dfrac{{}^-2(1) + 2}{1 - 1} = \dfrac{0}{0}$

no solution

Chapter 7 Solving Quadratic Equations

7-1 Solving by Backtracking

Pages 433–434 Problem Set A

1. Possible answer: The "−11" is in the wrong place; he's taking the square root of $2x$ and then subtracting 11, instead of subtracting 11 before taking the square root.

2. $\sqrt{2x} - 11 = 5$

3a.
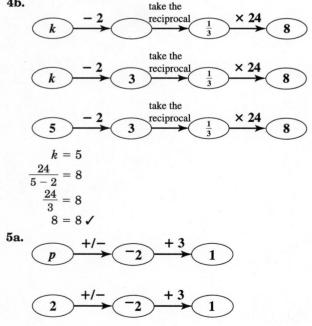

3b.

$x = 19$
$\sqrt{3(19) + 7} = 8$
$\sqrt{64} = 8$
$8 = 8\checkmark$

4a. Possible answer: $5 \to 3 \to \frac{1}{3} \to \frac{24}{3}$, or 8

4b.

$k = 5$
$\frac{24}{5 - 2} = 8$
$\frac{24}{3} = 8$
$8 = 8\checkmark$

5a.

$p = 2$

5b. You would have to add a variable as part of the backtracking, which can't be done.

6a. Possible answer: $5 \to {}^-5 \to {}^-2 \to {}^-4 \to {}^-1$

6b.
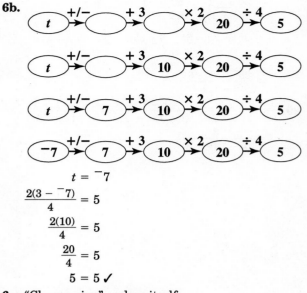

$t = {}^-7$
$\frac{2(3 - {}^-7)}{4} = 5$
$\frac{2(10)}{4} = 5$
$\frac{20}{4} = 5$
$5 = 5\checkmark$

6c. "Change sign" undoes itself.

7a. divide by the same number

7b. You can undo multiplication by $^-1$ by multiplying by $^-1$.

Page 435 Problem Set B

1.
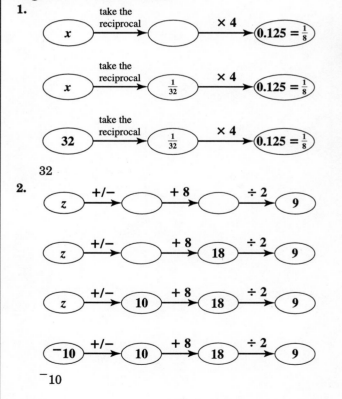

32

2.

$^-10$

3.

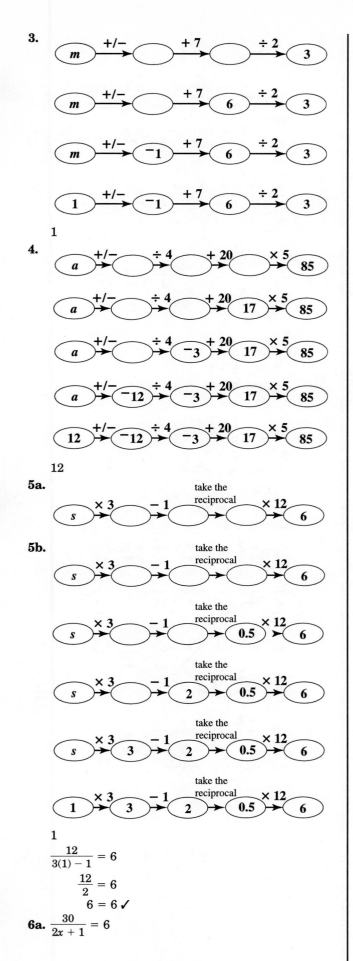

4.

5a.

5b.

$$\frac{12}{3(1) - 1} = 6$$

$$\frac{12}{2} = 6$$

$$6 = 6 ✓$$

6a. $\frac{30}{2x + 1} = 6$

6b.

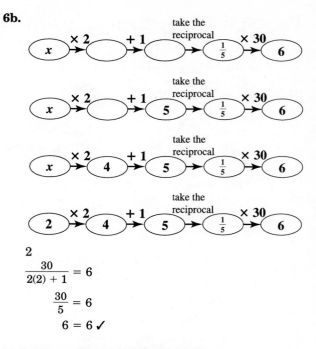

$$\frac{30}{2(2) + 1} = 6$$

$$\frac{30}{5} = 6$$

$$6 = 6 ✓$$

Page 435   Share and Summarize

1. Possible answer: $\frac{20}{\sqrt{2 - x}} = 5$

2. Answers will vary.

Pages 436–437   Problem Set C

1a.

1b.

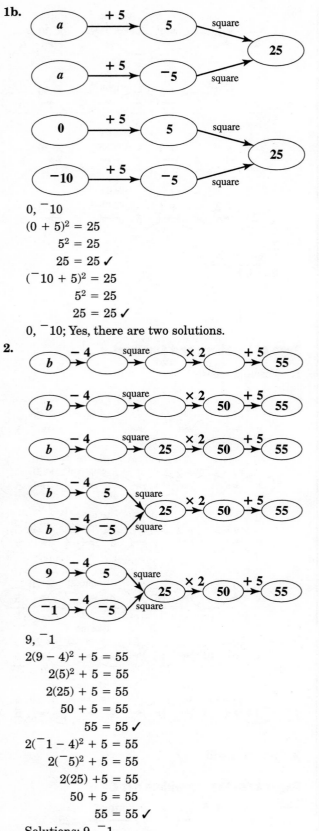

0, ⁻10

$(0 + 5)^2 = 25$

$5^2 = 25$

$25 = 25$ ✓

$(⁻10 + 5)^2 = 25$

$5^2 = 25$

$25 = 25$ ✓

0, ⁻10; Yes, there are two solutions.

2.

9, ⁻1

$2(9 - 4)^2 + 5 = 55$

$2(5)^2 + 5 = 55$

$2(25) + 5 = 55$

$50 + 5 = 55$

$55 = 55$ ✓

$2(⁻1 - 4)^2 + 5 = 55$

$2(⁻5)^2 + 5 = 55$

$2(25) + 5 = 55$

$50 + 5 = 55$

$55 = 55$ ✓

Solutions: 9, ⁻1

3.

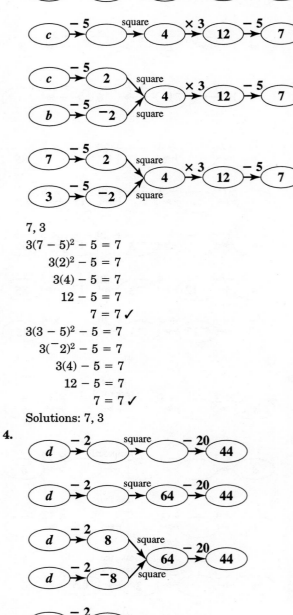

7, 3

$3(7 - 5)^2 - 5 = 7$

$3(2)^2 - 5 = 7$

$3(4) - 5 = 7$

$12 - 5 = 7$

$7 = 7$ ✓

$3(3 - 5)^2 - 5 = 7$

$3(⁻2)^2 - 5 = 7$

$3(4) - 5 = 7$

$12 - 5 = 7$

$7 = 7$ ✓

Solutions: 7, 3

4.

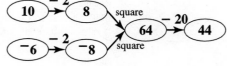

10, ⁻6

5.

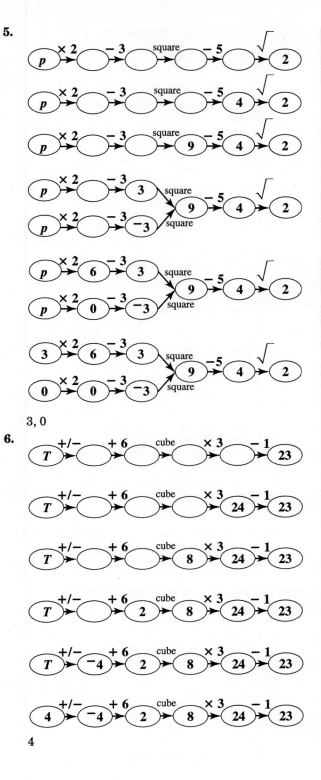

3, 0

6.

4

7.

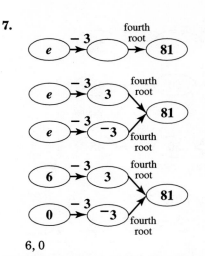

6, 0

8a. Because the variable d is being squared and is in the denominator.

8b. $\frac{360,000}{10^2} = \frac{360,000}{100} = 3,600$

$\frac{360,000}{20^2} = \frac{360,000}{400} = 900$

$\frac{360,000}{30^2} = \frac{360,000}{900} = 400$

$\frac{360,000}{50^2} = \frac{360,000}{2,500} = 144$

8c. The closer an object is to the light source, the brighter it is; the farther it is from the light source, the less bright it is.

8d.

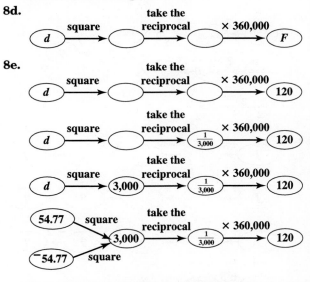

8e.

54.77; An object 54.77 ft from this light source has a brightness of 120 foot-candles.

Page 438   Problem Set D

1a. $(3 + \sqrt{5} - 3)^2 - 5 = (\sqrt{5})^2 - 5 = 5 - 5 = 0$

$(3 - \sqrt{5} - 3)^2 - 5 = (^-\sqrt{5})^2 - 5 = 5 - 5 = 0$

1b. 5.24, 0.76

2.

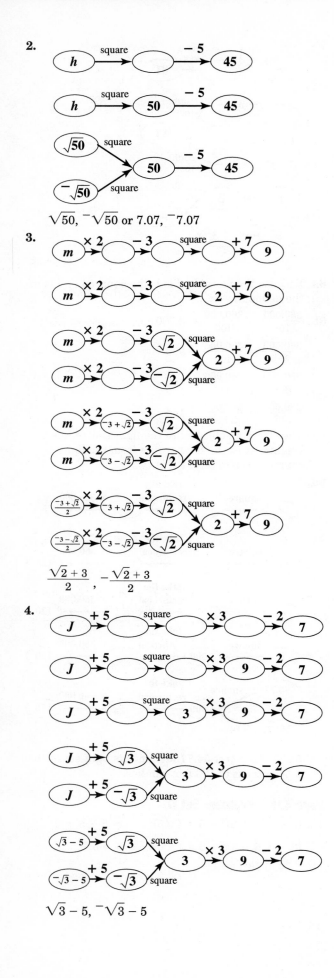

$\sqrt{50}$, $^-\sqrt{50}$ or 7.07, $^-$7.07

3.

$\dfrac{\sqrt{2}+3}{2}$, $-\dfrac{\sqrt{2}+3}{2}$

4.

$\sqrt{3}-5$, $^-\sqrt{3}-5$

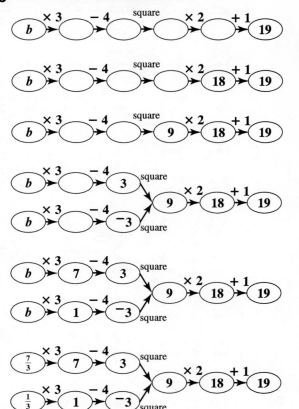

Backtrack through the flowchart, beginning at 19 and undoing each step: $19 - 1 = 18$, $18 \div 2 = 9$, the square roots of 9 are 3 and $^-$3, $3 + 4 = 7$ and $^-3 + 4 = 1$, $7 \div 3 = \dfrac{7}{3}$ and $1 \div 3 = \dfrac{1}{3}$. You must be careful when undoing the squaring, because there are two numbers that can give the same square.

Pages 439–441   On Your Own Exercises

1a.

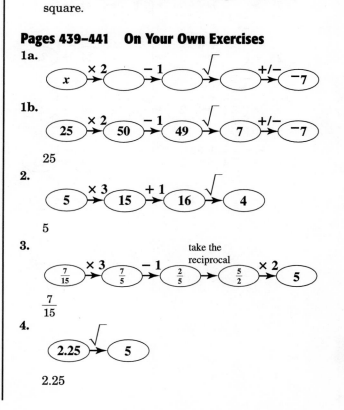

1b.

25

2.

5

3.

$\dfrac{7}{15}$

4.

2.25

5.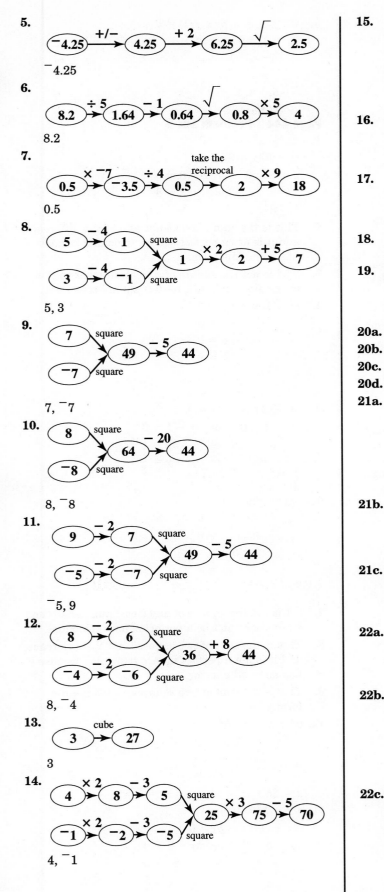

$-4.25 \xrightarrow{+/-} 4.25 \xrightarrow{+\,2} 6.25 \xrightarrow{\sqrt{}} 2.5$

$^-4.25$

6.

$8.2 \xrightarrow{\div\,5} 1.64 \xrightarrow{-\,1} 0.64 \xrightarrow{\sqrt{}} 0.8 \xrightarrow{\times\,5} 4$

8.2

7.

$0.5 \xrightarrow{\times\,^-7} -3.5 \xrightarrow{\div\,4} 0.5 \xrightarrow{\text{take the reciprocal}} 2 \xrightarrow{\times\,9} 18$

0.5

8.

$5 \xrightarrow{-\,4} 1 \xrightarrow{\text{square}} 1 \xrightarrow{\times\,2} 2 \xrightarrow{+\,5} 7$

$3 \xrightarrow{-\,4} -1 \xrightarrow{\text{square}}$

$5,\ 3$

9.

$7 \xrightarrow{\text{square}} 49 \xrightarrow{-\,5} 44$

$^-7 \xrightarrow{\text{square}}$

$7,\ ^-7$

10.

$8 \xrightarrow{\text{square}} 64 \xrightarrow{-\,20} 44$

$^-8 \xrightarrow{\text{square}}$

$8,\ ^-8$

11.

$9 \xrightarrow{-\,2} 7 \xrightarrow{\text{square}} 49 \xrightarrow{-\,5} 44$

$^-5 \xrightarrow{-\,2} ^-7 \xrightarrow{\text{square}}$

$^-5,\ 9$

12.

$8 \xrightarrow{-\,2} 6 \xrightarrow{\text{square}} 36 \xrightarrow{+\,8} 44$

$^-4 \xrightarrow{-\,2} ^-6 \xrightarrow{\text{square}}$

$8,\ ^-4$

13.

$3 \xrightarrow{\text{cube}} 27$

3

14.

$4 \xrightarrow{\times\,2} 8 \xrightarrow{-\,3} 5 \xrightarrow{\text{square}} 25 \xrightarrow{\times\,3} 75 \xrightarrow{-\,5} 70$

$^-1 \xrightarrow{\times\,2} ^-2 \xrightarrow{-\,3} ^-5 \xrightarrow{\text{square}}$

$4,\ ^-1$

15.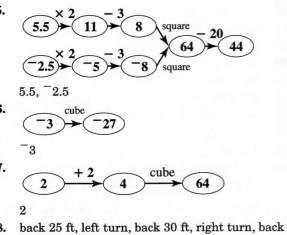

$5.5 \xrightarrow{\times\,2} 11 \xrightarrow{-\,3} 8 \xrightarrow{\text{square}} 64 \xrightarrow{-\,20} 44$

$^-2.5 \xrightarrow{\times\,2} ^-5 \xrightarrow{-\,3} ^-8 \xrightarrow{\text{square}}$

$5.5,\ ^-2.5$

16.

$^-3 \xrightarrow{\text{cube}} ^-27$

$^-3$

17.

$2 \xrightarrow{+\,2} 4 \xrightarrow{\text{cube}} 64$

2

18. back 25 ft, left turn, back 30 ft, right turn, back 15 ft, left turn, back 20 ft

19. Possible answer: No. The operations undo each other exactly, but her calculator gives only an approximation for $\sqrt{2}$. When it squares this value, the answer is not exactly 2.

20a. yes

20b. no

20c. yes

20d. no

21a.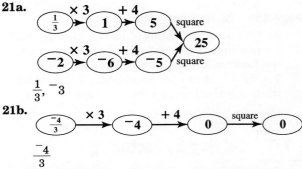

$\tfrac{1}{3} \xrightarrow{\times\,3} 1 \xrightarrow{+\,4} 5 \xrightarrow{\text{square}} 25$

$^-2 \xrightarrow{\times\,3} ^-6 \xrightarrow{+\,4} ^-5 \xrightarrow{\text{square}}$

$\tfrac{1}{3},\ ^-3$

21b.

$\tfrac{^-4}{3} \xrightarrow{\times\,3} ^-4 \xrightarrow{+\,4} 0 \xrightarrow{\text{square}} 0$

$\tfrac{^-4}{3}$

21c. Two solutions to Equation a, one to Equation b. This is because a positive number like 25 has two square roots, one positive and one negative, but 0 has only one square root, 0.

22a.

$5 \xrightarrow{\sqrt{}} \sqrt{5} \xrightarrow{\text{square}} 5$

5

22b.

$5 \xrightarrow{\text{square}} 25 \xrightarrow{\sqrt{}} 5$

$^-5 \xrightarrow{\text{square}}$

$5,\ ^-5$

22c. One solution to Equation a, two to Equation b. In Equation a, you first take the square root, so the solution must be a positive number. For Equation b, you first square, so the solution could be a negative number. If x is negative, say $^-5$, then $\sqrt{x^2}$ is not the same as x. In this case, it is 5.

23. $9a - 21$

24. $^-16b^2 + b$

25. $^-72c + 63c^2$

26. $d^2 + 9d + 18$

27. $2e^2 - 16e + 24$

28. $27f^2 + 87f - 10$

29. $g^2 + 14g + 49$

30. $9h^2 - 6h + 1$

31. $8j^3 + 24j^2 + 24j + 8$

32. $9k^2 + 12km + 4m^2$

33. $8d^2$

34. $1.575d^2$

35a. $2{,}500 \text{ g/m}^2 \times 0.035 \text{ oz/g} = 87.5 \text{ oz/m}^2$ and $87.5 \text{ oz/m}^2 \times \dfrac{1 \text{ m}^2}{1.09361^2 \text{ yd}^2} \approx 73.2 \text{ oz/yd}^2$

35b. Possible answer: A square meter of temperate rainforest produces about 57% of the plant material that a square meter of tropical rainforest produces. A square meter of tropical rainforest produces almost twice as much plant material as a square meter of temperate rainforest.

35c. 5.275×10^{10} kg; Possible explanation: $125 \text{ g/m}^2 \times \dfrac{1 \text{ kg}}{1{,}000 \text{ g}} \times \dfrac{1{,}000^2 \text{ m}^2}{1^2 \text{ km}^2} = 125{,}000 \text{ kg/km}^2$, and $125{,}000 \text{ kg/km}^2 \times 422{,}000 \text{ km}^2 = 5.275 \times 10^{10}$ kg

Page 440   In Your Own Words

Possible answer: Whenever an equation contains a variable that only appears in one term, you can use backtracking to solve it. The equation $7 + 3x = {}^-11$ can be solved using backtracking while the equation $x^2 + 2x = 4$ cannot.

7-2 Solving by Factoring

Page 442   Problem Set A

1. $(t - 1)(t - 3) = 0$

$t - 1 = 0$ or $t - 3 = 0$

$t = 1$ or $t = 3$

$1, 3$

2. $(s + 1)(2s + 3) = 0$

$s + 1 = 0$ or $2s + 3 = 0$

$s = {}^-1$ or $2s = {}^-3$

$s = {}^-1.5$

${}^-1, {}^-1.5$

3. $x(3x + 7) = 0$

$x = 0$ or $3x + 7 = 0$

$3x = {}^-7$

$x = \dfrac{-7}{3}$

$0, \dfrac{-7}{3}$

4. $(p + 4)(p + 4) = 0$

$p + 4 = 0$ or $p + 4 = 0$

$p = {}^-4$ or $p = {}^-4$

${}^-4$

5. $(2x + 1)(x + 8)(x - 1) = 0$

$2x + 1 = 0$ or $x + 8 = 0$ or $x - 1 = 0$

$2x = {}^-1$ or $x = {}^-8$ or $x = 1$

$x = {}^-0.5$

${}^-0.5, {}^-8, 1$

Page 444   Problem Set B

1. $x^2 - 64 = 0$

$(x + 8)(x - 8) = 0$

$x + 8 = 0$ or $x - 8 = 0$

$x = {}^-8$ or $x = 8$

$8, {}^-8$

2. This is the sum of two squares, not the difference; and it is not a perfect square trinomial because it has no middle term.

3. ${}^-64$ is not the square of a (real) number so the expression can't be a perfect square trinomial.

4. $k^2 - 16k + 64 = 0$

$(k - 8)^2 = 0$

$k - 8 = 0$

$k = 8$

8

5. $9y^2 - 1 = 0$

$(3y + 1)(3y - 1) = 0$

$3y + 1 = 0$ or $3y - 1 = 0$

$3y = {}^-1$ or $3y = 1$

$y = \dfrac{-1}{3}$ or $y = \dfrac{1}{3}$

$\dfrac{1}{3}, \dfrac{-1}{3}$

6. $9m^2 + 6m + 1 = 0$

$(3m + 1)^2 = 0$

$3m + 1 = 0$

$3m = {}^-1$

$m = \dfrac{-1}{3}$

$\dfrac{-1}{3}$

7. ${}^-1$ is not the square of any (real) number so the expression can't be a perfect square trinomial.

8. This is the sum of two squares, not the difference; and it is not a perfect square trinomial because it has no middle term.

9. This is the sum of two squares, so it's neither form.

10. $a^2 - 4ab + 4b^2 = 0$

$(a - 2b)^2 = 0$

$a - 2b = 0$

$a = 2b$

$a = 2b$

11. $4a^2 - b^2 = 0$

$(2a + b)(2a - b) = 0$

$2a + b = 0$ or $2a - b = 0$

$2a = {}^-b$ or $2a = b$

$a = \dfrac{-b}{2}$ or $a = \dfrac{b}{2}$

$a = \dfrac{b}{2}, \dfrac{-b}{2}$

Page 444   Share and Summarize

1. Possible answer: $x^2 + 12x + 36$ and $x^2 - 81$; x^2 and 81 are both perfect squares (of x and 9), so $x^2 - 81$ is the difference of two squares; $x^2 + 12x + 36$ can be rewritten as the square of a binomial, $(x + 6)^2$;

2. $4x^2 - 9 = 0$ can be rewritten as $(2x - 3)(2x + 3)$. This is equal to 0 only when one of the factors is equal to 0, so the only values of x that satisfy the equation are those that make $2x - 3$ or $2x + 3$ equal to 0, that is $x = 1.5, {}^-1.5$.

Page 446   Problem Set C

1. $m = 7, n = 1$
$(x + 7)(x + 1) = x^2 + (7 + 1)x + 7 \cdot 1$
$\qquad\qquad\qquad = x^2 + 8x + 7$
$x^2 + 8x + 7$

2. $m = 2, n = 5$
$(x + 2)(x + 5) = x^2 + (2 + 5)x + 2 \cdot 5$
$\qquad\qquad\qquad = x^2 + 7x + 10$
$x^2 + 7x + 10$

3. $m = {}^-4, n = {}^-5$
$(x - 4)(x - 5) = x^2 + ({}^-4 + {}^-5)x + {}^-4 \cdot {}^-5$
$\qquad\qquad\qquad = x^2 - 9x + 20$
$x^2 - 9x + 20$

4. $m = 2, n = {}^-3$
$(x + 2)(x - 3) = x^2 + (2 + {}^-3)x + 2 \cdot {}^-3$
$\qquad\qquad\qquad = x^2 - x - 6$
$x^2 - x - 6$

5. $m = {}^-2, n = 3$
$(x - 2)(x + 3) = x^2 + ({}^-2 + 3)x + {}^-2 \cdot 3$
$\qquad\qquad\qquad = x^2 + x - 6$
$x^2 + x - 6$

6. $m = 5, n = {}^-4$
$(x + 5)(x - 4) = x^2 + (5 + {}^-4)x + 5 \cdot {}^-4$
$\qquad\qquad\qquad = x^2 + x - 20$
$x^2 + x - 20$

7. $m + n = 7 = 6 + 1$
$mn = 6 = 6 \cdot 1$
$(x + 6)(x + 1)$

8. $m + n = {}^-7 = {}^-6 + {}^-1$
$mn = 6 = {}^-6 \cdot {}^-1$
$(x - 6)(x - 1)$

9. $m + n = {}^-4 = {}^-6 + 2$
$mn = {}^-12 = {}^-6 \cdot 2$
$(x - 6)(x + 2)$

10. $m + n = 4 = 6 + {}^-2$
$mn = {}^-12 = 6 \cdot {}^-2$
$(x - 2)(x + 6)$

11. $m + n = {}^-10 = {}^-8 + {}^-2$
$mn = 16 = {}^-8 \cdot {}^-2$
$x^2 - 10x + 16 = 0$
$(x - 2)(x - 8) = 0$
$x - 2 = 0 \ or \ x - 8 = 0$
$\qquad x = 2 \ or \qquad x = 8$
2, 8

12. $m + n = 6 = 8 + {}^-2$
$mn = {}^-16 = 8 \cdot {}^-2$
$x^2 + 6x - 16 = 0$
$(x - 2)(x + 8) = 0$
$x - 2 = 0 \ or \ x + 8 = 0$
$\qquad x = 2 \ or \qquad x = {}^-8$
2, ${}^-8$

Page 447   Problem Set D

1. $mn = 5$
$m + n = 6$
m and n must both be positive for the sum and the product to be positive.
$1 \cdot 5 = 5; 1 + 5 = 6 \checkmark$
$(x + 5)(x + 1)$

2. $mn = {}^-5$
$m + n = 4$
m and n must have opposite signs for the product to be negative.
$1 \cdot {}^-5 = {}^-5; 1 + {}^-5 = {}^-4$
${}^-1 \cdot 5 = {}^-5; {}^-1 + 5 = 4 \checkmark$
$(b + 5)(b - 1)$

3. $mn = 1$
$m + n = {}^-2$
m and n must both be negative for the product to be positive and the sum negative.
${}^-1 \cdot {}^-1 = 1; {}^-1 + {}^-1 = {}^-2 \checkmark$
$(w - 1)(w - 1) = (w - 1)^2$
$(w - 1)^2$

4. $mn = {}^-18$
$m + n = 9$
m and n must have opposite signs for the product to be negative.
$1 \cdot {}^-18 = {}^-18; 1 + {}^-18 = {}^-17$
${}^-1 \cdot 18 = {}^-18; {}^-1 + 18 = 17$
$2 \cdot {}^-9 = {}^-18; 2 + {}^-9 = {}^-7$
${}^-2 \cdot 9 = {}^-18; {}^-2 + 9 = 7$
$3 \cdot {}^-6 = {}^-18; 3 + {}^-6 = {}^-3$
${}^-3 \cdot 6 = {}^-18; {}^-3 + 6 = 3$
No combination of m and n will produce $mn = {}^-18$ and $m + n = 9$.
can't be factored

5. $mn = {}^-24$
$m + n = {}^-10$
m and n must have opposite signs for the product to be negative.
$1 \cdot {}^-24 = {}^-24; 1 + {}^-24 = {}^-23$
${}^-1 \cdot 24 = {}^-24; {}^-1 + 24 = 23$
$2 \cdot {}^-12 = {}^-24; 2 + {}^-12 = {}^-10 \checkmark$
$(s - 12)(s + 2)$

Chapter 7

6. $mn = 5$

$m + n = {}^-4$

m and n must both be negative for the product to be positive and the sum to be negative.

${}^-1 \cdot {}^-5 = 5; {}^-1 + {}^-5 = {}^-6$

No combination of m and n will produce $mn = 5$ and $m + n = {}^-4$.

can't be factored

7. $mn = {}^-12$

$m + n = 4$

m and n must have opposite signs for the product to be negative.

$1 \cdot {}^-12 = {}^-12; 1 + {}^-12 = {}^-11$

${}^-1 \cdot 12 = {}^-12; {}^-1 + 12 = 11$

$2 \cdot {}^-6 = {}^-12; 2 + {}^-6 = {}^-4$

${}^-2 \cdot 6 = {}^-12; {}^-2 + 6 = 4 ✓$

$w^2 + 4w - 12 = 0$

$(w - 2)(w + 6) = 0$

$w - 2 = 0$ or $w + 6 = 0$

$\qquad w = 2$ or $\qquad w = {}^-6$

$2, {}^-6$

8. $3a^2 + 18a + 15 = 3(a^2 + 6a + 5)$

$mn = 5$

$m + n = 6$

m and n must both be positive for the product and the sum to be positive.

$1 \cdot 5 = 5; 1 + 5 = 6 ✓$

$3(a^2 + 6a + 5) = 3(a + 5)(a + 1)$

$3(a + 5)(a + 1)$

9. $2b^2 + 8b - 10 = 2(b^2 + 4b - 5)$

$mn = {}^-5$

$m + n = 4$

m and n must have opposite signs for the product to be negative.

$1 \cdot {}^-5 = {}^-5; 1 + {}^-5 = {}^-4$

${}^-1 \cdot 5 = {}^-5; {}^-1 + 5 = 4 ✓$

$2(b^2 + 4b - 5) = 2(b + 5)(b - 1)$

$2(b + 5)(b - 1)$

10. $4x^2 - 8x + 8 = 4(x^2 - 2x + 2)$

$mn = 2$

$m + n = {}^-2$

m and n must both be negative for the product to be positive and the sum to be negative.

${}^-1 \cdot {}^-2 = 2; {}^-1 + {}^-2 = {}^-3$

No combination of m and n will produce $mn = 2$ and $m + n = {}^-2$.

$4(x^2 - 2x + 2)$; can't be factored further

11. $5t^2 + 25t - 70 = 5(t^2 + 5t - 14)$

$mn = {}^-14$

$m + n = 5$

m and n must have opposite signs for the product to be negative.

$1 \cdot {}^-14 = {}^-14; 1 + {}^-14 = {}^-13$

${}^-1 \cdot 14 = {}^-14; {}^-1 + 14 = 13$

$2 \cdot {}^-7 = {}^-14; 2 + {}^-7 = {}^-5$

${}^-2 \cdot {}^-7 = {}^-14; {}^-2 + 7 = 5 ✓$

$5(t^2 + 5t - 14) = 5(t + 7)(t - 2)$

$5(t + 7)(t - 2)$

12. $3x^2 - 11x - 4 = (3x + \_\_)(x - \_\_)$ or $(3x - \_\_)(x + \_\_)$

$1 \cdot {}^-4 = {}^-4$

${}^-1 \cdot 4 = {}^-4$

$2 \cdot {}^-2 = {}^-4$

Try these combinations in the parentheses to find the correct pair:

$(3x + 1)(x - 4) = 3x^2 - 12x + x - 4$

$\qquad = 3x^2 - 11x - 4 ✓$

13. $8x^2 + 2x - 3 = (\_\_x + 1)(\_\_x - 3)$ or $(\_\_x - 1)(\_\_x + 3)$

$1 \cdot 8 = 8$

$2 \cdot 4 = 8$

Try these combinations in the parentheses to find the correct pair:

$(x + 1)(8x - 3) = 8x^2 - 3x + 8x - 3$

$\qquad = 8x^2 + 5x - 3$

$(x - 1)(8x + 3) = 8x^2 + 3x - 8x - 3$

$\qquad = 8x^2 - 5x - 3$

$(2x + 1)(4x - 3) = 8x^2 - 6x + 4x - 3$

$\qquad = 8x^2 - 2x - 3$

$(2x - 1)(4x + 3) = 8x^2 + 6x - 4x - 3$

$\qquad = 8x^2 + 2x - 3 ✓$

Page 448   Share and Summarize

Possible answer:

Step 1: Check whether the expression is a perfect square trinomial or a difference of two squares. If so, use one of those special cases to solve the problem.

Step 2: If the terms contain a common factor, factor it out and then try factoring further.

Step 3: If the coefficient of the squared variable is 1, find all the factors of the constant term and decide whether you need to use two positive factors, two negative factors, or one positive and one negative factor.

Step 4: Try different combinations of factors to see if one set will work. If none of the combinations can be expanded to the original trinomial, the expression cannot be factored using integers.

Pages 449–450   Problem Set E

1. $4a + 3 = 6a + a^2$

$\qquad 3 = 2a + a^2$

$\qquad 0 = {}^-3 + 2a + a^2$

$\qquad 0 = a^2 + 2a - 3$

$\qquad 0 = (a - 1)(a + 3)$

$\qquad a = 1, {}^-3$

2. $\qquad b^2 - 12 = 4b$

$\qquad b^2 - 4b - 12 = 0$

$\qquad (b + 2)(b - 6) = 0$

$\qquad\qquad b = {}^-2, 6$

3. $c(c + 4) + 3c + 12 = 0$

$\qquad c^2 + 4c + 3c + 12 = 0$

$\qquad\quad c^2 + 7c + 12 = 0$

$\qquad\quad (c + 4)(c + 3) = 0$

$\qquad\qquad\qquad\qquad c = {}^-4, {}^-3$

4. $\qquad d + \dfrac{6}{d} = 5$

$\qquad\quad d^2 + 6 = 5d$

$\qquad d^2 - 5d + 6 = 0$

$\quad (d - 3)(d - 2) = 0$

$\qquad\qquad\qquad d = 3, 2$

5. $\dfrac{(x + 3)(x - 2)^2}{x - 2} = 3x - 3$

$\dfrac{(x + 3)(x - 2)\cancel{(x - 2)}}{\cancel{x - 2}} = 3x - 3$

$\qquad x^2 + x - 6 = 3x - 3$

$\qquad x^2 - 2x - 3 = 0$

$\qquad (x - 3)(x + 1) = 0$

$\qquad\qquad\qquad x = 3, {}^-1$

6a. Let x be Kenyon's number.

$\qquad x(x + 2) = 4x - 1$

$\qquad x^2 + 2x = 4x - 1$

$\qquad x^2 - 2x = {}^-1$

$\quad x^2 - 2x + 1 = 0$

$\quad (x - 1)(x - 1) = 0$

$\qquad\qquad\qquad x = 1$

6b. Kenyon's puzzle resulted in a quadratic expression that is a perfect square set equal to 0, so it has only one solution because 0 has only one square root.

7a. If w is the width, then

$w + 2$ is the length, and

$w(w + 2)$ is the area.

$w(w + 2) = 15$, where $w = $ width

7b. $\qquad w(w + 2) = 15$

$\qquad\quad w^2 + 2w = 15$

$\quad w^2 + 2w - 15 = 0$

$\quad (w + 5)(w - 3) = 0$

$\qquad\qquad\qquad w = {}^-5, 3$

Since ${}^-5$ can't be the length of a rug, only 3 makes sense.

7c. $w = 3$

$w + 2 = 5$

5 m by 3 m

8. $x + 20 = x^2$

$\qquad 20 = x^2 - x$

$\qquad 0 = x^2 - x - 20$

$\qquad 0 = (x - 5)(x + 4)$

$\qquad x = 5, {}^-4$

9. $\qquad x^2 + (x + 1)^2 = 145$

$\quad x^2 + x^2 + 2x + 1 = 145$

$\qquad 2x^2 + 2x - 144 = 0$

$\qquad 2(x^2 + x - 72) = 0$

$\qquad 2(x - 8)(x + 9) = 0$

$\qquad\qquad\qquad x = 8, {}^-9$

If $x = 8$, then the integers are 8 and $8 + 1 = 9$.

If $x = {}^-9$, then the integers are ${}^-9$ and ${}^-9 + 1 = {}^-8$.

The integers are 8 and 9, or ${}^-9$ and ${}^-8$.

10a. If $x - 2 = 5$, then $x = 7$.

Check $x = 7$ to see if it makes the original equation true:

$(7 + 1)(7 - 2) = 10$

$\qquad\quad 8 \cdot 5 = 10$

$\qquad\qquad 40 = 10$ ✗

She'd get $x = 7$, which doesn't satisfy the equation.

10b. No; it doesn't always work.

10c. $(x + 1)(x - 2) = 10$

$\qquad x^2 - x - 2 = 10$

$\qquad x^2 - x - 12 = 0$

$\quad (x - 4)(x + 3) = 0$

$\qquad\qquad\qquad x = 4, {}^-3$

If $x = 4$:

$(4 + 1)(4 - 2) = 10$

$\qquad\quad 5 \cdot 2 = 10$

$\qquad\qquad 10 = 10$ ✓

If $x = {}^-3$:

$({}^-3 + 1)({}^-3 - 2) = 10$

$\qquad\quad {}^-2 \cdot {}^-5 = 10$

$\qquad\qquad\quad 10 = 10$ ✓

10d. $(x + 5)(x - 2) = 30$

$\qquad x^2 + 3x - 10 = 30$

$\qquad x^2 + 3x - 40 = 0$

$\quad (x + 8)(x - 5) = 0$

$\qquad\qquad\qquad x = {}^-8, 5$

Page 450   Share and Summarize

1. Possible answer: A rug is 4 times as long as it is wide and has an area of 16 square feet. What are its length and width?

2. Possible answer:

In the above case, with w as the width,

$4w$ is the length and

$4w \cdot w = 4w^2$ is the area:

$\qquad\qquad 4w^2 = 16$

$\qquad\quad 4w^2 - 16 = 0$

$\quad (2w + 4)(2w - 4) = 0$

$\qquad\qquad\qquad w = 2 \text{ or } {}^-2$

The negative solution has no meaning in this problem, so the answer is width = 2 ft, length = $4 \cdot 2 = 8$ ft.

Pages 451–455   On Your Own Exercises

1. $(x + 5)(x + 7) = 0$

$\quad x + 5 = 0 \quad or \quad x + 7 = 0$

$\qquad\quad x = {}^-5 \quad or \qquad x = {}^-7$

${}^-5, {}^-7$

2. $(x - 5)(x + 7) = 0$
$x - 5 = 0 \ or \ x + 7 = 0$
$x = 5 \ or \quad x = {}^-7$
$5, \ {}^-7$

3. $(x - 5)(x - 7) = 0$
$x - 5 = 0 \ or \ x - 7 = 0$
$x = 5 \ or \quad x = 7$
$5, 7$

4. $(x + 5)(x - 7) = 0$
$x + 5 = 0 \quad or \ x - 7 = 0$
$x = {}^-5 \ or \quad x = 7$
${}^-5, 7$

5. difference of squares;
$\qquad x^2 - 49 = 0$
$(x + 7)(x - 7) = 0$
$x + 7 = 0 \quad or \ x - 7 = 0$
$\quad x = {}^-7 \ or \quad x = 7$
$x = 7, {}^-7$

6. neither form

7. neither form

8. perfect square trinomial
$x^2 - 14x + 49 = 0$
$\quad (x - 7)^2 = 0$
$\qquad x - 7 = 0$
$\qquad\qquad x = 7$

9. difference of squares
$\qquad 49 - x^2 = 0$
$(7 + x)(7 - x) = 0$
$7 + x = 0 \quad or \ 7 - x = 0$
$\quad x = {}^-7 \ or \qquad 7 = x$
$x = 7, {}^-7$

10. perfect square trinomial
$x^2 + 14x + 49 = 0$
$\quad (x + 7)^2 = 0$
$\qquad x + 7 = 0$
$\qquad\qquad x = {}^-7$

11. neither form

12. perfect square trinomial
$a^2x^2 + 4ab + b^2 = 0$
$\quad (ax + 2b)^2 = 0$
$\qquad ax + 2b = 0$
$\qquad\qquad ax = {}^-2b$
$\qquad\qquad x = \dfrac{-2b}{a}$

13. difference of squares
$\qquad m^2x^2 - n^2 = 0$
$(mx + n)(mx - n) = 0$
$mx + n = 0 \quad or \ mx - n = 0$
$\quad mx = {}^-n \ or \qquad mx = n$
$\qquad x = \dfrac{-n}{m} \ or \qquad x = \dfrac{n}{m}$
$x = \dfrac{n}{m}, \dfrac{-n}{m}$

14. neither form

15. $d^2 - 15d + 54$
$mn = 54$
$m + n = {}^-15$
m and n must both be negative for the product to be positive and the sum to be negative.
${}^-1 \cdot {}^-54 = 54; {}^-1 + {}^-54 = {}^-55$
${}^-2 \cdot {}^-27 = 54; {}^-2 + {}^-27 = {}^-29$
${}^-3 \cdot {}^-18 = 54; {}^-3 + {}^-18 = {}^-21$
${}^-6 \cdot {}^-9 = 54; {}^-6 + {}^-9 = {}^-15 \checkmark$
$(d - 9)(d - 6)$

16. $g^2 - g - 6$
$mn = {}^-6$
$m + n = {}^-1$
m and n must have opposite signs for the product to be negative.
$1 \cdot {}^-6 = {}^-6; 1 + {}^-6 = {}^-5$
${}^-1 \cdot 6 = {}^-6; {}^-1 + 6 = 5$
$2 \cdot {}^-3 = {}^-6; 2 + {}^-3 = {}^-1 \checkmark$
$(g - 3)(g + 2)$

17. $z^2 + 2z - 6$
$mn = {}^-6$
$m + n = 2$
m and n must have opposite signs for the product to be negative.
$1 \cdot {}^-6 = {}^-6; 1 + {}^-6 = {}^-5$
${}^-1 \cdot 6 = {}^-6; {}^-1 + 6 = 5$
$2 \cdot {}^-3 = {}^-6; 2 + {}^-3 = {}^-1$
${}^-2 \cdot 3 = {}^-6; {}^-2 + 3 = 1$
Can't be factored because none of the factors of 6 (6 and 1, or 3 and 2) have a difference of 2.

18. $h^2 - 3h - 28$
$mn = {}^-28$
$m + n = {}^-3$
m and n must have opposite signs for the product to be negative.
$1 \cdot {}^-28 = {}^-28; 1 + {}^-28 = {}^-27$
${}^-1 \cdot 28 = {}^-28; {}^-1 + 28 = 27$
$2 \cdot {}^-14 = {}^-28; 2 + {}^-14 = {}^-12$
${}^-2 \cdot 14 = {}^-28; {}^-2 + 14 = 12$
$4 \cdot {}^-7 = {}^-28; 4 + {}^-7 = {}^-3 \checkmark$
$(h - 7)(h + 4)$

19. $2x^2 - 8x - 10 = 2(x^2 - 4x - 5)$
$mn = {}^-5$
$m + n = {}^-4$
m and n must have opposite signs for the product to be negative.
$1 \cdot {}^-5 = {}^-5; 1 + {}^-5 = {}^-4 \checkmark$
$2(x - 5)(x + 1)$

20. $3c^2 - 9c + 6 = 3(c^2 - 3c + 2)$
$mn = 2$
$m + n = {}^-3$
m and n must both be negative for the product to be positive and the sum to be negative.
${}^-1 \cdot {}^-2 = 2; {}^-1 + {}^-2 = {}^-3 \checkmark$
$3(c - 2)(c - 1)$

21. $k^2 + 15k + 30 = 0$

$mn = 30$

$m + n = 15$

m and n must both be positive for the product and the sum to be positive.

$1 \cdot 30 = 30; 1 + 30 = 31$

$2 \cdot 15 = 30; 2 + 15 = 17$

$3 \cdot 10 = 30; 3 + 10 = 30$

$5 \cdot 6 = 30; 5 + 6 = 30$

Can't be factored because none of the factors of 30 (30 and 1, 15 and 2, 10 and 3, or 6 and 5) have a sum of 15.

22. $n^2 - 17n + 42 = 0$

$mn = 42$

$m + n = {}^-17$

m and n must both be negative for the product to be positive and the sum to be negative.

${}^-1 \cdot {}^-42 = 42; {}^-1 + {}^-42 = {}^-43$

${}^-2 \cdot {}^-21 = 42; {}^-2 + {}^-21 = {}^-23$

${}^-3 \cdot {}^-14 = 42; {}^-3 + {}^-14 = {}^-17 \checkmark$

$(n - 14)(n - 3) = 0$

$n - 14 = 0 \quad or \quad n - 3 = 0$

$n = 14 \quad or \quad n = 3$

$n = 3, 14$

23. $2b^2 - 21b + 10 = 0$

$(2b - 1)(b - 10) = 0$

$2b - 1 = 0 \ or \ b - 10 = 0$

$2b = 1 \ or \quad b = 10$

$b = 0.5, 10$

24. $8r^2 + 5r - 3 = 0$

$(8r - 3)(r + 1) = 0$

$8r - 3 = 0 \ or \ r + 1 = 0$

$8r = 3 \ or \quad r = {}^-1$

$r = \dfrac{3}{8}, {}^-1$

25. $\qquad 4x + x^2 = 21$

$x^2 + 4x - 21 = 0$

$(x - 3)(x + 7) = 0$

$\qquad\qquad x = 3, {}^-7$

26. $h^2 + 12 = 3h$

$h^2 - 3h + 12 = 0$

Factors of 12:

1, 12

2, 6

3, 4

Can't be solved by factoring (no factors of 12 add to 3).

27. $14e = e^2 + 24$

$0 = e^2 - 14e + 24$

$0 = (e - 12)(e - 2)$

$e = 12, 2$

28. $\qquad g^2 + 64 = 16g$

$g^2 - 16g + 64 = 0$

$\qquad (g - 8)^2 = 0$

$\qquad\quad g - 8 = 0$

$\qquad\qquad\quad g = 8$

29. $\qquad u^2 + 5u = 36$

$u^2 + 5u - 36 = 0$

$(u - 4)(u + 9) = 0$

$\qquad\qquad u = 4, {}^-9$

30. $(x + 3)(x - 4) = 30$

$x^2 - x - 12 = 30$

$x^2 - x - 42 = 0$

$(x - 7)(x + 6) = 0$

$\qquad\qquad x = 7, {}^-6$

31. $\qquad \dfrac{(x + 1)^3}{x + 1} = 5x + 5$

$\dfrac{(x + 1)(x + 1)(\cancel{x + 1})}{\cancel{x + 1}} = 5x + 5$

$x^2 + 2x + 1 = 5x + 5$

$x^2 - 3x - 4 = 0$

$(x - 4)(x + 1) = 0$

$\qquad\qquad x = 4, {}^-1$

The solution $x = {}^-1$ must be thrown out because the denominator of the original problem would be 0 if $x = {}^-1$.

$x = 4$

32. $\qquad n^2 + 6 = 5n$

$n^2 - 5n + 6 = 0$

$(n - 2)(n - 3) = 0$

$\qquad\qquad n = 2, 3$

33a. $(\sqrt{7})^2 = 7$

$\sqrt{7}$

33b. By thinking of 7 as a "square" (of $\sqrt{7}$), $4x^2 - 7$ can be thought of as the difference of two squares: $(2x + \sqrt{7})(2x - \sqrt{7})$.

34a. **i.** Figure B

ii. Figure D

iii. Figure A

iv. Figure C

34b. **i.** $D^2 - d^2$

$(D + d)(D - d)$

ii. $\pi(r + w)^2 - \pi r^2$

$\pi(r^2 + 2rw + w^2) - \pi r^2$

$\pi r^2 + 2\pi rw + \pi w^2 - \pi r^2$

$2\pi rw + \pi w^2$

$\pi w(2r + w)$

iii. $(d + w)^2 - d^2$

$d^2 + 2dw + w^2 - d^2$

$2dw + w^2$

$w(2d + w)$

iv. $4r^2 - \pi r^2$

$r^2(4 - \pi)$

35.
$$x^4 - 1 = 0$$
$$(x^2)^2 - 1 = 0$$
$$(x^2 + 1)(x^2 - 1) = 0$$
$$(x^2 + 1)(x + 1)(x - 1) = 0$$
$$x^2 + 1 = 0 \quad or \quad x + 1 = 0 \quad or \quad x - 1 = 0$$
$$x^2 = {}^-1 \quad or \quad x = 1 \quad or \quad x = {}^-1$$

$x^2 = {}^-1$ does not add any solutions since a real number squared cannot be negative.

$$x = 1, {}^-1$$

36.
$$x^8 - 1 = 0$$
$$(x^4)^2 - 1 = 0$$
$$(x^4 + 1)(x^4 - 1) = 0$$
$$(x^4 + 1)(x^2 + 1)(x^2 - 1) = 0$$
$$(x^4 + 1)(x^2 + 1)(x + 1)(x - 1) = 0$$
$$x^4 + 1 = 0 \quad or \quad x^2 + 1 = 0 \quad or \quad x + 1 = 0 \quad or \quad x - 1 = 0$$
$$x^4 = {}^-1 \quad or \quad x^2 = {}^-1 \quad or \quad x = {}^-1 \quad or \quad x = 1$$

$x^4 = {}^-1$ and $x^2 = {}^-1$ do not add any solutions since a real number raised to an even power cannot be negative.

$$x = 1, {}^-1$$

37.
$$x^3 - 16x = 0$$
$$x(x^2 - 16) = 0$$
$$x(x + 4)(x - 4) = 0$$
$$x = 0 \quad or \quad x + 4 = 0 \quad or \quad x - 4 = 0$$
$$x = {}^-4 \quad or \quad x = 4$$
$$x = 0, 4, {}^-4$$

38.
$$x^3 - 6x^2 + 9x = 0$$
$$x(x^2 - 6x + 9) = 0$$
$$x(x - 3)^2 = 0$$
$$x = 0 \quad or \quad x - 3 = 0$$
$$x = 3$$
$$x = 0, 3$$

39.
$$x^4 - 2x^2 + 1 = 0$$
$$(x^2 - 1)^2 = 0$$
$$(x + 1)(x - 1)(x + 1)(x - 1) = 0$$
$$(x + 1)^2(x - 1)^2 = 0$$
$$x + 1 = 0 \quad or \quad x - 1 = 0$$
$$x = {}^-1 \quad or \quad x = 1$$
$$x = 1, {}^-1$$

40.
$$x^4 + 2x^2 + 1 = 0$$
$$(x^2 + 1)^2 = 0$$
$$x^2 + 1 = 0$$
$$x^2 = {}^-1$$
no solution

41.
$$\frac{x^2 + 6x + 9}{x + 3} = 10$$
$$\frac{(x + 3)\cancel{(x + 3)}}{\cancel{x + 3}} = 10$$
$$x + 3 = 10$$
$$x = 7$$

42.
$$\frac{16x^2 - 81}{4x + 9} = 31$$
$$\frac{(4x - 9)\cancel{(4x + 9)}}{\cancel{4x + 9}} = 31$$
$$4x - 9 = 31$$
$$4x = 40$$
$$x = 10$$

43a. $a^2 - 4 = (a + 2)(a - 2)$

The denominator is equal to 0 when $a = 2$ or ${}^-2$.

43b. $\dfrac{5a + 10}{a^2 - 4} = \dfrac{5(a + 2)}{(a + 2)(a - 2)}$

$$\frac{5(a + 2)}{(a + 2)(a - 2)}$$

43c. $\dfrac{5\cancel{(a + 2)}}{\cancel{(a + 2)}(a - 2)} = \dfrac{5}{a - 2}$

$$\frac{5}{a - 2}$$

43d. If a is 2:

$\dfrac{5}{a - 2} = \dfrac{5}{2 - 2}$ is undefined.

If a is ${}^-2$:

$$\frac{5}{a - 2} = \frac{5}{{}^-2 - 2} = \frac{-5}{4}$$

43e. Possible answer: When I simplified, I removed one of the factors that made the original expression undefined.

43f. $\dfrac{2m + 1}{4m^2 - 1} = \dfrac{\cancel{2m + 1}}{\cancel{(2m + 1)}(2m - 1)}$

$$= \frac{1}{2m - 1}$$

where $2m - 1 \neq 0$ and $2m + 1 \neq 0$

$$2m - 1 \neq 0$$
$$2m \neq 1$$
$$m \neq 0.5$$
$$2m + 1 \neq 0$$
$$2m \neq {}^-1$$
$$m \neq {}^-0.5$$

$\dfrac{1}{2m - 1}$, where $m \neq {}^-0.5$ or 0.5

44a.

44b. The additional area is the size of the entire patio minus the original patio:

area of the entire patio: $(5 + d)^2$

area of the original patio: 5^2

$$(5 + d)^2 - 5^2 = 24$$

44c.
$$(5 + d)^2 - 5^2 = 24$$
$$25 + 10d + d^2 - 25 = 24$$
$$10d + d^2 = 24$$
$$d^2 + 10d - 24 = 0$$
$$(d + 12)(d - 2) = 0$$
$$d = {}^-12, 2$$
$d = {}^-12$ is meaningless in this situation
$d = 2$

45a.
$$\frac{1}{2}(n^2 + n) = 55$$
$$n^2 + \text{n} = 110$$
$$n^2 + n - 110 = 0$$
$$(n + 11)(n - 10) = 0$$
$$n = {}^-11, 10$$
$n = 10$ ($n = {}^-11$ doesn't make sense in this situation.)

45b.
$$\frac{1}{2}(n^2 + n) = 120$$
$$n^2 + n = 240$$
$$n^2 + n - 240 = 0$$
$$(n + 16)(n - 15) = 0$$
$$n = {}^-16, 15$$
$n = 15$ ($n = {}^-16$ doesn't make sense in this situation.)

45c.
$$\frac{1}{2}(n^2 + n) = 150$$
$$n^2 + n = 300$$
$$n^2 + n - 300 = 0$$
Factors of 300:
1, 300
2, 150
3, 100
4, 75
5, 60
6, 50
10, 30
12, 25
15, 20
can't be factored; 150 is not a triangular number.

45d.
$$\frac{1}{2}(n^2 + n) = 200$$
$$n^2 + n = 400$$
$$n^2 + n - 400 = 0$$
Factors of 400:
1, 400
2, 200
4, 100
5, 80
8, 50
10, 40
20, 20
can't be factored; 200 is not a triangular number.

45e.
$$\frac{1}{2}(n^2 + n) = 210$$
$$n^2 + n = 420$$
$$n^2 + n - 420 = 0$$
$$(n + 21)(n - 20) = 0$$
$$n = {}^-21, 20$$
$n = 20$ ($n = {}^-21$ doesn't make sense in this situation.)

46a.
$$\frac{n^2 - 3n}{2} = 20$$
$$n^2 - 3n = 40$$
$$n^2 - 3n - 40 = 0$$
$$(n - 8)(n + 5) = 0$$
$$n = 8, {}^-5$$
$n = 8$ ($n = {}^-5$ can't be the number of sides of a polygon.)

46b.
$$\frac{n^2 - 3n}{2} = 30$$
$$n^2 - 3n = 60$$
$$n^2 - 3n - 60 = 0$$
Factors of 60:
1, 60
2, 30
3, 20
4, 15
5, 12
6, 10
Can't be factored; there is no polygon with 30 diagonals.

46c.
$$\frac{n^2 - 3n}{2} = 35$$
$$n^2 - 3n = 70$$
$$n^2 - 3n - 70 = 0$$
$$(n - 10)(n + 7) = 0$$
$$n = 10, {}^-7$$
$n = 10$ ($n = {}^-7$ can't be the number of sides of a polygon.)

46d.
$$\frac{n^2 - 3n}{2} = 50$$
$$n^2 - 3n = 100$$
$$n^2 - 3n - 100 = 0$$
Factors of 100:
1, 100
2, 50
4, 25
5, 20
10, 10
Can't be factored; no polygon has 50 diagonals.

46e.
$$\frac{n^2 - 3n}{2} = 54$$
$$n^2 - 3n = 108$$
$$n^2 - 3n - 108 = 0$$
$$(n - 12)(n + 9) = 0$$
$$n = 12, {}^-9$$
$n = 12$ ($n = {}^-9$ can't be the number of sides of a polygon.)

47. 10

48. 4

49. collinear; Possible explanation: The line through the first two points has the equation $y = {}^-5x + 3$, and $(3, {}^-12)$ satisfies this equation.

50. not collinear; Possible explanation: The line through the first two points has the equation $y = 1.2x - 3$, but the third point doesn't satisfy this equation.

51. Linear; first differences are constant.

52. Neither; neither first nor second differences are constant.

53. Quadratic; second differences are constant.

54a. 2.352×10^{13} mi

54b. 2.94×10^{15} mi

54c. 2.91648×10^{15} mi

55. rotation symmetry

56. both

57. reflection symmetry

Page 453   In Your Own Words

Possible answer: If a quadratic equation of the form $x^2 + bx + c$ can be factored, it can be rewritten as the product of two linear expressions $(x + m)(x + n)$, where $b = m + n$ and $c = mn$. To factor and solve $x^2 + 13x + 30$ for example, I would follow these steps:

Step 1 Find the factors of 30: 1 and 30; 2 and 15; 3 and 10; 5 and 6.

Step 2 Choose the factors whose sum is 13: 3 and 10.

Step 3 Let $m = 3$ and $n = 10$ in $(x + m)(x + n)$ since $x^2 + (3 + 10)x + (3 \cdot 30) =$ $x^2 + (m + n)x + (mn)$: $(x + 3)(x + 10)$.

Step 4 Set $(x + 3)(x + 10)$ equal to 0 and solve for x.

$(x + 3)(x + 10) = 0$

$x + 3 = 0 \quad$ or $\quad x + 10 = 0$
$\qquad x = {}^-3 \qquad\qquad x = {}^-10$

7-3   Completing the Square

Page 457   Problem Set A

1.
$$(x - 3)^2 = 36$$
$$\sqrt{(x - 3)^2} = \pm\sqrt{36}$$
$$x - 3 = \pm6$$
$$x = 3 \pm 6$$
$$x = 9, {}^-3$$

2. $(k - 1)^2 - 25 = 0$
$$(k - 1)^2 = 25$$
$$\sqrt{(k - 1)^2} = \pm\sqrt{25}$$
$$k - 1 = \pm5$$
$$k = 1 \pm 5$$
$$k = 6, {}^-4$$

3. $2(r - 7)^2 = 32$
$$(r - 7)^2 = 16$$
$$\sqrt{(r - 7)^2} = \pm\sqrt{16}$$
$$r - 7 = \pm4$$
$$r = 7 \pm 4$$
$$r = 11, 3$$

4. $(a - 4)^2 + 2 = 0$
$$(a - 4)^2 = {}^-2$$
No real number squared can equal a negative number.
no solution

5. $2(b - 3)^2 + 5 = 55$
$$2(b - 3)^2 = 50$$
$$(b - 3)^2 = 25$$
$$\sqrt{(b - 3)^2} = \pm\sqrt{25}$$
$$b - 3 = \pm5$$
$$b = 3 \pm 5$$
$$b = 8, {}^-2$$

6. $3(2c + 5)^2 - 63 = 300$
$$3(2c + 5)^2 = 363$$
$$(2c + 5)^2 = 121$$
$$\sqrt{(2c + 5)^2} = \pm\sqrt{121}$$
$$2c + 5 = \pm11$$
$$2c = {}^-5 \pm 11$$
$$c = \frac{{}^-5 \pm 11}{2}$$
$$c = 3, {}^-8$$

7.
$$(x - 4)^2 = 3$$
$$\sqrt{(x - 4)^2} = \pm\sqrt{3}$$
$$x - 4 = \pm\sqrt{3}$$
$$x = 4 \pm\sqrt{3}$$

8. $2(r - 3)^2 = {}^-10$
$$(r - 3)^2 = {}^-5$$
No real number squared can equal a negative number.
no solution

9. $4(x + 2)^2 - 3 = 0$
$$4(x + 2)^2 = 3$$
$$(x + 2)^2 = \frac{3}{4}$$
$$\sqrt{(x + 2)^2} = \pm\sqrt{\frac{3}{4}}$$
$$x + 2 = \pm\sqrt{\frac{3}{4}}$$
$$x = {}^-2 \pm\sqrt{\frac{3}{4}}$$

10. 7. 5.73, 2.27; 9. ${}^-1.13, {}^-2.87$

Page 458   Problem Set B

1a. $x^2 + 6x + 9 = (x + 3)^2$

1b. $b^2 + 9$ cannot be factored using integers.

1c. $x^2 + 6x + 4$ cannot be factored using integers.

1d. $m^2 + 12m - 36$ cannot be factored using integers.

1e. $m^2 - 12m + 36 = (m - 6)^2$

1f. $y^2 + y + \frac{1}{4} = \left(y + \frac{1}{2}\right)^2$

1g. $r^2 - 16 = (r + 4)(r - 4)$ which is not a perfect square.

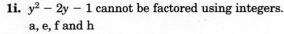

1h. $1 + 2r + r^2 = (1 + r)^2$

1i. $y^2 - 2y - 1$ cannot be factored using integers.

a, e, f and h

2a. $4p^2 + 4p + 1 = (2p + 1)^2$

2b. $4q^2 + 4q + 4$ cannot be factored using integers.

2c. $4s^2 - 4s - 1$ cannot be factored using integers.

2d. $4t^2 - 4t + 1 = (2t - 1)^2$

2e. $4y^2 + 9$ cannot be factored using integers.

2f. $4w^2 + 12w + 9 = (2w + 3)^2$

a, d, and f

3. If the expression is in the form $ax^2 + bx + c$, the coefficient of x^2 and the constant c should both be perfect squares. The coefficient of x should be ± 2 times the product of the square roots of these two perfect squares.

Page 459 Problem Set C

1. $x^2 - 18x + 81 = (x - 9)^2$

$81, (x - 9)^2$

2. $x^2 + 22x + 121 = (x + 11)^2$

$121, (x + 11)^2$

3. $k^2 - 3k + \frac{9}{4} = \left(k - \frac{3}{2}\right)^2$

$\frac{9}{4}, \left(k - \frac{3}{2}\right)^2$

4. $25m^2 + 10m + 1 = (5m + 1)^2$

$1, (5m + 1)^2$

5. $16r^2 - 8r + 1 = (4r - 1)^2$

$+ 1, (4r - 1)^2$

6. $4z^2 - 12z + 9 = (2z - 3)^2$

$+ 9 = (2z - 3)^2$

Page 459 Share and Summarize

1. If you can get a quadratic equation into the form $expression^2 = constant$, you can solve it by taking the square root of both sides.

2. If a trinomial is in the form $ax^2 + bx + c$, b should be equal to $\pm 2\sqrt{ac}$.

Page 460 Problem Set D

1. $x^2 + 6x + 15 = x^2 + 6x + 9 + 6$
$= (x + 3)^2 + 6$

$6, 6$

2. $k^2 - 6k + 30 = k^2 - 6k + 9 + 21$
$= (k - 3)^2 + 21$

$21, 21$

3. $s^2 + 6s - 1 = s^2 + 6s + 9 - 10$
$= (s + 3)^2 - 10$

$10, 3, 10$

4. $r^2 - 6r - 21 = r^2 - 6r + 9 - 30$
$= (r - 3)^2 - 30$

$- 30, - 3, - 30$

5. $m^2 + 12m + 30 = m^2 + 12m + 36 - 6$
$= (m + 6)^2 - 6$

$(m + 6)^2 - 6$

6. $h^2 - 5h = h^2 - 5h + \frac{25}{4} - \frac{25}{4}$
$= \left(h - \frac{5}{2}\right)^2 - \frac{25}{4}$

$\left(h - \frac{5}{2}\right)^2 - \frac{25}{4}$

7. $9r^2 + 18r - 20 = 9r^2 + 18r + 9 - 29$
$= (3r + 3)^2 - 29$

$(3r + 3)^2 - 29$

8. $9n^2 - 6n + 11 = 9n^2 - 6n + 1 + 10$
$= (3n - 1)^2 + 10$

$(3n - 1)^2 + 10$

Page 460 Problem Set E

1.
$$x^2 - 8x - 9 = 0$$
$$x^2 - 8x + 16 - 25 = 0$$
$$(x - 4)^2 - 25 = 0$$
$$(x - 4)^2 = 25$$
$$\sqrt{(x - 4)^2} = \pm\sqrt{25}$$
$$x - 4 = \pm 5$$
$$x = 4 \pm 5$$
$$x = 9, {}^-1$$

$x = 9, {}^-1$

2.
$$w^2 - 8w + 6 = 0$$
$$w^2 - 8w + 16 - 10 = 0$$
$$(w - 4)^2 - 10 = 0$$
$$(w - 4)^2 = 10$$
$$\sqrt{(w - 4)^2} = \pm\sqrt{10}$$
$$w - 4 = \pm\sqrt{10}$$
$$w = 4 \pm \sqrt{10}$$

$w = 4 \pm \sqrt{10}$

3.
$$9m^2 + 6m - 8 = 0$$
$$9m^2 + 6m + 1 - 9 = 0$$
$$(3m + 1)^2 - 9 = 0$$
$$(3m + 1)^2 = 9$$
$$\sqrt{(3m + 1)^2} = \pm\sqrt{9}$$
$$3m + 1 = \pm 3$$
$$3m = {}^-1 \pm 3$$
$$m = \frac{2}{3}, \frac{-4}{3}$$

$m = \frac{2}{3}, \frac{-4}{3}$

Page 461 Problem Set F

1.
$$x^2 - 4x + 4 - \frac{9}{2} = 0$$
$$(x - 2)^2 - \frac{9}{2} = 0$$
$$(x - 2)^2 = \frac{9}{2}$$
$$\sqrt{(x - 2)^2} = \pm\sqrt{\frac{9}{2}}$$
$$x - 2 = \pm\frac{3}{\sqrt{2}}$$
$$x = 2 \pm \frac{3}{\sqrt{2}}$$

2.
$$2m^2 - 12m + 7 = 0$$
$$m^2 - 6m + \frac{7}{2} = 0$$
$$m^2 - 6m + 9 - \frac{11}{2} = 0$$
$$(m - 3)^2 - \frac{11}{2} = 0$$
$$(m - 3)^2 = \frac{11}{2}$$
$$\sqrt{(m - 3)^2} = \pm\sqrt{\frac{11}{2}}$$
$$m - 3 = \pm\sqrt{\frac{11}{2}}$$
$$m = 3 \pm\sqrt{\frac{11}{2}}$$

3a. $x^2 - \frac{2}{3}x - \frac{1}{6} = 0$

3b. 2; $9x^2 - 6x - \frac{3}{2} = 0$

3c. Possible solution:
$$9x^2 - 6x - \frac{3}{2} = 0$$
$$9x^2 - 6x + 1 - \frac{5}{2} = 0$$
$$(3x - 1)^2 - \frac{5}{2} = 0$$
$$(3x - 1)^2 = \frac{5}{2}$$
$$\sqrt{(3x - 1)^2} = \pm\sqrt{\frac{5}{2}}$$
$$3x - 1 = \pm\sqrt{\frac{5}{2}}$$
$$3x = 1 \pm \sqrt{\frac{5}{2}}$$
$$x = \frac{1}{3}\left(1 \pm \sqrt{\frac{5}{2}}\right)$$
$$x = \frac{1}{3}\left(1 + \sqrt{\frac{5}{2}}\right), \frac{1}{3}\left(1 - \sqrt{\frac{5}{2}}\right)$$

4. If you rewrite the equation as $x^2 - 16x + 64 = 0$, the left side is already a perfect square.
$(x - 8)^2 = 0$ simplifies to $x - 8 = 0$ since 0 only has one square root. $x = 8$ is the only solution.

5. $g^2 - 4g + 4 + 7 = 0$
$$(g - 2)^2 + 7 = 0$$
$$(g - 2)^2 = {}^-7$$

The next step would involve taking the square root of a negative number, which can't be done.

Page 461 Share and Summarize

1. Possible answer:
$$4x^2 - 4x - 15 = 0$$
Complete the square by adding 1 to both sides.
$$4x^2 - 4x + 1 - 15 = 1$$
$$(2x - 1)^2 - 15 = 1$$
$$(2x - 1)^2 = 16$$
$$\sqrt{(2x - 1)^2} = \pm\sqrt{16}$$
$$2x - 1 = \pm 4$$
$$2x = 1 \pm 4$$
$$x = \frac{1 \pm 4}{2}$$
$$x = \frac{5}{2}, \frac{-3}{2}$$

2. Divide through by the leading coefficient so that the equation is in the form $x^2 + \frac{b}{a}x + \frac{c}{a} = 0$. For example, $2x^2 + 4x - 10 = 0$ becomes $x^2 + 2x - 5 = 0$. It's now easy to complete the square: $x^2 + 2x - 5 + 1 = 1$, so $(x + 1)^2 = 6$.

Pages 462–465 On Your Own Exercises

1.
$$(x + 3)^2 = 25$$
$$\sqrt{(x + 3)^2} = \pm\sqrt{25}$$
$$x + 3 = \pm 5$$
$$x = {}^-3 \pm 5$$
$$x = 2, {}^-8$$

2.
$$(r - 8)^2 + 3 = 52$$
$$(r - 8)^2 = 49$$
$$\sqrt{(r - 8)^2} = \pm\sqrt{49}$$
$$r - 8 = \pm 7$$
$$r = 8 \pm 7$$
$$r = 15, 1$$

3.
$$(2m + 1)^2 - 4 = 117$$
$$(2m + 1)^2 = 121$$
$$\sqrt{(2m + 1)^2} = \pm\sqrt{121}$$
$$2m + 1 = \pm 11$$
$$2m = {}^-1 \pm 11$$
$$m = 5, {}^-6$$

4.
$$3(x - 3)^2 = 30$$
$$(x - 3)^2 = 10$$
$$\sqrt{(x - 3)^2} = \pm\sqrt{10}$$
$$x - 3 = \pm\sqrt{10}$$
$$x = 3 \pm \sqrt{10}$$

5.
$${}^-2(y - 7)^2 + 4 = 0$$
$${}^-2(y - 7)^2 = {}^-4$$
$$(y - 7)^2 = 2$$
$$\sqrt{(y - 7)^2} = \pm\sqrt{2}$$
$$y - 7 = \pm\sqrt{2}$$
$$y = 7 \pm \sqrt{2}$$

6. $4(2z + 3)^2 - 2 = {}^-1$

$4(2z + 3)^2 = 1$

$(2z + 3)^2 = \dfrac{1}{4}$

$\sqrt{(2z + 3)^2} = \pm\sqrt{\dfrac{1}{4}}$

$2z + 3 = \pm\dfrac{1}{2}$

$2z = {}^-3 \pm \dfrac{1}{2}$

$z = \dfrac{-5}{4}, \dfrac{-7}{4}$

7. $x^2 - 8x + 16 = (x - 4)^2$

8. $b^2 + 9b + \dfrac{81}{4} = \left(b + \dfrac{9}{2}\right)^2$

9. $81d^2 - 90d + 25 = (9d - 5)^2$

10. $r^2 - 6r + 1 = r^2 - 6r + 9 + {}^-8$

$= (r - 3)^2 - 8$

${}^-8, {}^-3, 8$

11. $r^2 + 6r + 6 = r^2 + 6r + 9 - 3$

$= (r + 3)^2 - 3$

$+3, {}^-3$

12. $p^2 - 16p + 60 = p^2 - 16p + 64 - 4$

$= (p - 8)^2 - 4$

$(p - 8)^2 - 4$

13. $g^2 - 3g - 1 = g^2 - 3g + 2.25 - 3.25$

$= (g - 1.5)^2 - 3.25$

$(g - 1.5)^2 - 3.25$

14. $a^2 + 10a + 101 = a^2 + 10a + 25 + 76$

$= (a + 5)^2 + 76$

$(a + 5)^2 + 76$

15. $4x^2 + 4x + 2 = 4x^2 + 4x + 1 + 1$

$= (2x + 1)^2 + 1$

$(2x + 1)^2 + 1$

16. $m^2 + 2m - 11 = 0$

$m^2 + 2m + 1 - 12 = 0$

$m^2 + 2m + 1 = 12$

$(m + 1)^2 = 12$

$\sqrt{(m + 1)^2} = \pm\sqrt{12}$

$m + 1 = \pm\sqrt{12}$

$m = {}^-1 \pm 2\sqrt{3}$

17. $b^2 - 3b = 3b + 7$

$b^2 - 6b - 7 = 0$

$b^2 - 6b + 9 - 16 = 0$

$(b - 3)^2 - 16 = 0$

$(b - 3)^2 = 16$

$\sqrt{(b - 3)^2} = \pm\sqrt{16}$

$b - 3 = \pm 4$

$b = 3 \pm 4$

$b = 7, {}^-1$

18. $x^2 - 6x = {}^-5$

$x^2 - 6x + 5 = 0$

$x^2 - 6x + 9 - 4 = 0$

$(x - 3)^2 - 4 = 0$

$(x - 3)^2 = 4$

$\sqrt{(x - 3)^2} = \pm\sqrt{4}$

$x - 3 = \pm 2$

$x = 3 \pm 2$

$x = 5, 1$

19. $a^2 + 10a + 26 = 0$

$a^2 + 10a + 25 + 1 = 0$

$(a + 5)^2 + 1 = 0$

$(a + 5)^2 = {}^-1$

The square of a real number cannot be negative.
no solutions

20. $2x^2 + 4x - 1 = 0$

$x^2 + 2x - \dfrac{1}{2} = 0$

$x^2 + 2x + 1 - \dfrac{3}{2} = 0$

$(x + 1)^2 - \dfrac{3}{2} = 0$

$(x + 1)^2 = \dfrac{3}{2}$

$\sqrt{(x + 1)^2} = \pm\sqrt{\dfrac{3}{2}}$

$x + 1 = \pm\sqrt{\dfrac{3}{2}}$

$x = {}^-1 \pm \sqrt{\dfrac{3}{2}}$

21. $2u^2 + 3u - 2 = 0$

$u^2 + \dfrac{3}{2}u - 1 = 0$

$u^2 + \dfrac{3}{2}u + \dfrac{9}{16} - \dfrac{25}{16} = 0$

$\left(u + \dfrac{3}{4}\right)^2 - \dfrac{25}{16} = 0$

$\left(u + \dfrac{3}{4}\right)^2 = \dfrac{25}{16}$

$\sqrt{\left(u + \dfrac{3}{4}\right)^2} = \pm\sqrt{\dfrac{25}{16}}$

$u + \dfrac{3}{4} = \pm\dfrac{5}{4}$

$u = \dfrac{-3}{4} \pm \dfrac{5}{4}$

$u = {}^-2, \dfrac{1}{2}$

22. Stephen's puzzle has no solution. The equation is $(x - 1)^2 + 5 = 4$. An equivalent equation is $(x - 1)^2 = {}^-1$, and since $(x - 1)^2$ must be at least 0, the puzzle has no solution. Consuela's puzzle has one solution. The equation is $(x - 1)^2 + 1 = 1$. An equivalent equation is $(x - 1)^2 = 0$, and 0 has only one square root. Kwame's puzzle has two solutions. The equation is $(2x - 5)^2 + 1 = 10$. An equivalent equation is $(2x - 5)^2 = 9$, and 9 has two square roots.

23.
$$^-16(t - 1)^2 + 20 = 0$$
$$^-16(t - 1)^2 = {}^-20$$
$$(t - 1)^2 = \frac{5}{4}$$
$$\sqrt{(t - 1)^2} = \pm\sqrt{\frac{5}{4}}$$
$$t - 1 = \pm\frac{\sqrt{5}}{2}$$
$$t = 1 \pm \frac{\sqrt{5}}{2}$$
$$t \approx 2.12, \; {}^-0.12$$

$t \approx 2.12$ s ($t \approx {}^-0.12$ doesn't make sense in this situation.)

24a. i.
$$x^2 + 6x + 15 = 0$$
$$x^2 + 6x + 9 + 6 = 0$$
$$(x + 3)^2 + 6 = 0; \text{ no solution;}$$

$(x + 3)^2 + 6 = 0$; no solution; Possible explanation: $(x + 3)^2$ would have to be $^-6$, and a square can't be negative.

ii.
$$x^2 + 6x + 5 = 0$$
$$x^2 + 6x + 9 - 4 = 0$$
$$(x + 3)^2 - 4 = 0$$

$(x + 3)^2 - 4 = 0$; There will be solutions. Possible explanation: $(x + 3)^2$ must be 4, which has two square roots.

24b. If $c > 0$, the equation has no solutions because $(x + a)^2$ must be ≥ 0 and if you add a positive number, the result can't be 0. If $c \leq 0$, there will be solutions because $(x + a)^2$ would have to equal ^-c which is ≥ 0 and so has at least one solution.

25a. Possible answer: 4 ft and 6 ft, which gives an area that is too small (24 ft² instead of 25 ft²).

25b. If x is the length of the shorter side, $x(x + 2) = 25$.
$$x(x + 2) = 25$$
$$x^2 + 2x - 25 = 0$$
$$x^2 + 2x + 1 - 26 = 0$$
$$(x + 1)^2 - 26 = 0$$
$$(x + 1)^2 = 26$$
$$\sqrt{(x + 1)^2} = \pm\sqrt{26}$$
$$x + 1 = \pm\sqrt{26}$$
$$x = {}^-1 \pm \sqrt{26}$$

Since x is the side of a rectangle, only the positive answer makes sense. The shorter side is $\sqrt{26} - 1$ ft; the longer side is $\sqrt{26} - 1 + 2 = \sqrt{26} + 1$ ft.

26a. 101

26b. 100

26c. $100(101) = 10{,}100$

26d. twice

26e. $10{,}100 \div 2 = 5{,}050$

26f. Write two rows of numbers 1 to n, one in reverse order. There are n pairs of numbers, and each pair adds to $n + 1$, so the sum of all the pairs is $n(n + 1)$. Since each number is counted twice, S is half of the sum of all the pairs, so
$$S = \frac{n(n + 1)}{2}.$$

26g.
$$\frac{n(n + 1)}{2} = 91$$
$$n(n + 1) = 182$$
$$n^2 + n - 182 = 0$$
$$n^2 + n + \frac{1}{4} - 182.25 = 0$$
$$\left(n + \frac{1}{2}\right)^2 - 182.25 = 0$$
$$\left(n + \frac{1}{2}\right)^2 = 182.25$$
$$\sqrt{\left(n + \frac{1}{2}\right)^2} = \pm\sqrt{182.25}$$
$$n + \frac{1}{2} = \pm 13.5$$
$$n = {}^-0.5 \pm 13.5$$
$$n = 13, \; {}^-14$$

The negative answer doesn't make sense for this problem, so $n = 13$. She added the numbers from 1 to 13.

27. $a = 2, b = {}^-7, c = 5$

28. $a = 9, b = {}^-8, c = {}^-2$

29. $a = 3.5, b = 2, c = 3$

30. $a = 1, b = 0, c = {}^-1$

31. $a = 1, b = 0, c = 4$

32. $a = 3.5, b = 1, c = {}^-7$

33.

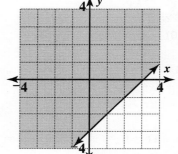

34.

35.

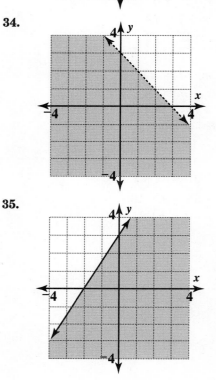

36a. N
36b. K
36c. P
36d. T
36e. R
36f. M
36g. Q
36h. S
36i. L

Page 464   In Your Own Words

Possible answer: If a quadratic equation is in the form of a perfect square, you can easily rewrite it as the square of a binomial and solve the equation by taking the square root of each side. This technique reduces a quadratic equation into a linear equation, simplifying the process for solving quadratic equations.

7-4   The Quadratic Formula

Pages 467–468   Problem Set A

1. $a = 2, b = 3, c = 0$

$$x = \frac{^-3 \pm \sqrt{3^2 - 4(2)(0)}}{2(2)}$$

$$x = \frac{^-3 \pm \sqrt{9 - 0}}{4}$$

$$x = \frac{^-3 \pm 3}{4}$$

$$x = 0 \ or \ \frac{-3}{2}$$

2. $a = 7, b = 1, c = {}^-3$

$$x = \frac{^-1 \pm \sqrt{1^2 - 4(7)(^-3)}}{2(7)}$$

$$x = \frac{^-1 \pm \sqrt{1 + 84}}{14}$$

$$x = \frac{^-1 \pm \sqrt{85}}{14}$$

3. $a = {}^-1, b = 2, c = 3$

$$x = \frac{^-2 \pm \sqrt{2^2 - 4(^-1)(3)}}{2(^-1)}$$

$$x = \frac{^-2 \pm \sqrt{4 + 12}}{^-2}$$

$$x = \frac{^-2 \pm 4}{^-2}$$

$$x = 3 \ or \ {}^-1$$

4. $6x + 2 = x^2$

$$0 = x^2 - 6x - 2$$

$$a = 1, b = {}^-6, c = {}^-2$$

$$x = \frac{6 \pm \sqrt{(^-6)^2 - 4(1)(^-2)}}{2(1)}$$

$$x = \frac{6 \pm \sqrt{36 + 8}}{2}$$

$$x = \frac{6 \pm \sqrt{44}}{2}$$

$$x = \frac{6 \pm 2\sqrt{11}}{2}$$

$$x = 3 \pm \sqrt{11}$$

5.

$$2x^2 = x - 5$$

$$2x^2 - x + 5 = 0$$

$$a = 2, b = {}^-1, c = 5$$

$$x = \frac{1 \pm \sqrt{(^-1)^2 - 4(2)(5)}}{2(2)}$$

$$x = \frac{1 \pm \sqrt{1 - 40}}{4}$$

$$x = \frac{1 \pm \sqrt{^-39}}{4}$$

You can't take the square root of a negative number.

no solutions

6. $a = 1, b = 0, c = {}^-12$

$$x = \frac{0 \pm \sqrt{0^2 - 4(1)(^-12)}}{2(1)}$$

$$x = \frac{0 \pm \sqrt{0 + 48}}{2}$$

$$x = \frac{\pm 4\sqrt{3}}{2}$$

$$x = \pm 2\sqrt{3}$$

7.

$$x^2 = 5x$$

$$x^2 - 5x = 0$$

$$a = 1, b = {}^-5, c = 0$$

$$x = \frac{5 \pm \sqrt{(^-5)^2 - 4(1)(0)}}{2(1)}$$

$$x = \frac{5 \pm \sqrt{25 - 0}}{2}$$

$$x = \frac{5 \pm 5}{2}$$

$$x = 0 \ or \ 5$$

8.

$$x(x - 6) = 3$$

$$x^2 - 6x - 3 = 0$$

$$a = 1, b = {}^-6, c = {}^-3$$

$$x = \frac{6 \pm \sqrt{(^-6)^2 - 4(1)(^-3)}}{2(1)}$$

$$x = \frac{6 \pm \sqrt{36 + 12}}{2}$$

$$x = \frac{6 \pm \sqrt{48}}{2}$$

$$x = \frac{6 \pm 4\sqrt{3}}{2}$$

$$x = 3 \pm 2\sqrt{3}$$

9a. $x^2 + 3x + 2 = 0$

$$(x + 2)(x + 1) = 0$$

$$x = {}^-2 \ or \ {}^-1$$

9b. $x^2 + 3x + 2 = 0$

$$a = 1, b = 3, c = 2$$

$$x = \frac{^-3 \pm \sqrt{3^2 - 4(1)(2)}}{2(1)}$$

$$x = \frac{^-3 \pm \sqrt{9 - 8}}{2}$$

$$x = \frac{^-3 \pm \sqrt{1}}{2}$$

$$x = \frac{^-3 \pm 1}{2}$$

$$x = {}^-2 \ or \ {}^-1$$

9c. Answers will vary.

9d. 1, 3 and 7

1. $x^2 - 5x + 6 = 0$

$(x - 3)(x - 2) = 0$

$x = 3, 2$

could have factored

2. $w^2 - 6w + 9 = 0$

$(w - 3)^2 = 0$

$w = 3$

could have factored

3. $t^2 + 4t + 1 = 0$

$a = 1, b = 4, c = 1$

$t = \dfrac{^-4 \pm \sqrt{4^2 - 4(1)(1)}}{2(1)}$

$t = \dfrac{^-4 \pm \sqrt{16 - 4}}{2}$

$t = \dfrac{^-4 \pm \sqrt{12}}{2}$

$t = \dfrac{^-4 \pm 2\sqrt{3}}{2}$

$t = {^-2} \pm \sqrt{3}$

probably couldn't have factored

4. $x^2 - x + 2 = 0$

$a = 1, b = {^-1}, c = 2$

$x = \dfrac{1 \pm \sqrt{(^-1)^2 - 4(1)(2)}}{2(1)}$

$x = \dfrac{1 \pm \sqrt{1 - 8}}{2}$

$x = \dfrac{1 \pm \sqrt{^-7}}{2}$

You can't take the square root of a negative number.

no solutions; couldn't have factored

5. $k^2 + 4k + 2 = 0$

$a = 1, b = 4, c = 2$

$k = \dfrac{^-4 \pm \sqrt{(4)^2 - 4(1)(2)}}{2(1)}$

$k = \dfrac{^-4 \pm \sqrt{16 - 8}}{2}$

$k = \dfrac{^-4 \pm \sqrt{8}}{2}$

$k = \dfrac{^-4 \pm 2\sqrt{2}}{2}$

$k = {^-2} \pm \sqrt{2}$

probably couldn't have factored

6. $3g^2 - 2g - 2 = 0$

$a = 3, b = {^-2}, c = {^-2}$

$g = \dfrac{2 \pm \sqrt{(^-2)^2 - 4(3)(^-2)}}{2(3)}$

$g = \dfrac{2 \pm \sqrt{4 + 24}}{6}$

$g = \dfrac{2 \pm \sqrt{28}}{6}$

$g = \dfrac{2 \pm 2\sqrt{7}}{6}$

$g = \dfrac{1 \pm \sqrt{7}}{3}$

probably couldn't have factored

7. $z^2 - 12z + 36 = 0$

$(z - 6)^2 = 0$

$z = 6$

could have factored

8. $2e^2 + 7e + 6 = 0$

$a = 2, b = 7, c = 6$

$g = \dfrac{^-7 \pm \sqrt{(7)^2 - 4(2)(6)}}{2(2)}$

$g = \dfrac{^-7 \pm \sqrt{49 - 48}}{4}$

$g = \dfrac{^-7 \pm \sqrt{1}}{4}$

$g = \dfrac{^-7 \pm 1}{4}$

$g = {^-2}, {^-1.5}$

probably couldn't have factored

9. $x^2 + x = 15 - x$

$x^2 + 2x - 15 = 0$

$(x + 5)(x - 3) = 0$

$x = {^-5}, 3$

could be factored

10. $3n^2 + 14 = 8n^2 + 3n$

$0 = 5n^2 + 3n - 14$

$a = 5, b = 3, c = {^-14}$

$n = \dfrac{^-3 \pm \sqrt{3^2 - 4(5)(^-14)}}{2(5)}$

$n = \dfrac{^-3 \pm \sqrt{9 + 280}}{10}$

$n = \dfrac{^-3 \pm \sqrt{289}}{10}$

$n = \dfrac{^-3 \pm 17}{10}$

$n = {^-2}, 1.4$

probably couldn't have been factored

Page 468   Share and Summarize

1. When you complete the square using a, b, and c instead of actual numbers for the coefficients, you get the quadratic formula.

2a. factoring and backtracking

2b. completing the square and the quadratic formula

3. Possible answers: Factoring is convenient when the factors are easy to find. Backtracking is convenient for an equation in the form $a(bx + c)^2 + d = e$. Completing the square is easy when the coefficient of the x^2 term is 1 and the coefficient of the x term is even. Otherwise, the quadratic formula is likely to be the easiest method.

Pages 469–470   Problem Set C

1a. If x is the width in meters, then $x + 1$ is the length in meters

$x(x + 1) = 4$

$x^2 + x - 4 = 0$

1b. $a = 1, b = 1, c = {}^-4$

$$x = \frac{{}^-1 \pm \sqrt{1^2 - 4(1)({}^-4)}}{2(1)}$$

$$x = \frac{{}^-1 \pm \sqrt{1 + 16}}{2}$$

$$x = \frac{{}^-1 \pm \sqrt{17}}{2}$$

Only the positive solution makes sense in this context, so the width is $\frac{{}^-1+\sqrt{17}}{2}$ m ≈ 156 cm, and the length is $1 + \frac{{}^-1+\sqrt{17}}{2} = \frac{1+\sqrt{17}}{2}$ m ≈ 256 cm.

2. If x is the width in meters, then $x + 2$ is the length in meters

$$x(x + 2) = 6$$
$$x^2 + 2x - 6 = 0$$
$$a = 1, b = 2, c = {}^-6$$

$$x = \frac{{}^-2 \pm \sqrt{2^2 - 4(1)({}^-6)}}{2(1)}$$

$$x = \frac{{}^-2 \pm \sqrt{4 + 24}}{2}$$

$$x = \frac{{}^-2 \pm \sqrt{28}}{2}$$

$$x = \frac{{}^-2 \pm 2\sqrt{7}}{2}$$

$$x = {}^-1 \pm \sqrt{7}$$

Only the positive solution makes sense in this context, so the width is $\sqrt{7} - 1$ m ≈ 165 cm, and the length is $2 + {}^-1 + \sqrt{7} = 1 + \sqrt{7}$ m ≈ 365 cm

3. $h = 0$

$$0 = {}^-16t^2 + 30t$$
$$16t^2 - 30t = 0$$
$$2t(8t - 15) = 0$$
$$2t = 0 \quad or \quad 8t - 15 = 0$$
$$t = 0, 1\frac{7}{8}$$

Since $t = 0$ is when the ball left the ground, the ball returns to the ground after $1\frac{7}{8}$ s, or 1.875 s.

4a. $s = 5, v = 30$

$$h = 30t - 16t^2 + 5$$

4b. $5 + 30t - 16t^2 = 0$ or

$$16t^2 - 30t - 5 = 0$$
$$a = 16, b = {}^-30, c = {}^-5$$

$$x = \frac{30 \pm \sqrt{({}^-30)^2 - 4(16)({}^-5)}}{2(16)}$$

$$x = \frac{30 \pm \sqrt{900 + 320}}{32}$$

$$x = \frac{30 \pm \sqrt{1,220}}{32}$$

Only the positive solution makes sense in this context, so $t = \frac{30 + \sqrt{1,220}}{32} \approx 2.03$ s.

5.
$$^-16t^2 + 100 = 0$$
$$100 = 16t^2$$
$$t^2 = 6.25$$
$$t = 2.5 \, or \, {}^-2.5$$
$$t = {}^-2.5 \text{ makes no sense in this context.}$$
$$t = 2.5 \text{ s}$$

Pages 470–471   Problem Set D

1. $A = 5 + 2p$

2. $U = 20 - 2p$

3a. $T = A \cdot U$
$$T = 5 \cdot 20 = 100$$
$$100$$

3b. $T = A \cdot U$
$$T = (5 + 2p)(20 - 2p)$$
$$T = 100 + 30p - 4p^2$$

3c. $T = 100$
$$100 = 100 + 30p - 4p^2$$
$$4p^2 - 30p = 0$$
$$p(4p - 30) = 0$$
$$p = 0 \text{ and } 7.5$$

3d. The rating decreases when $100 + 30p - 4p^2 < 100$.

$$100 + 30p - 4p^2 < 100$$
$$^-4p^2 + 30p < 0$$

Consider the equation
$$^-4p^2 + 30p = 0$$
$$p({}^-4p + 30) = 0$$
$$p = 0 \quad or \quad {}^-4p + 30 = 0$$
$$^-4p = {}^-30$$
$$p = 7.5$$

Check values less than 0, between 0 and 7.5 and greater than 7.5 to see if they make the inequality true.

If $p = {}^-1$, then
$$^-4p^2 + 30p = {}^-4({}^-1)^2 + 30({}^-1)$$
$$= {}^-4 - 30$$
$$= {}^-34 \text{ which is} < 0 \checkmark$$

If $p = 1$, then
$$^-4p^2 + 30p = {}^-4(1)^2 + 30(1)$$
$$= {}^-4 + 30$$
$$= 26 \text{ which is not} < 0 ✗$$

If $p = 8$, then
$$^-4p^2 + 30p = {}^-4(8)^2 + 30(8)$$
$$= {}^-256 + 240$$
$$= {}^-16 \text{ which is} < 0 \checkmark$$

So a decrease in beds or an increase of more than 750 would decrease T.

3e. i. $100 + 30p - 4p^2 = 140$

$$0 = 4p^2 - 30p + 40$$

$a = 4, b = {}^-30, c = 40$

$$p = \frac{30 \pm \sqrt{({}^-30)^2 - 4(4)(40)}}{2(4)}$$

$$p = \frac{30 \pm \sqrt{900 - 640}}{8}$$

$$p = \frac{30 \pm \sqrt{260}}{8}$$

$$p = \frac{30 \pm 2\sqrt{65}}{8}$$

$$p = \frac{15 \pm \sqrt{65}}{4} \approx 5.77 \text{ or } 1.73$$

ii. From 3e part i, when $p = 5.77$ or 1.73,
$T = 140$

Check values less than 1.73, between 1.73 and 5.77 and greater than 5.77 to see if they make $100 + 30p - 4p^2 > 140$.

If $p = 0$, then

$100 + 30p - 4p^2 = 100 + 30(0) - 4(0)^2$
$= 100$ which is not > 140 ✗

If $p = 2$, then

$100 + 30p - 4p^2 = 100 + 30(2) - 4(2)^2$
$= 100 + 60 - 16$
$= 144$ which is > 140 ✓

If $p = 6$, then

$100 + 30p - 4p^2 = 100 + 30(6) - 4(6)^2$
$= 100 + 180 - 144$
$= 136$ which is not > 140 ✗

values between 5.77 and 1.73

3f. Add between 173 and 577 beds

Page 471 Share and Summarize

If the equation is quadratic, express it in the form $ax^2 + bx + c$ and then substitute the values of a,

b, and c into the formula $x = \dfrac{{}^-b \pm \sqrt{b^2 - 4ac}}{2a}$.

Pages 472–473 Problem Set E

1a. Possible answer: $x^2 \geq 0$, so $x^2 + 1 \geq 1$, so $x^2 + 1$ can't be equal to 0.

1b. $a = 1, b = 0, c = 1$

$b^2 - 4ac = 0^2 - 4(1)(1)$
$= 0 - 4$
$= {}^-4$

${}^-4$, negative

1c. Equations will vary; the value of $b^2 - 4ac$ will be negative.

Possible answer:

$x^2 + 7 = 0$

$a = 1, b = 0, c = 7$

$b^2 - 4ac = 0^2 - 4(1)(7)$
$= 0 - 28$
$= {}^-28$

negative

2a. $(x - 3)(x + 5) = 0$

$x^2 + 2x - 15 = 0$

$a = 1, b = 2, c = {}^-15$

$b^2 - 4ac = 2^2 - 4(1)({}^-15)$
$= 4 + 60$
$= 64$

64, positive

2b. Equations will vary; the value of $b^2 - 4ac$ will be positive.

Possible answer:

$(x + 1)(x + 2) = 0$

$x^2 + 3x + 2 = 0$

$a = 1, b = 3, c = 2$

$b^2 - 4ac = 3^2 - 4(1)(2)$
$= 9 - 8$
$= 1$

1, positive

3a. $x^2 + 2x + 1 = 0$

$a = 1, b = 2, c = 1$

$b^2 - 4ac = 2^2 - 4(1)(1)$
$= 4 - 4$
$= 0$

3b. Equations will vary; the value of $b^2 - 4ac$ will be 0.

Possible answer:

$(x + 2)^2 = 0$

$x^2 + 4x + 4 = 0$

$a = 1, b = 4, c = 4$

$b^2 - 4ac = 4^2 - 4(1)(4)$
$= 16 - 16$
$= 0$

0

4a. under the radical sign

4b. Negative values; if the expression is negative, you're trying to take the square root of a negative number, so there are no solutions.

4c. 0; if the expression is 0, there is only one square root (you add and subtract 0, which gives the same value for the solution).

4d. Positive values; if the expression is positive, there are two square roots (when you add and subtract $\sqrt{b^2 - 4ac}$ you get two different values).

Page 474 Problem Set F

1. $a = 2, b = {}^-9, c = 5$

$b^2 - 4ac = ({}^-9)^2 - 4(2)(5)$
$= 81 - 40$
$= 41$

$b^2 - 4ac$ is positive, so there are 2 solutions.

2. $a = 3, b = {}^-7, c = 9$

$b^2 - 4ac = ({}^-7)^2 - 4(3)(9)$
$= 49 - 108$
$= {}^-59$

$b^2 - 4ac$ is negative, so there are 0 solutions.

3a. $30t - 16t^2 = 100$

3b. $^-16t^2 + 30t - 100 = 0$

or

$16t^2 - 30t + 100 = 0$

3c. $a = 16, b = {}^-30, c = 100$

$b^2 - 4ac = ({}^-30)^2 - 4(16)(100)$

$\qquad\qquad = {}^-5{,}500$

$^-5{,}500$

3d. No; the value of $b^2 - 4ac$ is negative, so the equation has no solutions.

4a. $30t - 16t^2 = M$

4b. $^-16t^2 + 30t - M = 0$

or

$16t^2 - 30t + M = 0$

4c. The graph reaches its highest point at only 1 point.

1

4d. It must be 0.

4e. $a = 16, b = {}^-30, c = M$

$b^2 - 4ac = 0$

$({}^-30)^2 - 4(16)(M) = 0$

$900 - 64M = 0$

$^-64M = {}^-900$

$M = \dfrac{900}{64} = \dfrac{225}{16} \approx 14.06$

4f. about 14.06 ft

4g. $^-16t^2 + 30t - \dfrac{225}{16} = 0$

$a = {}^-16, b = 30, c = -\dfrac{225}{16}$

$t = \dfrac{{}^-30 \pm \sqrt{30^2 - 4({}^-16)\left(-\dfrac{225}{16}\right)}}{2({}^-16)}$

$t = \dfrac{{}^-30 \pm \sqrt{900 - 900}}{{}^-32}$

$t = \dfrac{{}^-30 \pm \sqrt{0}}{{}^-32}$

$t = \dfrac{{}^-30 \pm 0}{32}$

$t = \dfrac{15}{16} \approx 0.94$ s

Page 475   Share and Summarize

1. Write the equation in the form $ax^2 + bx + c$ and compute $b^2 - 4ac$. If this value is positive, there are two solutions; if it is equal to 0, there is one solution; and if it is negative, there are no solutions.

2. Possible answer: Look at the value of $b^2 - 4a(c - d)$; if it's positive or 0, y is d for at least one x value; if it's negative, y is never d.

Pages 475–478   Lab

1. Answers will vary.

2. Rectangles and explanations will vary.

3. approximately 1.62

4. Answers will vary.

5. $\dfrac{x + 1}{x}$

6. $\dfrac{x}{1} = \dfrac{x + 1}{x}$

Multiply both sides of the equation by x to get x out of the denominator.

$x^2 = x + 1$ or $x^2 - x - 1 = 0$

7. $x^2 - x - 1 = 0$

$a = 1, b = {}^-1, c = {}^-1$

$x = \dfrac{1 \pm \sqrt{({}^-1)^2 - 4(1)({}^-1)}}{2(1)}$

$x = \dfrac{1 \pm \sqrt{1 + 4}}{2}$

$x = \dfrac{1 \pm \sqrt{5}}{2}$; approximately 1.618, $^-0.681$

8. Only 1.618 makes sense; the side lengths of a rectangle must be positive.

9. approximately 1.618

10. The values are very close.

11. Answers will vary.

12a. Since it is a square, the ratio is $\dfrac{1}{1}$ or 1.

12b. $\dfrac{2}{1}$ or 2

12c. $\dfrac{3}{2}$ or 1.5

12d. Answers will vary, but the ratio should be close to the golden ratio.

13. $1 + 1 = 2$

$1 + 2 = 3$

$2 + 3 = 5$

$3 + 5 = 8$

$5 + 8 = 13$

$8 + 13 = 21$

13 and 21; Possible explanation: For each new number, add the two previous numbers.

14. $\dfrac{F_4}{F_3} = \dfrac{3}{2} = 1.5$

$\dfrac{F_5}{F_4} = \dfrac{5}{3} = 1.667$

$\dfrac{F_6}{F_5} = \dfrac{8}{5} = 1.6$

$\dfrac{F_7}{F_6} = \dfrac{13}{8} = 1.625$

$\dfrac{F_8}{F_7} = \dfrac{21}{13} \approx 1.615$

$\dfrac{F_9}{F_8} = \dfrac{34}{21} \approx 1.619$

$\dfrac{F_{10}}{F_9} = \dfrac{55}{34} \approx 1.618$

15. They seem to be getting closer and closer to the golden ratio.

16. Answers will vary.

1. $2x^2 + 5x = 0$

   $a = 2, b = 5, c = 0$

   $x = \dfrac{-5 \pm \sqrt{5^2 - 4(2)(0)}}{2(2)}$

   $x = \dfrac{-5 \pm \sqrt{25 - 0}}{4}$

   $x = \dfrac{-5 \pm 5}{4}$

   $x = -2.5$ and 0

2. $\boxed{5x^2 + 7x + 4 = 0}$

   $a = 5, b = 7, c = 4$

   $x = \dfrac{-7 \pm \sqrt{7^2 - 4(5)(4)}}{2(5)}$

   $x = \dfrac{-7 \pm \sqrt{49 - 80}}{10}$

   $x = \dfrac{-7 \pm \sqrt{-31}}{10}$

   You can't take the square root of a negative number.
   no solutions

3. $c^2 - 10 = 0$

   $a = 1, b = 0, c = -10$

   $c = \dfrac{0 \pm \sqrt{0^2 - 4(1)(-10)}}{2(1)}$

   $c = \dfrac{0 \pm \sqrt{40}}{2}$

   $c = \dfrac{\pm 2\sqrt{10}}{2}$

   $c = \pm\sqrt{10}$

4. $b^2 + 10 = 0$

   $a = 1, b = 0, c = 10$

   $b = \dfrac{0 \pm \sqrt{0^2 - 4(1)(10)}}{2(1)}$

   $b = \dfrac{\pm\sqrt{-40}}{2}$

   You can't take the square root of a negative number
   no solutions

5. factoring:

   $$9x^2 - 16 = 0$$
   $$(3x + 4)(3x - 4) = 0$$
   $$x = \pm\dfrac{4}{3}$$

   quadratic formula:

   $a = 9, b = 0, c = -16$

   $x = \dfrac{0 \pm \sqrt{0^2 - 4(9)(-16)}}{2(9)}$

   $x = \dfrac{\pm\sqrt{576}}{18}$

   $x = \dfrac{\pm 24}{18}$

   $x = \pm\dfrac{4}{3}$

6. If w is the width in centimeters, then $2w + 2$ is the length in centimeters

   $$w(2w + 2) = 320$$
   $$2w^2 + 2w = 320$$
   $$2w^2 + 2w - 320 = 0$$

   $a = 2, b = 2, c = -320$

   $w = \dfrac{-2 \pm \sqrt{2^2 - 4(2)(-320)}}{2(2)}$

   $w = \dfrac{-2 \pm \sqrt{4 + 2,560}}{4}$

   $w = \dfrac{-2 \pm \sqrt{2,564}}{4}$

   $w = \dfrac{-2 \pm 2\sqrt{641}}{4}$

   $w = \dfrac{-1 \pm \sqrt{641}}{2}$

   The width is $\dfrac{-1 \pm \sqrt{641}}{2} \approx 12.16$ cm (-13.16 doesn't make sense in the context) and the length is $2 \cdot 12.16 + 2 = 26.32$ cm.

7a. $2t(60 - t) = 0$

   $120t - 2t^2 = 0$

   $a = -2, b = 120, c = 0$

   $t = \dfrac{-120 \pm \sqrt{120^2 - 4(-2)(0)}}{2(-2)}$

   $t = \dfrac{-120 \pm \sqrt{14,400}}{-4}$

   $t = \dfrac{-120 \pm 120}{-4}$

   $t = 0$ and 60

   60 s

7b. $2t(60 - t) = 1,200$

   $120t - 2t^2 = 1,200$

   $$0 = 2t^2 - 120t + 1,200$$

   $a = 2, b = -120, c = 1,200$

   $t = \dfrac{120 \pm \sqrt{(-120)^2 - 4(2)(1,200)}}{2(2)}$

   $t = \dfrac{120 \pm \sqrt{14,400 - 9600}}{4}$

   $t = \dfrac{120 \pm \sqrt{4,800}}{4}$

   $t = \dfrac{120 \pm 40\sqrt{3}}{4}$

   $t = 30 \pm 10\sqrt{3}$ or approximately 12.68 s and 47.32 s

8. $a = 1, b = 2, c = 3$

   $b^2 - 4ac = 2^2 - 4(1)(3)$

   $\qquad\qquad = 4 - 12$

   $\qquad\qquad = -8$

   no solutions because $b^2 - 4ac$ is negative (-8)

9. $a = 1, b = -2, c = -3$

   $b^2 - 4ac = (-2)^2 - 4(1)(-3)$

   $\qquad\qquad = 4 + 12$

   $\qquad\qquad = 16$

   two solutions because $b^2 - 4ac$ is positive (16)

10. $a = 9, b = 12, c = 4$

   $b^2 - 4ac = 12^2 - 4(9)(4)$

   $\qquad\qquad = 144 - 144$

   $\qquad\qquad = 0$

   1 solution because $b^2 - 4ac$ is 0

11a. No; to find when it might, you'd solve
$40t - 16t^2 + 5 = 100$ or $^-16t^2 + 40t - 95 = 0$,
but since $b^2 - 4ac = {}^-4{,}480$, which is negative,
the equation has no solutions.

11b. Yes; to find whether it will, you'd solve
$40t - 16t^2 + 5 = 15$ or $^-16t^2 + 40t - 10 = 0$;
since $b^2 - 4ac = 960$, which is positive, the
equation has solutions.

11c. $40t - 16t^2 + 5 = M$, where M is the maximum
point.
$$^-16t^2 + 40t + 5 - M = 0$$
$$a = {}^-16, b = 40, c = 5 - M$$
There is only one maximum point, so
$b^2 - 4ac = 0$.
$$b^2 - 4ac = 0$$
$$40^2 - 4(^-16)(5 - M) = 0$$
$$1{,}600 + 64(5 - M) = 0$$
$$1{,}600 + 320 - 64M = 0$$
$$1{,}920 - 64M = 0$$
$$^-64M = {}^-1{,}920$$
$$M = 30$$
30 ft

12a. Possible answers:
$(x - 8)(x + 1.5) = 0$ or $(x - 8)(2x + 3) = 0$

12b. $(x - 8)(x + 1.5) = 0$
$x^2 - 6.5x - 12 = 0$
$2x^2 - 13x - 24 = 0$
Yes, he was correct.

12c. Possible answers: An advantage of using the
quadratic formula is that you can be sure it will
work. A disadvantage is that it can be extra
work to rearrange an equation to fit in the form
$ax^2 + bx + c = 0$ and then apply the formula.

13a. Possible answer: $x = 1$

13b.
$$3x + \frac{1}{x} = 4$$
$$3x^2 + 1 = 4x$$
$$3x^2 - 4x + 1 = 0$$
$$a = 3, b = {}^-4, c = 1$$
$$x = \frac{4 \pm \sqrt{(^-4)^2 - 4(3)(1)}}{2(3)}$$
$$x = \frac{4 \pm \sqrt{16 - 12}}{6}$$
$$x = \frac{4 \pm \sqrt{4}}{6}$$
$$x = \frac{4 \pm 2}{6}$$
$$x = 1 \text{ or } \frac{1}{3}$$

14. The left side is equal to 0 when $x^2 - 2x - 2 = 0$.
$$a = 1, b = {}^-2, c = {}^-2$$
$$x = \frac{2 \pm \sqrt{(^-2)^2 - 4(1)(^-2)}}{2(1)}$$
$$x = \frac{2 \pm \sqrt{4 + 8}}{2}$$
$$x = \frac{2 \pm \sqrt{12}}{2}$$
$$x = \frac{2 \pm 2\sqrt{3}}{2}$$
$$x = 1 \pm \sqrt{3}$$

15. Possible answer:
The equation can be factored as:
$x(x^2 - 2x - 2) = 0$
At least one of the factors must be equal to 0 for
the equation to be true.
$x = 0 \ \ or \ \ x^2 - 2x - 2 = 0$
From problem 14, $x = 1 \pm \sqrt{3}$
$x = 0, 1 + \sqrt{3}$, and $1 - \sqrt{3}$

16. Let m stand for the number of monkeys in the
troop. Then $\left(\dfrac{m}{8}\right)^2 + 12 = m$
$$\left(\frac{m}{8}\right)^2 + 12 = m$$
$$\frac{m^2}{64} + 12 = m$$
$$m^2 + 768 = 64m$$
$$m^2 - 64m + 768 = 0$$
$$a = 1, b = {}^-64, c = 768$$
$$m = \frac{64 \pm \sqrt{(^-64)^2 - 4(1)(768)}}{2(1)}$$
$$m = \frac{64 \pm \sqrt{4{,}096 - 3{,}072}}{2}$$
$$m = \frac{64 \pm \sqrt{1{,}024}}{2}$$
$$m = \frac{64 \pm 32}{2}$$
$m = 16$ or 48; Both answers make sense.

17a. $x^2 - 3x - 7 = 0$
$$a = 1, b = {}^-3, c = {}^-7$$
$$x = \frac{3 \pm \sqrt{(^-3)^2 - 4(1)(^-7)}}{2(1)}$$
$$x = \frac{3 \pm \sqrt{9 + 28}}{2}$$
$$x = \frac{3 \pm \sqrt{37}}{2} \approx 4.54 \text{ and } ^-1.54$$

17b.

17c. $^-1.54 < x < 4.54$

17d. $x \leq {}^-1.54$ or $x \geq 4.54$

17e. $^-1.54 \leq x \leq 4.54$

18a. $x(x - 1) = 0$
$x = 0, 1$

18b. 0.5 is between 0 and 1
$0.5(0.5 - 1) = 0.5(^-0.5)$
$\qquad\qquad\quad = {}^-0.25$

negative

18c. no; Possible explanation: If $x^2 - x + 1 = 0$, $b^2 - 4ac = {}^-3$ and there are no solutions.

18d. yes; Possible explanation: If $x^2 - x - 1 = 0$, $b^2 - 4ac = 5$, and there are two solutions.

18e.

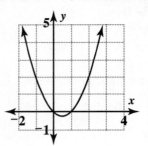

18f. If m is the minimum, $x^2 - x = m$, or $x^2 - x - m = 0$ has exactly one solution. So $b^2 - 4ac = 1 + 4m = 0$. Therefore, $4m = {}^-1$ and $m = {}^-0.25$.

19a. If the width is w, the height is $\frac{1}{2}(20 - 2w) = 10 - w$. The area is $(10 - w)w = 10w - w^2$.

19b. There is a maximum area.

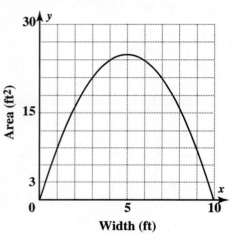

Width (ft)

19c. If the frame has a maximum area M, w satisfies the equation $10w - w^2 = M$ or $w^2 - 10w + M = 0$. For this equation, $b^2 - 4ac = 100 - 4M$. At the maximum, there is only one solution, so $100 - 4M = 0$ and $M = 25$.

19d. $M = 25$ satisfies the equation $w^2 - 10w + M = 0$ from above. So, $w^2 - 10w + 25 = 0$. $(w - 5)(w - 5) = 0$ $w = 5$ From 19a, the height is $10 - w = 10 - 5 = 5$ 5 ft by 5 ft

20. $B = 3(0.2^r)$

21. $B = 12(0.4^r)$

22. $b = 5,000(1.08)^t$

23. $b = c\left(\frac{15}{16}\right)^{24}$

24a. They increase at a steady rate.

24b. They increase, slowly at first and then more quickly.

24c. They decrease, quickly at first and then more slowly.

25a. Possible answer: 40 blue, 60 orange

25b. Possible answer: 27 blue, 73 orange

25c. 25 blue, 75 orange

Page 481   In Your Own Words

Possible answer: The solutions of $ax^2 + bx + c = d$ are the x-intercepts of the graph $y = ax^2 + bx + c$. To quickly find the number of solutions in a quadratic equation, use the following rules:

If $b^2 - 4ac < 0$, then there are no solutions.

If $b^2 - 4ac = 0$, then there is one solution.

If $b^2 - 4ac > 0$, then there are two solutions.

If $ax^2 + bx + c = d$ has no solutions then the graph does not have any x-intercepts.

Review and Self-Assessment

Pages 483–484   Strategies and Applications

1a. squaring

1b. taking the reciprocal

1c. changing sign

1d. taking the square root; consider positive and negative roots

2. yes;

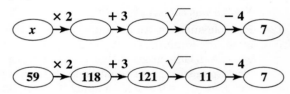

59

3. yes;

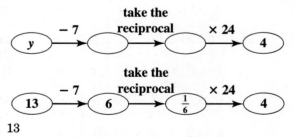

13

4. No; the input variable appears twice.

5. No; the input variable appears twice.

6. yes;

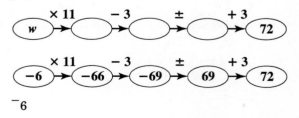

${}^-6$

7. yes;

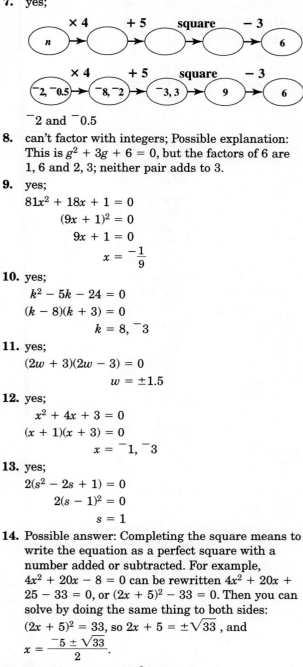

−2 and −0.5

8. can't factor with integers; Possible explanation: This is $g^2 + 3g + 6 = 0$, but the factors of 6 are 1, 6 and 2, 3; neither pair adds to 3.

9. yes;

$$81x^2 + 18x + 1 = 0$$
$$(9x + 1)^2 = 0$$
$$9x + 1 = 0$$
$$x = -\frac{1}{9}$$

10. yes;

$$k^2 - 5k - 24 = 0$$
$$(k - 8)(k + 3) = 0$$
$$k = 8, \, ^-3$$

11. yes;

$$(2w + 3)(2w - 3) = 0$$
$$w = \pm 1.5$$

12. yes;

$$x^2 + 4x + 3 = 0$$
$$(x + 1)(x + 3) = 0$$
$$x = \, ^-1, \, ^-3$$

13. yes;

$$2(s^2 - 2s + 1) = 0$$
$$2(s - 1)^2 = 0$$
$$s = 1$$

14. Possible answer: Completing the square means to write the equation as a perfect square with a number added or subtracted. For example, $4x^2 + 20x - 8 = 0$ can be rewritten $4x^2 + 20x + 25 - 33 = 0$, or $(2x + 5)^2 - 33 = 0$. Then you can solve by doing the same thing to both sides: $(2x + 5)^2 = 33$, so $2x + 5 = \pm\sqrt{33}$, and $x = \dfrac{^-5 \pm \sqrt{33}}{2}$.

15. Possible answer: $12x^2 + 5x - 3 = 0$

16. Completing the square using the equation $ax^2 + bx + c = 0$

17. This is the quadratic formula, which works only if d is 0.

18. If the value is negative, there are no solutions; if it's 0, there is one solution; if it's positive, there are two solutions.

Page 485 Demonstrating Skills

19. $a^2 + 3a = a(a + 3)$

$a(a + 3)$

20. $2b^2 - 2 = 2(b^2 - 1)$
$$= 2(b + 1)(b - 1)$$
$2(b + 1)(b - 1)$

21. $c^2 + 14c + 49 = (c + 7)^2$

$(c + 7)^2$

22. $8d^2 - 8d + 2 = 2(4d^2 - 4d + 1)$
$$= 2(2d - 1)^2$$
$2(2d - 1)^2$

23. $e^2 + 8e - 9 = (e + 9)(e - 1)$

$(e + 9)(e - 1)$

24. $f^2 + 7f + 10 = (f + 5)(f + 2)$

$(f + 5)(f + 2)$

25. $4g^2 + 12g - 3 = 4g^2 + 12g + 9 - 12$
$$= (2g + 3)^2 - 12$$
$(2g + 3)^2 - 12$

26. $h^2 - 10h + 7 = h^2 - 10h + 25 - 18$
$$= (h - 5)^2 - 18$$
$(h - 5)^2 - 18$

27. $2j^2 + 24j = 2(j^2 + 12j)$
$$= 2(j^2 + 12j + 36) - 2(36)$$
$$= 2(j + 6)^2 - 72$$
$2(j + 6)^2 - 72$

28.
$$k^2 + 10 = 20k - 90$$
$$k^2 - 20k + 100 = 0$$
$$a = 1, b = \, ^-20, c = 100$$
$$b^2 - 4ac = (^-20)^2 - 4(1)(100)$$
$$= 400 - 400$$
$$= 0$$
1 solution

29. $2m^2 + 3m + 3 = \, ^-5$
$$2m^2 + 3m + 8 = 0$$
$$a = 2, b = 3, c = 8$$
$$b^2 - 4ac = 3^2 - 4(2)(8)$$
$$= 9 - 64$$
$$= \, ^-55$$
0 solutions

30. $\sqrt{3n + 1} = 13$
$$(\sqrt{3n + 1})^2 = 13^2$$
$$3n + 1 = 169$$
$$3n = 168$$
$$n = 56$$
56

31. $\dfrac{60}{^-(2p - 3)} = 12$
$$60 = \, ^-12(2p - 3)$$
$$60 = \, ^-24p + 36$$
$$24 = \, ^-24p$$
$$^-1 = p$$
$^-1$

32. $(7q + 3)(q - 8) = 0$
$$7q + 3 = 0 \quad or \quad q - 8 = 0$$
$$7q = \, ^-3 \quad or \quad q = 8$$
$$q = \frac{-3}{7}$$
$-\dfrac{3}{7}, 8$

33. $(10r + 4)(5r + 4) = {}^-2$
$50r^2 + 60r + 16 = {}^-2$
$50r^2 + 60r + 18 = 0$
$2(25r^2 + 30r + 9) = 0$
$2(5r + 3)^2 = 0$
$5r + 3 = 0$
$5r = {}^-3$
$r = \dfrac{-3}{5}$
$-\dfrac{3}{5}$

34. $4s^2 + 3s - 40 = 3s - 41$
$4s^2 + 1 = 0$
$a = 4, b = 0, c = 1$
$b^2 - 4ac = 0^2 - 4(4)(1)$
$= 0 - 16$
$= {}^-16$
no solution

35. $t^2 - 100 = 0$
$t^2 = 100$
$t = \pm 10$

36. $2u^2 - 4u = 14$
$2u^2 - 4u - 14 = 0$
$2(u^2 - 2u - 7) = 0$
$a = 1, b = {}^-2, c = {}^-7$
$u = \dfrac{2 \pm \sqrt{({}^-2)^2 - 4(1)({}^-7)}}{2(1)}$
$u = \dfrac{2 \pm \sqrt{4 + 28}}{2}$
$u = \dfrac{2 \pm \sqrt{32}}{2}$
$u = \dfrac{2 \pm 4\sqrt{2}}{2}$
$u = 1 \pm 2\sqrt{2}$

37. $9v^2 - 3 = 4v^2 + 32$
$5v^2 - 35 = 0$
$5(v^2 - 7) = 0$
$v^2 - 7 = 0$
$v^2 = 7$
$v = \pm \sqrt{7}$

38. $5w^2 = 8w$
$5w^2 - 8w = 0$
$w(5w - 8) = 0$
$w = 0 \quad or \quad 5w - 8 = 0$
$5w = 8$
$w = \dfrac{8}{5}$
$0, \dfrac{8}{5}$

39. $3 - 9x - x^2 = 17$
$0 = x^2 + 9x + 14$
$0 = (x + 2)(x + 7)$
$x + 2 = 0 \quad or \quad x + 7 = 0$
$x = {}^-2 \qquad\qquad x = {}^-7$
${}^-2, {}^-7$

Chapter 8 Functions and Their Graphs

8-1 Functions

Page 490 Problem Set A

1. $5 \times 2 + 7 = 10 + 7 = 17$
2. $^-4 \times 2 + 7 = ^-8 + 7 = ^-1$
3. $x \times 2 + 7 = ^-10$
   $$x \times 2 = ^-17$$
   $$x = ^-17 \div 2$$
   $$x = ^-8.5$$
4. no; Possible explanation: If you double a number, there's only one possible answer; when you add 7 to that answer, there's still only one possible result.
5. $x \times 2 + 7 = 2x + 7$
6. Possible answer: It's a linear relationship like those we've studied throughout the year. The graph of the function would be a line.
7. no; Possible explanation: The same input will produce different outputs in the two machines. For example, an input of 0 produces output 7 in Function A and output 14 in Function B; Function A = $2x + 7$ and Function B = $(x + 7)2$.
8. $(2x + 7) - 7 = 2x$
   $2x \div 2 = x$
   Subtract 7. Then divide by 2.

Page 491 Problem Set B

1. yes
2. yes
3. no
4. no
5. Any prime number; 2, 3, 5, 7, and 11 are the first few possibilities.
6. Yes; any prime number will produce the output *yes*.
7. It's not possible. There is no way to know, just from the output *yes*, which prime number was entered. Likewise, there is no way to know from the output *no* which composite number was entered.

Page 491 Problem Set C

1. 3
2. 3
3. Any number; 0, $-\frac{1}{2}$, 101, and π are some examples.
4. Yes; every input produces the output 3, so it could have been any number.

5. For any input, there is only one possible output: 3. No input produces more than one output.
6. Possible answer: Because it always gives the same constant value as an output.
7. No machine will work. There is no way to know, just from the output 3, which number was entered.

Page 492 Share and Summarize

Possible answer: Gabriela is right; it is a function. Ben is right that different inputs produce the same output, but that's OK. The rule for a function is that every input has only one possible output, and that's true here.

Page 493 Problem Set D

1. $(2 \cdot 0 + 1)^2 = 1^2 = 1$
   $(2 \cdot {}^-1 + 1)^2 = ({}^-1)^2 = 1$
   $(2 \cdot 1 + 1)^2 = 3^2 = 9$
   $\left(2 \cdot \dfrac{1}{2} + 1\right)^2 = 2^2 = 4$
   $\left(2 \cdot {}^-\dfrac{1}{2} + 1\right)^2 = 0^2 = 0$

   Possible table:

Input	Output
0	1
$^-1$	1
1	9
$\frac{1}{2}$	4
$^-\frac{1}{2}$	0

2. Yes; for each input, there is only one possible output.
3a. $y = (2x + 1)^2$
3b. All describe his rule.
3c. $g(x) = (2x + 1)^2$ and $p(t) = (2t + 1)^2$

Pages 493–494 Problem Set E

1a. $y = (2x + 1)^2$
1b. Possible graph:

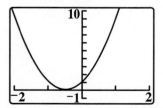

2. Graphs a, c, e, and g represent functions, because there is only one *y* value for each *x* value. Graphs b, d, and f do not, because a single *x* value produces more than one possible *y* value.

Page 495 Problem Set F

1. $f(2)$ represents the distance a skydiver has fallen after 2 s. Its value is $4.9(2^2) = 19.6$ m.
2. $4.9(10^2) = 4.9 \times 100 = 490$ m

3. no; Possible explanation: ⁻3 as an input would be 3 s before the jump, but a skydiver isn't falling before the jump, so the calculation won't tell you anything meaningful.

Page 496   Problem Set G

1. all real numbers
2. nonnegative numbers (positive or 0)
3. $1 - x \neq 0$
   $x \neq 1$
   all real numbers except 1
4. nonzero integers
5. integers
6a. $2{,}523 \times 6 = 15{,}138$
6b. Positive nonintegers and negative numbers can't be inputs; you can't have a partial ant or negative ants.
6c. $g(a) = 6a$

Page 496   Share and Summarize

1. Possible answers: 7 more than ⁻3 times the input; 3 times the input number subtracted from 7; $f(t) = 7 - 3t$; $f(t) = {}^{-}3t + 7$.

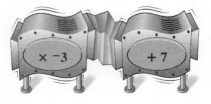

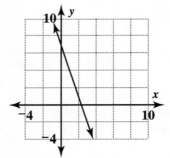

Input	Output
0	7
⁻1	10
1	4
$\frac{2}{3}$	5

2. no

Page 497   Problem Set H

1. 6 m; From the equation, Tala is holding the stone when $t = 0$ (it has not yet been thrown), and $h(0) = 6$. From the graph, the height of the graph on the h-axis when $t = 0$ is 6 m.
2. about 5 m above the water; Possible explanation: Tala releases the stone about 6 m above the water; since she's probably about 1.5 m tall, 5 m would mean the stone is released a little below shoulder height.

---

3. at about 0.8 s and about 2.2 s
4. between about 0.8 s and about 2.2 s
5. about 17 m
6. about 1.5 s
7. 17.48 m

Page 498   Problem Set I

1. $C(1) \approx \dfrac{21(1)}{1^2 + 1.3(1) + 2.9} \approx 4.04$ g/L

   $C(6) \approx \dfrac{21(6)}{6^2 + 1.3(6) + 2.9} \approx 2.70$ g/L

   $C(10) \approx \dfrac{21(10)}{10^2 + 1.3(10) + 2.9} \approx 1.81$ g/L

   These represent the concentration of the anesthetic 1 min, 6 min, and 10 min after it is administered.
2. about 4.5 g/L
3. about 1.7 min
4. 4.46 g/L at 1.70 min
5. about 20 s
6. Possible answer: about 40 s, since the concentration will stay high for at least 3 min after that

Page 499   Share and Summarize

1. Maximum value is 5 when $x = 0$.
2. Maximum value is 14 when $x = 2$.
3. no maximum value
4. Maximum value is 1 when $x = {}^{-}270$ and 90.

Page 500   Problem Set J

1.

Input	0.5	1	1.5	2	2.5	3
Width	2.5	2	1.5	1	0.5	0
Perimeter	6	6	6	6	6	6

2. It decreases by the same amount.
3. Possible equation: $W = 3 - L$
4.

Length	0.5	1	1.5	2	2.5	3
Width	2.5	2	1.5	1	0.5	0
Area	1.25	2	2.25	2	1.25	0

5. $A(L) = L(3 - L)$ or $A(L) = 3L - L^2$
6.

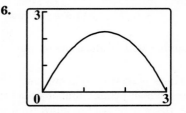

7. 1.5 m each

Page 501   Problem Set K

1. $40 \div 2 = 20$ $2 \cdot 2 + 20 = 24$
   $40 \div 4 = 10$ $2 \cdot 4 + 10 = 18$
   $40 \div 8 = 5$ $2 \cdot 8 + 5 = 21$
   $40 \div 10 = 4$ $2 \cdot 10 + 4 = 24$

Width, W	1.5	2	2.5	3
Length, L	1.5	1	0.5	0
Amount of Fencing	6	6	6	6

2. $L = \dfrac{40}{W}$

3. $2W + \dfrac{40}{W}$

4. The amount of fencing is a minimum (about 17.9 m) when the width is about 4.5 m, but there is not much practical difference in the fencing length for widths between 4 m and 5 m.

Page 502 Share and Summarize

1. By graphing the function $f(x) = x + \dfrac{1}{x}$, you see that the minimum total is 2 when $x = 1$.

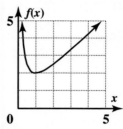

2. There doesn't appear to be a maximum. Possible explanation: The value of $f(x)$ is always a little greater than the value of the input x, because you add the positive value of $\dfrac{1}{x}$ to it. Since x has no maximum value, neither does $f(x)$.

Pages 502–503 Lab

1. Answers will vary.

2. Answers will vary. The actual maximum is for a side length of 1 in., giving a volume of 18 in³. It's possible that no student in class created this box; students should find the best approximation in the class.

3.

Side Length of Square	0	0.5	1	1.5	2	2.5
Height of Box	0	0.5	1	1.5	2	2.5
Length of Box	8	7	6	5	4	3
Width of Box	5	4	3	2	1	0

4.

Side Length of Square	0	0.5	1	1.5	2	2.5
Height of Box	0	0.5	1	1.5	2	2.5
Length of Box	8	7	6	5	4	3
Width of Box	5	4	3	2	1	0
Volume of Box	0	14	18	15	8	0

the one with a square of side length 1 in.

5a. x

5b. $8 - 2x$

5c. $5 - 2x$

5d. $x(8 - 2x)(5 - 2x)$

6. $v(x) = x(8 - 2x)(5 - 2x)$

7.

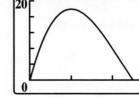

$x = 1$ in. appears to give the maximum volume.

8a. about 1.59 in. or 1.6 in.; Possible explanation: I looked at the graph of $v = x(11 - 2x)(8.5 - 2x)$.

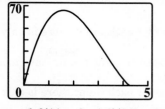

8b. $v = 1.6(11 - 2 \cdot 1.6)(8.5 - 2 \cdot 1.6) = 12.48 \cdot 5.3 = 66.144$ or about 66 in³

9. See student work.

Pages 504–513 On Your Own Exercises

1a. $10 \div 2 = 5$

1b. $\dfrac{-2}{3} \div 2 = \dfrac{-2}{3} \cdot \dfrac{1}{2} = \dfrac{-1}{3}$

1c. $1.5 \div 2 = 0.75$

1d. $x \div 2 = \dfrac{x}{2}$

1e. $x \div 2 = {}^-9$
$x = {}^-18$

1f. a "$\times 2$" machine

2a. $\dfrac{4 \cdot 4}{3 \cdot 3} = \dfrac{16}{9}$

2b. $\dfrac{{}^-4 \cdot {}^-4}{{}^-3 \cdot {}^-3} = \dfrac{16}{9}$

2c. $x \cdot x = 9$
$x^2 = 9$
$x = \sqrt{9}$
$x = 3$ or ${}^-3$

2d. There is no such function machine. A machine that finds square roots will give two values, $\pm\sqrt{x}$, for every input x, and one that finds only positive square root will give an incorrect response when the input to the "Square" machine is negative.

3a. $(1.5 - 1) \times \dfrac{1}{2} = 0.5 \times \dfrac{1}{2} = 0.25$

3b. $({}^-3 - 1) \times \dfrac{1}{2} = {}^-4 \times \dfrac{1}{2} = {}^-2$

3c. $(11 - 1) \times \dfrac{1}{2} = 10 \times \dfrac{1}{2} = 5$

3d. $\dfrac{x - 1}{2}$

3e. $\dfrac{x - 1}{2} = {}^-8$
$x - 1 = {}^-16$
$x = {}^-15$

3f. $\dfrac{x - 1}{2} \times 2 = x - 1$
$x - 1 + 1 = x$
Multiply by 2. Then add 1.
Possible answer:

4. A function; there is one such ratio (always equal to π) for every circle.

5. Not a function; each team has more than one member.

6. Not a function; CDs usually have more than one song.

7. function, because for each input there is only one output

8. not a function; because some inputs have more than one output

9. function, because for each input there is only one output

10a.
$(({}^-3)^2 - 2) \div 2 = \dfrac{7}{2}$
$(({}^-2)^2 - 2) \div 2 = 1$
$(({}^-1)^2 - 2) \div 2 = \dfrac{-1}{2}$
$((0)^2 - 2) \div 2 = {}^-1$
$((1)^2 - 2) \div 2 = \dfrac{-1}{2}$
$((2)^2 - 2) \div 2 = 1$
$((3)^2 - 2) \div 2 = \dfrac{7}{2}$

Input, I	Output, O
−3	$\dfrac{7}{2}$
−2	1
−1	$-\dfrac{1}{2}$
0	−1
1	$-\dfrac{1}{2}$
2	1
3	$\dfrac{7}{2}$

10b.

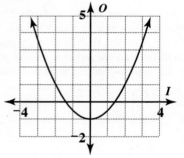

10c. Yes; each input has only one output.

11a. $g(t)$, $h(z)$, $b = a^2 + a + 1$, and $F(X)$; they all produce the appropriate outputs.

11b. $8^2 + 8 + 1 = 73$
$10^2 + 10 + 1 = 111$
$11^2 + 11 + 1 = 133$
73, 111, and 133 are missing, associated with 8, 10, and 11, respectively.

12a. $s(8) = 4.9(8)^2 = 4.9 \cdot 64 = 313.6$ m
the distance the rock falls in 8 s

12b. $s(9) = 4.9(9)^2 = 4.9 \cdot 81 = 396.9$ m
$s(10) = 4.9(10)^2 = 4.9 \cdot 100 = 490$ m

12c. $600 = 4.9t^2$
$t^2 = 600 \div 4.9$
$t = \sqrt{600 \div 4.9} \approx \sqrt{122.44} \approx 11.066$
after about 11.066 s

12d. t is between 0 (including 0) and about 11.066.

13. all real numbers

14. $x + 1 \neq 0$
$x \neq {}^-1$
all real numbers except ${}^-1$

15. $x + 1 \neq 0$
$x \neq {}^-1$
$x - 1 \neq 0$
$x \neq 1$
all real numbers except ${}^-1$ and 1

16. Graphs c and d; they have values of x that are associated with two or more values of y. *not a func*

17a. $h(4) = 6 + 20(4) - 4.9(4)^2 =$
$6 + 80 - 78.4 = 7.6$ m
the height of the stone after 4 s

17b. $h(3) = 6 + 20(3) - 4.9(3)^2 =$
$6 + 60 - 44.1 = 21.9$ m

17c.

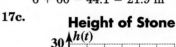
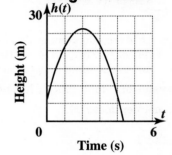

17d. about 26.5 m, about 2 s

18a. $0(0 - 7) = 0$
${}^-1(1 - 7) = 6$
${}^-2(2 - 7) = 10$
${}^-3(3 - 7) = 12$
${}^-4(4 - 7) = 12$
${}^-5(5 - 7) = 10$
${}^-6(6 - 7) = 6$
${}^-7(7 - 7) = 0$

s	$P(s)$
0	0
1	6
2	10
3	12
4	12
5	10
6	6
7	0

18b. Possible answer: If the deli sets its sandwich price at $7.00, it will not sell enough to make a profit.

18c. ${}^-3.25(3.25 - 7) = 12.1875 \approx 12.19$
${}^-3.5(3.5 - 7) = 12.25$
${}^-3.75(3.75 - 7) = 12.1875 \approx 12.19$
$3.50

Possible table:

s	P(s)
3.25	12.19
3.5	12.25
3.75	12.19

18d. $12.25 \times \$100 = \$1,225$

19. $f(0) = 0$

$f(1) = 200 - 5 = 195$

$f(10) = 2,000 - 500 = 1,500$

$f(19) = 3,800 - 1,805 = 1,995$

$f(20) = 4,000 - 2,000 = 2,000$

$f(21) = 4,200 - 2,205 = 1,995$

$f(30) = 6,000 - 4,500 = 1,500$

The maximum value is 2,000. The value that yields the maximum value is 20.

Possible calculator screens:

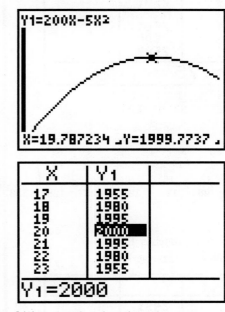

20. $k(0) = 4 + 0 - 0 = 4$

$k(0.4) = 4 + 1.6 - 0.64 = 4.96$

$k(0.5) = 4 + 2 - 1 = 5$

$k(0.6) = 4 + 2.4 - 1.44 = 4.96$

$k(1) = 4 + 4 - 4 = 4$

The maximum value is 5. The value that yields the maximum value is 0.5.

Possible calculator screens:

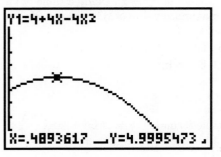

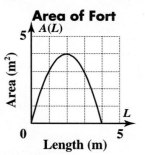

21a.

Length (m)	0.5	1	1.5	2	2.5	3	3.5
Width (m)	3.5	3	2.5	2	1.5	1	0.5
Perimeter (m)	8	8	8	8	8	8	8

21b. Possible function: $W(L) = 4 - L$

21c.

Length (m)	0.5	1	1.5	2	2.5	3	3.5
Width (m)	3.5	3	2.5	2	1.5	1	0.5
Perimeter (m)	8	8	8	8	8	8	8
Area (m²)	1.75	3	3.75	4	3.75	3	1.75

21d. $A(L) = L(4 - L)$ or $A(L) = 4L - L^2$

21e.

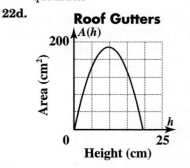

21f. 2 m by 2 m

22a. $39 - 4 \cdot 2 = 31$ $4 \cdot 31 = 124$

$39 - 8 \cdot 2 = 23$ $8 \cdot 23 = 184$

$39 - 12 \cdot 2 = 15$ $12 \cdot 15 = 180$

$39 - 16 \cdot 2 = 7$ $16 \cdot 7 = 112$

Height (cm), h	4	8	12	16
Width (cm), w	31	23	15	7
Area (cm²), A	124	184	180	112

22b. $w = 39 - 2h$

22c. $A(h) = h(39 - 2h) = 39h - 2h^2$

quadratic

22d.

Roof Gutters

22e. about 10 cm (9.75 cm exactly)

23.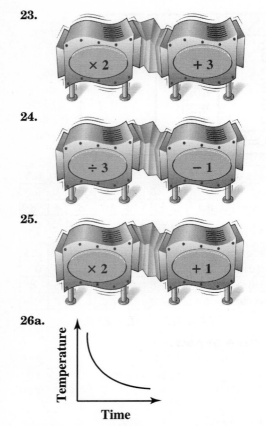

24.

25.

26a.

Temperature (vertical axis) vs. Time (horizontal axis)

26b. Yes; there is just one temperature for any given time.

27a. Add 180° to each previous measure.

Polygon	Sum of Interior Angles
Triangle	180°
Square	360°
Pentagon	540°
Hexagon	720°
Heptagon	900°
Octagon	1,080°
Nonagon	1,260°
Decagon	1,440°
11-gon	1,620°
Dodecagon	1,800°

27b. $g(s) = 180(s - 2)$

27c. Whole numbers greater than or equal to 3; the number of sides must be a whole number, and 3 is the smallest such input since a triangle is the polygon with the least number of sides.

28. Possible function: $f(x) = \dfrac{1}{x^2 - 9}$

29. Possible function: $f(x) = \sqrt{x}$

30. Possible function: $f(x) = \sqrt{-x}$

31. $f(^-0.5) = {}^-0.5 + 0.5^2 = {}^-0.25$

$(^-0.5, {}^-0.25)$

Possible calculator screen:

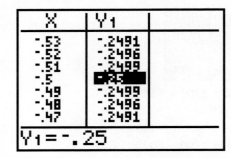

32. $f(0.5) = 1 - 0.5 + 0.5^2 = 0.75$

$(0.5, 0.75)$

Possible calculator screen:

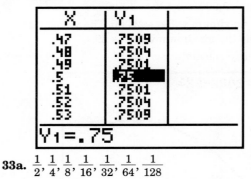

33a. $\dfrac{1}{2}, \dfrac{1}{4}, \dfrac{1}{8}, \dfrac{1}{16}, \dfrac{1}{32}, \dfrac{1}{64}, \dfrac{1}{128}$

33b. $\dfrac{16}{32} + \dfrac{8}{32} + \dfrac{4}{32} + \dfrac{2}{32} + \dfrac{1}{32} = \dfrac{31}{32}$

33c. $\dfrac{32}{64} + \dfrac{16}{64} + \dfrac{8}{64} + \dfrac{4}{64} + \dfrac{2}{64} + \dfrac{1}{64} = \dfrac{63}{64}$

33d. $\dfrac{64}{128} + \dfrac{32}{128} + \dfrac{16}{128} + \dfrac{8}{128} + \dfrac{4}{128} + \dfrac{2}{128} + \dfrac{1}{128} = \dfrac{127}{128}$

33e. The sum approaches 1.

34. Possible calculator screen:

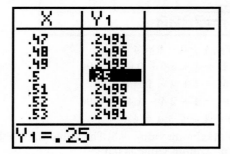

0.25; If one number is x, the other is $1 - x$, so the product is $x(1 - x)$. Using a table of values, the maximum value of $x(1 - x)$ is 0.25 (when $x = 0.5$).

35a. $0.25 \cdot 0.25 \cdot 8 = 0.5 \text{ in}^3$

$12 \cdot 0.5 = 6 \text{ in}^3$

35b. $V = 8xy$

35c. $y = \dfrac{6}{8x}$ or $y = \dfrac{3}{4x}$

35d. Possible formulas: $S = 2(8x) + 2(8)\left(\dfrac{3}{4x}\right) + 2x\left(\dfrac{3}{4x}\right)$ or $S = 16x + \dfrac{12}{x} + \dfrac{3}{2}$

35e.

x	s
0.25 in.	53.5 in²
0.5 in.	33.5 in²
0.75 in.	29.5 in²
1 in.	29.5 in²
1.5 in.	33.5 in²
3 in.	53.5 in²

35f. $x = 0.75$ and $y = \dfrac{3}{4(0.75)} = 1$ (or $x = 1$ and

$y = \dfrac{3}{4(1)} = 0.75$)

0.75 in. by 1 in. by 8 in.

36. $\dfrac{32.2}{x} = \dfrac{92}{100}$

$92\,x = 3{,}220$

$x = 35$

37. $\dfrac{90}{125} = \dfrac{n}{100}$

$125n = 9{,}000$

$n = 72$

72%

38. $\dfrac{x}{36} = \dfrac{81}{100}$

$100\,x = 2{,}916$

$x = 29.16$

39. $7^{23\,-\,15} = 7^8$

40. $7^{3\,\times\,10} = 7^{30}$

41. $\dfrac{1}{7^{11}} = 7^{-11}$

42. Possible answer:

43. Graph b

44. Graph d

45. Graph a

46. Graph c

47. 19, 19

48. $k^2 - 14k + 49 + 21 = (k - 7)^2 + 21$

49. $b^2 + 5b + \dfrac{25}{4} - \dfrac{28}{4} = \left(b + \dfrac{5}{2}\right)^2 - 7$

50a. Measurements will vary.

about 2.75 in²

50b. Scale factors are given as a linear dimension. So find the square roots of each of areas.

$\sqrt{1.59} \approx 1.261$ and $\sqrt{2.75} \approx 1.658$

There are $5{,}280 \times 12$, or $63{,}360$, inches in a mile.

$1.261 \times 63{,}360 \div 1.658 \approx 48{,}189$

about 48,200

50c. $4 \times 48{,}200 = 192{,}800$

$192800 \div 63{,}360 \approx 3.04$

about 3 mi

Page 511   In Your Own Words

Possible answer: The function "Input: a number; Output: 1 less than double the number" can be represented by the algebraic equation $f(x) = 2x - 1$. The function "Input: the name of a color; Output: the number of letters that make up that name" cannot be represented by an algebraic equation. Both of my examples are functions because there is only one output value for each input value.

8-2   Graphs of Functions

Page 515   Problem Set A

1a.

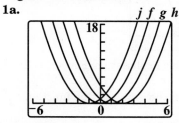

1b. All four graphs have the same shape. Each is a translation of f: g, 1 unit to the right; h, 2 units to the right; and j, 1 unit to the left.

1c. Possible answer:

$m(x) = (x + 3)^2$

$k(x) = (x - 4)^2$

2a.

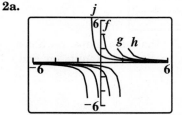

2b. All four graphs have the same shape. Each is a translation of f: g, 1 unit to the right; h, 2 units to the right; and j, 1 unit to the left.

2c. Possible answer:

$m(x) = \dfrac{1}{x + 2}$

$k(x) = \dfrac{1}{x - 5}$

3. They are similar in that the graph of the next function in each set is translated 1 unit to the right of the graph of the previous function. They are different in that the functions in each set are of different types: Problem 1 has quadratic functions, and Problem 2 has inverse variations.

4. $g(x) = (x - 1)^2$; Possible explanation: For $g(x) = (x - 1)^2$, the output is 9 for an input of 4, so $(4, 9)$ is on the graph of this function.

Page 516   Problem Set B

1a. i. $g(x) = 2^{x\,-\,2}$

ii. $h(x) = 2^{x\,-\,3}$

iii. $j(x) = 2^{x\,+\,3}$

1b.

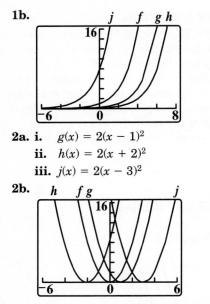

2a. i. $g(x) = 2(x - 1)^2$
ii. $h(x) = 2(x + 2)^2$
iii. $j(x) = 2(x - 3)^2$

2b.

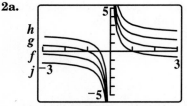

3. $j(x) = 2^{x+3}$; Possible explanation: For $j(x) = 2^{x+3}$, the output is 1 for an input of ⁻3, so (⁻3, 1) is on the graph of this function.

Page 517   Problem Set C

1a.

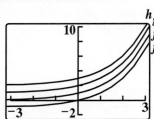

1b. All four graphs have the same shape. Each is a translation of f: g, 1 unit up; h, 2 units up; and j, 1 unit down.

1c. Possible answer:
$m(x) = 2^x - 4$
$k(x) = 2^x + 5$

2a.

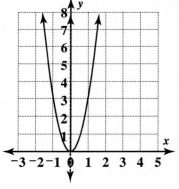

2b. All four graphs have the same shape. Each is a translation of f: g, 1 unit up; h, 2 units up; and j, 1 unit down.

2c. Possible answer:
$m(x) = \dfrac{1}{x} + 4$

$k(x) = \dfrac{1}{x} - 5$

3. They are similar in that the graph of each function in a set is translated 1 unit up from the graph of the previous function. They are different in that the functions in each set are of different types: Problem 1 has exponential functions, and Problem 2 has inverse variations.

4. $g(x) = \dfrac{1}{x} + 1$; Possible explanation: For $g(x) = \dfrac{1}{x} + 1$, the output is $\dfrac{4}{3}$ for an input of 3, so $\left(3, \dfrac{4}{3}\right)$ is on the graph of this function.

Page 517   Share and Summarize

1. Possible answer: No matter what type of function f and g are, they will have the same shape, but g will be translated h units to the left (if h is positive) or right (if h is negative) of f.

2. Possible answer: No matter what type of function f and g are, they will have the same shape, but g will be translated h units above (if h is positive) or below (if h is negative) f.

3. Treat a as the input of the function and calculate the output. If the output is b, the point (a, b) is on the graph.

Page 519   Problem Set D

1. domain: all real numbers
range: $f(x) > 0$

2. domain: all real numbers except $s = $ ⁻3
range: all real numbers except 0

3. domain: all real numbers
range: all real numbers

4. domain: the 50 states
range: the 50 state capitals

5. domain: all real numbers
range: all integers

Pages 520–521   Problem Set E

1a. Graph i: Function f; Graph ii: Function g

1b.

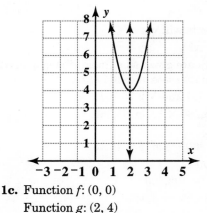

1c. Function f: (0, 0)
Function g: (2, 4)

1d. $f(x) \geq 0, g(x) \geq 4$

1e. The range starts at the y value of the vertex (the minimum).

2a. $x = {}^-2; ({}^-2, {}^-1)$

2b. g; Possible explanation: It's the only one with vertex $({}^-2, {}^-1)$.

2c. $f(x) \geq 1$, vertex $({}^-2, 1)$

$g(x) \geq {}^-1$, vertex $({}^-2, {}^-1)$

$h(x) \leq 1$, vertex $(2, 1)$

$i(x) \geq {}^-1$, vertex $(2, {}^-1)$

2d. The range is greater than or equal to, or less than or equal to, the y-coordinate of the maximum or minimum point.

3a. $x = 3$

3b. $(3, {}^-1)$

4a. Possible functions: $f(x) = (x - 3)^2 + 4$ or $f(x) = {}^-2(x - 3)^2 + 4$

4b. yes; Possible functions: $f(x) = 3(x - 3)^2 + 4$ and $f(x) = {}^-4(x - 3)^2 + 4$; there are an infinite number.

5a. f is a translation of g, h units horizontally and k units vertically.

5b. $(0, 0); (h, k)$

Page 522   Problem Set F

1a.
$$f(x) = x^2 + 8x + 7$$
$$f(x) - 7 + 16 = x^2 + 8x + 16$$
$$f(x) + 9 = (x + 4)^2$$
$$f(x) = (x + 4)^2 - 9$$

1b. $x = {}^-4$

1c. $({}^-4, {}^-9)$

1d.

2a.
$$f(x) = -x^2 + 4x + 1$$
$$f(x) - 1 = {}^-(x^2 - 4x)$$
$$f(x) - 1 - 4 = {}^-(x^2 - 4x - 4)$$
$$f(x) - 5 = {}^-(x - 2)^2$$
$$f(x) = {}^-(x - 2)^2 + 5$$

2b. $x = 2$

2c. $(2, 5)$

2d.

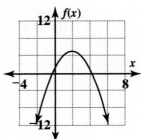

3a.
$$f(x) = x^2 - 6x - 3$$
$$f(x) + 3 = x^2 - 6x$$
$$f(x) + 3 + 9 = x^2 - 6x + 9$$
$$f(x) + 12 = (x - 3)^2$$
$$f(x) = (x - 3)^2 - 12$$

3b. $x = 3$

3c. $(3, {}^-12)$

3d.

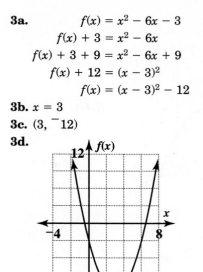

Page 522   Share and Summarize

The end value of the range is the y value of the vertex.

Page 523   Problem Set G

1. ${}^-1, 2$

2. $x = \dfrac{1}{2}$

3. The reflection of the left x-intercept is the right x-intercept.

4. $\dfrac{3}{2}$ units

5. $3(x^2 - x - 2) = 0$

$3(x + 1)(x - 2) = 0$

${}^-1, 2$

6. $\dfrac{1}{2} - {}^-1 = \dfrac{3}{2}$ and $2 - \dfrac{1}{2} = \dfrac{3}{2}$

Page 524   Problem Set H

1a. $(2, 0)$ and $({}^-3, 0)$

1b. $\dfrac{2 + ({}^-3)}{2} = -\dfrac{1}{2} = {}^-0.5$

$f({}^-0.5) = ({}^-0.5 - 2)({}^-0.5 + 3) = {}^-6.25$

$({}^-0.5, {}^-6.25)$

1c.

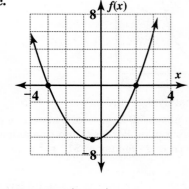

2a. $(5, 0)$ and $\left(-\dfrac{1}{2}, 0 \right)$

2b. $\dfrac{5 + {}^{-}\frac{1}{2}}{2} = 2.25$

$f(2.25) = {}^{-}(2.25 - 5)(2 \cdot 2.25 + 1) = 15.125$

(2.25, 15.125)

2c.

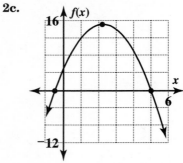

3a. $x^2 - 3x - 40 = (x - 8)(x + 5)$

(8, 0) and (${}^{-}5$, 0)

3b. $\dfrac{8 + {}^{-}5}{2} = \dfrac{3}{2} = 1.5$

$f(1.5) = 1.5^2 - 3(1.5) - 40 = {}^{-}42.25$

(1.5, ${}^{-}42.25$)

3c.

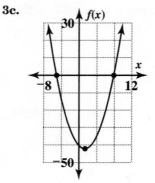

4. $f(t) = (t + 4)(t - 3)$, ${}^{-}4$ and 3

Page 524   Share and Summarize

Possible answer: Find the mean of the solution, m. The vertex is $(m, f(m))$.

Page 526   Problem Set I

1. $L(h) = 10h$

2. $D(h) = 2^h$

3.

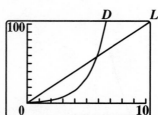

4. two, approximately 0.11 and 5.9

5. For more than about 5.9 h, you earn more money with the doubling plan. For less than this amount of time, you earn more money at \$10 per hour.

Pages 526–527   Problem Set J

1. $1{,}100 \cdot 1.1 = 1{,}210$

$1{,}210 \cdot 1.1 = 1{,}331$

Hour	Bacteria
1	1,100
2	1,210
3	1,331

2. $p(x) = 1{,}000(1.1^x)$

3. Possible calculator screen:

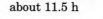

about 7.3 h

4. Possible answers: I graphed p and estimated when $p(x) = 2{,}000$. *Or*, I graphed p and $y = 2{,}000$ and looked at where they crossed.

5. $p(x) = 3{,}000$ or $1{,}000(1.1^x) = 3{,}000$

Possible calculator screen:

about 11.5 h

Page 527   Problem Set K

1. $f(x) = x^3$ and $g(x) = 2x - 0.5$

2. Possible calculator screen:

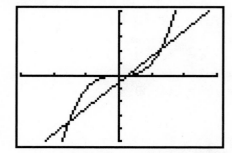

three, since the lines intersect three times

3. Possible answer: ${}^{-}1.53$, 0.26, 1.27

4a. The x-axis (or the x-intercepts)

4b. Possible calculator screen:

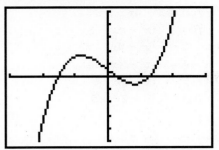

⁻1.53, 0.26, 1.27

4c. Answers will vary. Most students will find it easier to estimate the *x* values using Hakeem's method.

Page 527 Share and Summarize

1. exactly

$$100k = 10$$
$$k = 0.1$$

2. approximately

Possible calculator screen:

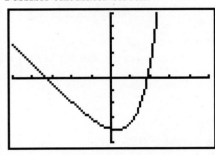
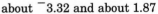

about ⁻3.32 and about 1.87

3. approximately

Possible calculator screen:

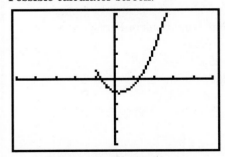

about ⁻0.72 and about 1.22

Pages 528–537 On Your Own Exercises

1a.

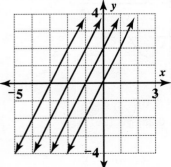

1b.

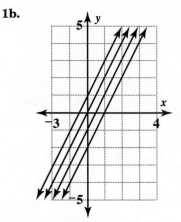

1c. Possible answer: All eight graphs are parallel lines.

1d. Possible answer: Each function in Part a is shifted horizontally 2 units to the left of the previous function; in Part b the shifts are vertical and occur 1 unit at a time.

1e. Answers will vary. Functions will be of the form $y = 2(x + a)$ for Part a and $y - a = 2(x - 1)$ for Part b.

1f. $y - 3 = 2(x - 1)$; Substitute $x = 3$ and $y = 7$ in the equations to find the correct one.

2a.

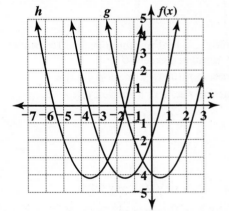

2b. The graph of *g* is the same shape as the graph of *f* but shifted 2 units to the right. The graph of *h* is the same shape as the graph of *f* but shifted 2 units to the left.

3. $g(x) = \dfrac{1}{x - 5}$

4. $g(x) = x^2 + x + 1$

5. $g(x) = \dfrac{1}{x - 2}$

6. $g(x) = (x + 5)^2$

7.

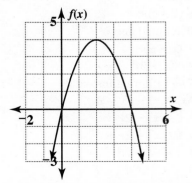

domain: All real numbers; range: $f(x) \le 4$

8.

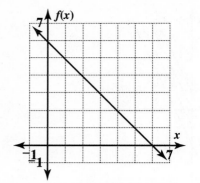

domain: all real numbers; range: all real numbers

9.

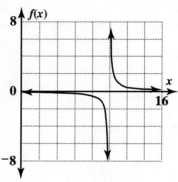

domain: all real numbers except 10; range: all real numbers except 0

10a. Function f: (0, 1); Function g: (1, 2)

10b. Function f: $x = 0$; Function g: $x = 1$

10c.

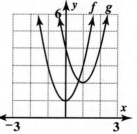

11a. $x = 2$; (2, 3)

11b. h; The graph has its vertex at (2, 3), as does the function h.

12. $(^-3, 4)$; $x = ^-3$; $f(x) \leq 4$

13. $(5, ^-9)$; $p = 5$; $g(p) \geq ^-9$

14. $(^-6, ^-3)$; $x = ^-6$; $h(x) \geq ^-3$

15a. Possible function:
$$f(x) = 6 + (x + 2)^2$$

15b. yes; Possible functions:
$$g(x) = 6 - (x + 2)^2$$
$$h(x) = 6 + 2(x + 2)^2$$
There are an infinite number.

16a.
$$f(x) = x^2 - 2x - 6$$
$$f(x) + 6 = x^2 - 2x$$
$$f(x) + 6 + 1 = x^2 - 2x + 1$$
$$f(x) + 7 = (x - 1)^2$$
$$f(x) = (x - 1)^2 - 7$$

16b. $x = 1$

16c. $(1, ^-7)$

17a.
$$f(x) = 3 + 4x - x^2$$
$$f(x) = ^-(x^2 - 4x - 3)$$
$$f(x) - 3 = ^-(x^2 - 4x)$$
$$f(x) - 3 - 4 = ^-(x^2 - 4x + 4)$$
$$f(x) - 7 = ^-(x - 2)^2$$
$$f(x) = ^-(x - 2)^2 + 7$$

17b. $x = 2$

17c. (2, 7)

18a.
$$f(x) = x^2 + 8x - 1$$
$$f(x) + 1 = x^2 + 8x$$
$$f(x) + 1 + 16 = x^2 + 8x + 16$$
$$f(x) + 17 = -(x + 4)^2$$
$$f(x) = -(x + 4)^2 - 17$$

18b. $x = ^-4$

18c. $(^-4, ^-17)$

19a. $^-1.5, 3.5$; Possible explanation: The parabola appears to cross the x-axis about halfway between -1 and -2 and halfway between 3 and 4.

19b. $\dfrac{^-2 \pm \sqrt{2^2 - 4(^-1)(5)}}{2(^-1)} = \dfrac{^-2 \pm \sqrt{24}}{^-2} = 1 \pm \sqrt{6}$

$1 - \sqrt{6}, 1 + \sqrt{6}$

The approximations in the answer to Part a are very close.

19c. (1, 6)

19d. $x = 1$

19e. $\sqrt{6}$ units

20a. Possible answer: $^-0.25, 0.75$

20b. $\dfrac{\frac{1}{2} \pm \sqrt{\left(-\frac{1}{2}\right)^2 - 4(1)\left(-\frac{3}{16}\right)}}{2(1)} = \dfrac{\frac{1}{2} \pm \sqrt{1}}{2} = \dfrac{1}{4} \pm \dfrac{1}{2}$

$^-0.25, 0.75$

The approximations in Part a are accurate.

20c. $(0.25, ^-0.25)$

20d. $x = 0.25$

20e. 0.5 unit

21a. (3, 0) and $(^-0.5, 0)$

21b. $x = 1.25$; $(1.25, ^-3.0625)$

21c.

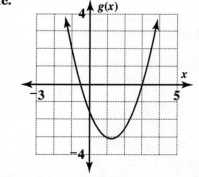

22a. (1, 0) and $(^-1.5, 0)$

22b. $x = ^-0.25$, $(^-0.25, ^-3.125)$

22c.

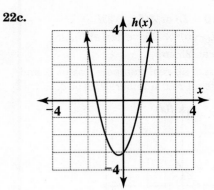

23a. $(1, 0)$ and $(^-5, 0)$

23b. $x = {^-}2; ({^-}2, 9)$

23c.

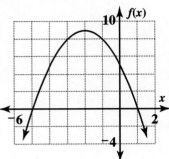

24.

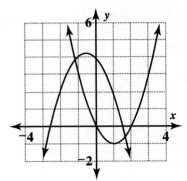

two solutions

25.

two solutions

26.

no solutions

27.

three solutions: $^-2.2$, 0, and 2.2

28.

one solution: about 2.6

29.

one solution: about 2.2

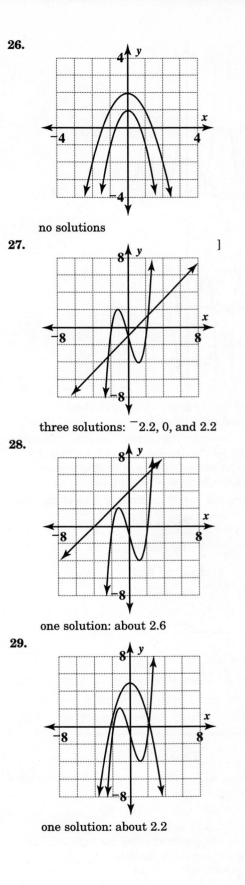

30a.

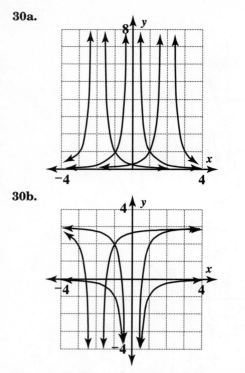

30b.

30c. Each of the six graphs consists of two curves that are mirror images.

30d. Possible answer: The second and third functions in Part a are horizontal shifts of the first; in Part b the curves have been shifted vertically and one has been shifted horizontally as well.

30e. Answers will vary. Functions will be of the form $y = \dfrac{1}{(x + a)^2}$ for Part a and $y = \dfrac{^-1}{(x + a)^2}$ or $y = 3 - \dfrac{1}{(x + a)^2}$ for Part b.

31a.

Height of Ball

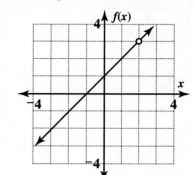

31b. The graph will be the same shape but translated 2 units to the right.

31c. $h(t) = 6 + 60(t - 2) - 16(t - 2)^2$

31d. When the first ball is on its way down; the graphs would intersect after the first ball has reached its maximum height.

32. $g(x) = 2^{x + 5} - 3$

33. $g(x) = 2(x + 1)^2 - 1$

34. $g(x) = (x + 3)^3 - (x + 4) - 1$

35. $g(x) = {}^-1 + \dfrac{1}{(x + 4)^2 + 1}$

36a. $W = 10 - L$

36b. $A(L) = L(10 - L)$ or $A(L) = 10L - L^2$

36c. $A(L) = {}^-(L - 5)^2 + 25$; vertex at (5, 25)

36d. 5 cm by 5 cm, 25 cm^2

37. The domain is all real numbers except 2, and the range is all real numbers except 3.

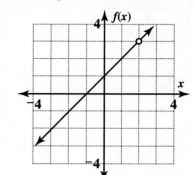

38a.
$$f(x) = 4x^2 - 8x - 1$$
$$f(x) + 1 = 4(x^2 - 2x)$$
$$f(x) + 1 + 4 = 4(x^2 - 2x + 1)$$
$$f(x) + 5 = 4(x - 1)^2$$
$$f(x) = 4(x - 1)^2 - 5$$

38b. $x = 1$

38c. $(1, {}^-5)$

39a.
$$f(x) = {}^-2x^2 + 4x + 1$$
$$f(x) - 1 = {}^-2(x^2 - 2x)$$
$$f(x) - 1 - 2 = {}^-2(x^2 + {}^-2x + 1)$$
$$f(x) - 3 = {}^-2(x - 1)^2$$
$$f(x) = {}^-2(x - 1)^2 + 3$$

39b. $x = 1$

39c. $(1, 3)$

40a.
$$f(x) = {}^-x^2 - 3x - 3$$
$$f(x) + 3 = {}^-(x^2 - 3x)$$
$$f(x) + 3 - \frac{9}{4} = {}^-\left(x^2 - 3x + \frac{9}{4}\right)$$
$$f(x) + \frac{3}{4} = {}^-\left(x - \frac{3}{2}\right)^2$$
$$f(x) = {}^-\left(x - \frac{3}{2}\right)^2 - \frac{3}{4}$$
$$f(x) = {}^-(x + 1.5)^2 - 0.75$$

40b. $x = {}^-1.5$

40c. $({}^-1.5, {}^-0.75)$

41.

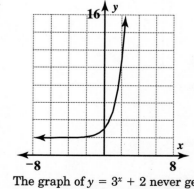

The graph of $y = 3^x + 2$ never gets below the line $y = 2$, so you can never have $3^x + 2 = 0$.

42a. $^-2, {}^-1, 1$

42b. $^-2$

42c.

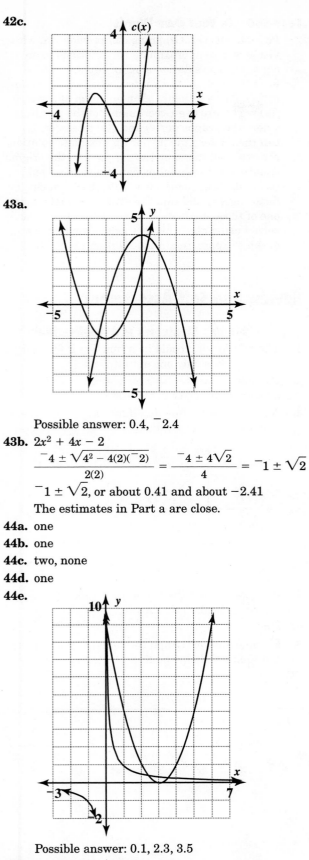

43a.

Possible answer: 0.4, ⁻2.4

43b. $2x^2 + 4x - 2$

$$\frac{^-4 \pm \sqrt{4^2 - 4(2)(^-2)}}{2(2)} = \frac{^-4 \pm 4\sqrt{2}}{4} = {}^-1 \pm \sqrt{2}$$

$^-1 \pm \sqrt{2}$, or about 0.41 and about −2.41
The estimates in Part a are close.

44a. one

44b. one

44c. two, none

44d. one

44e.

Possible answer: 0.1, 2.3, 3.5

45a. Possible answer: 0, 1, 2, 3

45b. Possible answer: ⁻5, ⁻4, 7, 10

46a. rectangular: $R(x) = x^2$
cylindrical: $C(x) = \pi(x - 1)^2$

46b.

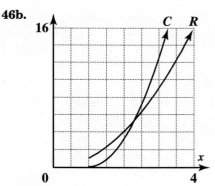

46c. about 2.3

47. Possible answer:

48. linear but not a direct variation

49. a direct variation

50. nonlinear

51. linear but not a direct variation

52. $\dfrac{1 - 12}{3 - 8} = \dfrac{^-11}{^-5} = \dfrac{11}{5}; \dfrac{12 - (^-10)}{8 - (^-1)} = \dfrac{22}{9}; \dfrac{11}{5} \neq \dfrac{22}{9};$
no

53. $\dfrac{9 - 2}{^-2 - 2} = \dfrac{7}{^-4}; \dfrac{2 - (^-1.5)}{2 - 4} = \dfrac{3.5}{^-2}; \dfrac{2 - (9)}{2 - (^-2)} = \dfrac{^-7}{4} = $
$\dfrac{7}{^-4} = \dfrac{3.5}{^-2} = \dfrac{^-7}{4}$ yes

54. $\dfrac{22 - 1}{15 - 0} = \dfrac{21}{15} = \dfrac{7}{5}; \dfrac{1 - (^-6)}{0 - (5)} = \dfrac{7}{^-5}; \dfrac{7}{5} \neq \dfrac{7}{^-5}$ no

55. $^-\sqrt{7s + 2} = {}^-10$
$\quad\quad 7s + 2 = 100$
$\quad\quad\quad\quad 7s = 98$
$\quad\quad\quad\quad\; s = 14$

56. $^-\dfrac{1}{z + 7} = {}^-1$
$\quad z + 7 = 1$
$\quad\quad\; z = {}^-6$

57. $x = \dfrac{^-3 \pm \sqrt{9 - 4(1)(^-6)}}{2} = \dfrac{^-3 \pm \sqrt{33}}{2}$

58. $16k^2 + 8k + 1 = 0$
$\quad\quad (4k + 1)^2 = 0$
$\quad\quad\quad 4k + 1 = 0$
$\quad\quad\quad\quad\quad 4k = {}^-1$
$\quad\quad\quad\quad\quad\; k = {}^-0.25$

59. Possible answer: If the chosen number is x, you get $\left(\dfrac{9x + 6}{3} - 2\right) \div x = 3x \div x$, which always equals 3.

60a.

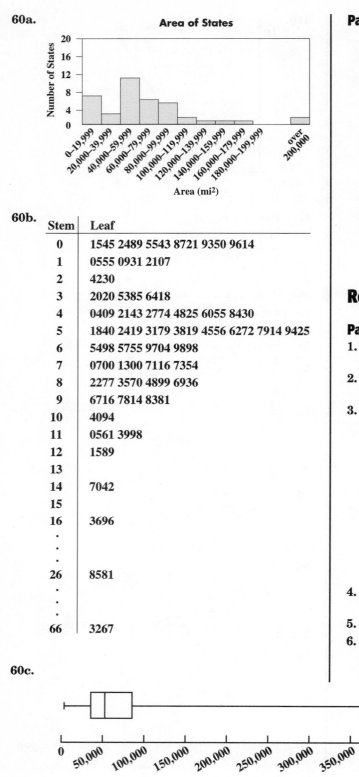

Area of States

Number of States (y-axis: 0, 4, 8, 12, 16, 20)

Area (mi²) — x-axis: 0–19,999 / 20,000–39,999 / 40,000–59,999 / 60,000–79,999 / 80,000–99,999 / 100,000–119,999 / 120,000–139,999 / 140,000–159,999 / 160,000–179,999 / 180,000–199,999 / over 200,000

60b.

Stem	Leaf
0	1545 2489 5543 8721 9350 9614
1	0555 0931 2107
2	4230
3	2020 5385 6418
4	0409 2143 2774 4825 6055 8430
5	1840 2419 3179 3819 4556 6272 7914 9425
6	5498 5755 9704 9898
7	0700 1300 7116 7354
8	2277 3570 4899 6936
9	6716 7814 8381
10	4094
11	0561 3998
12	1589
13	
14	7042
15	
16	3696
.	
.	
.	
26	8581
.	
.	
66	3267

60c.

A box-and-whisker plot on a number line from 0 to 700,000 (marks every 50,000).

Page 535 In Your Own Words

Possible answer: Graphing can provide you with a visual way to approximate the solutions to an equation. The solution(s) of an equation of the form $f(x) = 0$ are the x-intercept(s) of the graph of $f(x)$. The solution(s) of an equation of the form $f(x) = g(x)$ are the x-coordinates of the point(s) where the graphs of $f(x)$ and $g(x)$ intersect. You can then determine if your approximate solutions are exact solutions by testing them in the original equation. If the equation can be easily solved using algebraic methods such as backtracking or factoring, I would find the exact solution(s) using one of those methods. If the equation is not easily solved using algebraic methods, I would use a graph to approximate the solution(s).

Review and Self-Assessment

Pages 538–540   Strategies and Applications

1. The relationship could be a function if for every input there is only one output.

2. Possible answers: $y^2 = x$; *or* $y = \pm\sqrt{x}$; *or* input: a state, output: a city in the state

3. A graph is not a function if for any x value there is more than one y value.

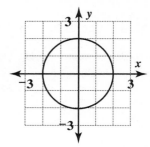

4. Possible answer: the height over time of a stone tossed vertically into the air

5. $k(n) \geq {}^{-}4$

6. Possible answer: Graph the function or complete the square to help you find its vertex.

7a. $A(x) = x(11 - x)$

7b. 30.25 cm^2

7c. 5.5 cm by 5.5 cm

8. about 510 m, attained approximately 10 s after launch

9. The graph of g is the same shape as f, translated 10 units up and 2 units to the left. The graph of h is the same shape as f, translated 3 units down and 2 units to the right.

10. $h(t) = 4(t - 3)^2 - 3$

11. Possible function: $y = 2(x + 6)^2 + 1$

12. Possible answer: The y value of the vertex is an extreme value for the range of the function, so the range is either all values greater than or equal to that value, or all values less than or equal to that value.

13. One method is setting $g(x) = 0$ to find the x-intercepts, $^-2$ and $^-4$. The line of symmetry is midway between the x-intercepts, at $x = {}^-3$. The vertex is thus $(^-3, {}^-1)$. Another method is to find the product and rewrite the function, $g(x) = 8 + 6x + x^2$. Then complete the square to rewrite it again, giving $g(x) = (x + 3)^2 - 1$. Again, the vertex is $(^-3, {}^-1)$.

14. Possible answer: The line of symmetry lies halfway between the x-intercepts; this gives the x-coordinate of the vertex, which is $(x, f(x))$.

15. Graph $y = x^3$ and $y = 2x^2 + 1$ and find the x values of their points of intersection.

16. two solutions; Possible explanation: The function $f(x) = x^2 + 2x - 3$ is a parabola opening up with vertex $(^-1, {}^-4)$ and $y = x - 2$ is a line with a positive slope that intersects the parabola twice.

Pages 540–541   Demonstrating Skills

17.

Input	Output
$^-2$	$^-3$
$^-1$	$^-3$
0	$^-1$
1	3
2	9

18.

Input	Output
$^-4$	$\frac{1}{8}$
$^-2$	$\frac{1}{6}$
0	$\frac{1}{4}$
2	$\frac{1}{2}$
4	undefined

19a–c.

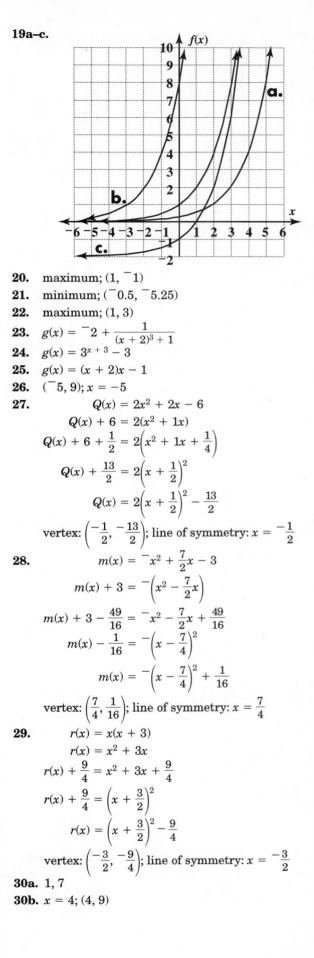

20. maximum; $(1, {}^-1)$

21. minimum; $(^-0.5, {}^-5.25)$

22. maximum; $(1, 3)$

23. $g(x) = {}^-2 + \dfrac{1}{(x + 2)^3 + 1}$

24. $g(x) = 3^{x + 3} - 3$

25. $g(x) = (x + 2)x - 1$

26. $(^-5, 9); x = -5$

27.
$$Q(x) = 2x^2 + 2x - 6$$
$$Q(x) + 6 = 2(x^2 + 1x)$$
$$Q(x) + 6 + \frac{1}{2} = 2\left(x^2 + 1x + \frac{1}{4}\right)$$
$$Q(x) + \frac{13}{2} = 2\left(x + \frac{1}{2}\right)^2$$
$$Q(x) = 2\left(x + \frac{1}{2}\right)^2 - \frac{13}{2}$$
vertex: $\left(-\dfrac{1}{2}, -\dfrac{13}{2}\right)$; line of symmetry: $x = \dfrac{-1}{2}$

28.
$$m(x) = {}^-x^2 + \frac{7}{2}x - 3$$
$$m(x) + 3 = {}^-\left(x^2 - \frac{7}{2}x\right)$$
$$m(x) + 3 - \frac{49}{16} = {}^-x^2 - \frac{7}{2}x + \frac{49}{16}$$
$$m(x) - \frac{1}{16} = {}^-\left(x - \frac{7}{4}\right)^2$$
$$m(x) = {}^-\left(x - \frac{7}{4}\right)^2 + \frac{1}{16}$$
vertex: $\left(\dfrac{7}{4}, \dfrac{1}{16}\right)$; line of symmetry: $x = \dfrac{7}{4}$

29.
$$r(x) = x(x + 3)$$
$$r(x) = x^2 + 3x$$
$$r(x) + \frac{9}{4} = x^2 + 3x + \frac{9}{4}$$
$$r(x) + \frac{9}{4} = \left(x + \frac{3}{2}\right)^2$$
$$r(x) = \left(x + \frac{3}{2}\right)^2 - \frac{9}{4}$$
vertex: $\left(-\dfrac{3}{2}, -\dfrac{9}{4}\right)$; line of symmetry: $x = \dfrac{-3}{2}$

30a. 1, 7

30b. $x = 4; (4, 9)$

30c.

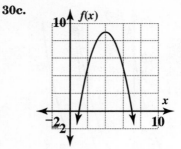

31. ‾1, 1.5

32. Rewrite the equation as $x^2 + 2x + 1 = 0$ and solve by factoring or using the quadratic formula; $x = {}^-1$.

Chapter 9 Probability

9-1 Counting Strategies

Pages 545–546 Lab

1. Predictions will vary.
2. 1 cheese only pizza
   4 single-topping pizzas: M, A, T, G
   6 two-topping pizzas: MA, MT, MG, AT, AG, TG
   4 three-topping pizzas: MAT, MAG, MTG, ATG
   1 four-topping pizza: MATG
   $1 + 4 + 6 + 4 + 1 = 16$ pizzas
3. 1 cheese only pizza
   1 single-topping pizza
   $1 + 1 = 2$ pizzas
4. 1 cheese only pizza
   2 single-topping pizzas
   1 two-topping pizza
   $1 + 2 + 1 = 4$ pizzas
5. 1 cheese only pizza
   3 single-topping pizzas
   3 two-topping pizzas
   1 three-topping pizza
   $1 + 3 + 3 + 1 = 8$ pizzas
6.

Toppings	1	2	3
Different Pizzas	2	4	8

7. Possible answer: The number of different pizzas doubles with each topping added. Eight different pizzas can be made from 3 toppings, so there should be 16 different pizzas from 4 toppings. This is what I found in Question 2.
8. $16 \times 2 = 32$ pizzas
   1 cheese only pizza
   5 single-topping pizzas
   10 two-topping pizzas
   10 three-topping pizzas
   5 four-topping pizzas
   1 five-topping pizza
   $1 + 5 + 10 + 10 + 5 + 1 = 32$ pizzas
9. 6 toppings: $32 \times 2 = 64$
   7 toppings: $64 \times 2 = 128$
   8 toppings: $128 \times 2 = 256$
   9 toppings: $256 \times 2 = 512$
   10 toppings: $512 \times 2 = 1{,}024$
   11 toppings: $1{,}024 \times 2 = 2{,}048$
   12 toppings: $2{,}048 \times 2 = 4{,}096$

Toppings	1	2	3	4	5	6	7	8	9	10	11	12
Different Pizzas	2	4	8	16	32	64	128	256	512	1,024	2,048	4,096

10. Reports will vary.

Pages 547–548 Problem Set A

1. Ally/Brevin, Ally/Carol, Ally/Doug
2. Brevin/Carol, Brevin/Doug
3. Carol/Doug
4a. If students did Problems 1–3 correctly, they will have listed each pair exactly once.
4b. 6 pairs; Ally/Brevin, Ally/Carol, Ally/Doug, Brevin/Carol, Brevin/Doug, Carol/Doug
5a. 1
5b. $\frac{1}{6}$

Page 548 Problem Set B

1. $\frac{1}{6} = \frac{2}{12}$
2. Answers will vary.
3. Total draws will vary; $\frac{1}{6}$ of the total.
4. Answers will vary.

Page 549 Problem Set C

1a. Evan/Ally, Evan/Brevin, Evan/Carol, Evan/Doug
   4
1b. 10
1c. AB, AC, AD, AE, BC, BD, BE, CD, CE, DE
2a. 4 pairs; AE, BE, CE, DE
2b. $\frac{4}{10}$, or $\frac{2}{5}$

Page 550 Problem Set D

1. $\frac{4}{10}$
2. $\frac{7}{10}$
3. $\frac{6}{10}$
4. $\frac{9}{10}$
5. $\frac{3}{10}$
6. $\frac{1}{10}$
7. Possible question: What is the probability that the next game involves Carol and either Ally or Doug?
8. Answers will vary.

Page 550 Share and Summarize

Count all the outcomes that produce the event and divide by the total number of outcomes in the sample space.

Page 552 Problem Set E

1. Predictions will vary.
2. ABCD, ABDC, ACBD, ACDB, ADBC, ADCB
3. After deciding that A is first, all that is being rearranged are the other three CDs.
4. It doesn't matter which CD is first; there are still exactly three other CDs being rearranged.

5.

B First	C First	D First
BACD	CABD	DABC
BADC	CADB	DACB
BCAD	CBAD	DBAC
BCDA	CBDA	DBCA
BDAC	CDAB	DCAB
BDCA	CDBA	DCBA

6. 24 orders; multiply the number of lists by the total number of lists.

7. Answers will vary.

8. 5 lists of 24 = 120

Pages 553–554 Problem Set F

1. BCAD, BCDA, ABCD, DBCA, ADBC, DABC
$\frac{6}{24}$, or $\frac{1}{4}$

2. BCDA, BDCA, CBDA, CDBA, DBCA, DCBA
$\frac{6}{24}$, or $\frac{1}{4}$

3. ABCD, ABDC, ACBD, ACDB, ADBC, ADCB, BACD, BADC, BCAD, BCDA, BDAC, BDCA, DABC, DACB, DBAC, DBCA, DCBA, DCAB
$\frac{18}{24}$, or $\frac{3}{4}$

4. BACD, BADC, BCAD, BCDA, BDAC, BDCA, CBAD, CBDA, CDBA, DBAC, DBCA, DCBA
$\frac{12}{24}$, or $\frac{1}{2}$

5. DBCA, DCBA
$\frac{2}{24}$, or $\frac{1}{12}$

6. CBAD
$\frac{1}{24}$

7. ABCD, ACBD, ADCB, ACDB
$\frac{4}{24}$, or $\frac{1}{6}$

8. No matter which CD is last, there are exactly 6 ways of arranging the other three CDs.

9. No matter whether A is first or last—or, for that matter, second or third—there are exactly 6 ways of arranging the other three CDs.

10. C has 6 out of 24 chances of being played first. So, it must have 24 − 6 = 18 chances out of 24 of *not* being played first.

11. $1 - \frac{1}{4} = \frac{3}{4}$
Possible explanation: I subtracted from 1.

12. $1 - p$

13. Possible answer: A is played first.

14. Possible answer: A is not played first and D is not played last.

15. Possible answer: A is played.

16. Possible answer: B is played immediately after A, A is not played first, and C is not played last.

Page 554 Share and Summarize

1a. $n = 2$
$2 - 1 = 1$
There is one way to put 1 CD in order.
$2 \times 1 = 2$ ways; yes

1b. $n = 3$
$3 - 1 = 2$
There are 2 ways to put 2 CDs in order.
$3 \times 2 = 6$ ways; yes
$n = 4$
$4 - 1 = 3$
There are 6 ways to put 3 CDs in order.
$4 \times 6 = 24$ ways; yes

1c. For n CDs, there are n choices for the first disc. After that, you must arrange the remaining $n - 1$ CDs, so there are $n \times$ (the number of ways to put $n - 1$ in order) ways to do it.

1d. $n = 5$
$5 - 1 = 4$
There are 24 ways to put 4 CDs in order.
$5 \times 24 = 120$ ways to put 5 CDs in order
$n = 6$
$6 - 1 = 5$
There are 120 ways to put 5 CDs in order.
$6 \times 120 = 720$ ways to put 6 CDs in order
$n = 7$
$7 - 1 = 6$
There are 720 ways to put 6 CDs in order.
$6 \times 720 = 720$ ways to put 6 CDs in order
$7 \times 6 = 5,040$ ways to put 7 CDs in order

2. no; Possible explanation: She is counting each outcome twice. In this situation order is not important; for example, Ally/Carol is the same as Carol/Ally. Lucita's method counts these outcomes separately.

Page 555 Problem Set G

1. 3-7, 4-6, 5-5; 6 pairs
2. 0-11, 1-10, 2-9, 3-8, 4-7, 5-6; 6 pairs
3. 0-12, 1-11, 2-10, 3-9, 4-8, 5-7, 6-6; 7 pairs

4.

Sum	10	11	12	13	14	15	16
Number of Pairs	6	6	7	7	8	9	9

5.

Sum	20	27	40	80	100	275
Number of Pairs	11	14	21	41	51	138

6a. even sums: $\frac{s}{2} + 1$, or $\frac{s+2}{2}$
odd sums: $\frac{s}{2} + \frac{1}{2}$, or $\frac{s+1}{2}$

6b. Possible answer: For even totals—for example S = 100—you start writing the pairs 1-99, 2-98, 3-97, until 50-50, which is 50 pairs, half of 100. Then there is one extra pair 0-100, so the number of pairs is $1 + \frac{s}{2}$.

For odd totals, like 101, you start the same way—1-100, 2-99, 3-98, until 50-51—but because half of 101 is 50.5, which isn't a whole number, the counting stops at 50, which is $\frac{s}{2} - \frac{1}{2}$, or $\frac{s-1}{2}$.
There is one extra pair, 0-101, so you add a pair, giving $\frac{s}{2} + \frac{1}{2}$, or $\frac{s+1}{2}$.

1a. 11

1b. $\frac{6}{11}$; Of the 11 pairs, 6 include a number greater than 14: 0-20, 1-19, 2-18, 3-17, 4-16, and 5-15.

2a. 51

2b. 10 pairs: 41-59, 42-58, 43-57, 44-56, 45-55, 46-54, 47-53, 48-52, 49-51, 50-50

2c. $\frac{10}{51}$

3a. $\frac{55+1}{2} = \frac{56}{2} = 28$

3b. 7 pairs: 0-55, 1-54, 2-53, 3-52, 4-51, 5-50, 6-49

3c. $28 - 7 = 21$

$\frac{21}{28}$, or $\frac{3}{4}$

Page 557   Problem Set I

1. 9; $\frac{x}{3} = 3$ only when $x = 9$.

2. No; 1-2-6 is considered the same as 6-2-1.

3. 0-0-9, 0-1-8, 0-2-7, 0-3-6, 0-4-5; 5 triples

4a. If it has a 0, it would have been listed in Problem 3. If I listed it here, it would be counted twice.

4b. 1-1-7, 1-2-6, 1-3-5, 1-4-4; 4 triples

5. 2-2-5, 2-3-4, 3-3-3

Smallest Number in Triple	0	1	2	3
Number of Triples	5	4	2	1

6. The higher numbers have been used in the triples already counted.

7. 12

8. $\frac{5}{12}$; $\frac{0}{12}$, or 0

9. The sum of the triples must be 12.

0-0-12, 0-1-11, 0-2-10, 0-3-9, 0-4-8, 0-5-7, 0-6-6

1-1-10, 1-2-9, 1-3-8, 1-4-7, 1-5-6

2-2-8, 2-3-7, 2-4-6, 2-5-5

3-3-6, 3-4-5

4-4-4

19

Page 557   Share and Summarize

Possible answer: The sum of the four numbers would have to be $4m$, so I would start by finding all the sets that include two or more 0s, then one 0 and at least one 1, then one 0 and at least one 2 but no 1s, then one 0 and at least one 3 but no 1s or 2s, and so on. I would then do the same with 1s instead of 0s, and exclude 0 from the triples. Then I would do the same with 2s, excluding 0s and 1s, and so on.

Pages 558–564   On Your Own Exercises

1a. AB, AC, BC

1b. $\frac{1}{3}$

1c. 15 pairs; AB, AC, AD, AE, AF, BC, BD, BE, BF, CD, CE, CF, DE, DF, EF

1d. $\frac{9}{15}$, or $\frac{3}{5}$

1e. $\frac{10}{15}$, or $\frac{2}{3}$

2a.

Player	Matches to Play	Number of Matches
A	AB, AC, AD, AE, AF, AG	6
B	BC, BD, BE, BF, BG	5
C	CD, CE, CF, CG	4
D	DE, DF, DG	3
E	EF, EG	2
F	FG	1
G		0

2b. Predictions will vary.

2c. Predictions will vary.

2d. See the table in Part a.

2e. The numbers decrease by 1. Possible explanation: Since the person for a particular row must play everyone else, the number of matches is equal to the number of remaining players—but for each row, you are reducing the number of players being considered by 1.

2f. 21

2g. 28; add all the numbers from 1 to 7.

3a. $4 \cdot 3 \cdot 2 \cdot 1 = 24$

3b. $3 \cdot 2 \cdot 1 = 6$

$24 - 6 = 18$

3c. $3 \cdot 2 \cdot 1 = 6$

4a. $4 \cdot 3 \cdot 2 \cdot 1 = 24$

4b. $3 \cdot 2 \cdot 1 = 6$

$\frac{6}{24}$, or $\frac{1}{4}$

4c. $24 - 6 = 18$

$\frac{18}{24}$, or $\frac{3}{4}$

4d. $2 \cdot 3 \cdot 2 \cdot 1 = 12$

$\frac{12}{24}$, or $\frac{1}{2}$

4e. $\frac{4}{24}$, or $\frac{1}{6}$

5a. 0-26, 1-25, 2-24, 3-23, 4-22, 5-21, 6-20, 7-19, 8-18, 9-17, 10-16, 11-15, 12-14, 13-13

5b. 14

5c. $\frac{12}{14}$, or $\frac{6}{7}$; In 12 of the 14 pairs listed, at least one number is greater than or equal to 15.

5d. $\frac{2}{14}$, or $\frac{1}{7}$; In 2 of the 14 pairs listed, both numbers are less than 15.

6a. $\frac{480+2}{2} = \frac{482}{2} = 241$

6b. 180; Possible explanation: For one number to be greater than 300, the other must be between 0 and 179. There are 180 such pairs.

7a. 0-0-15, 0-1-14, 0-2-13, 0-3-12, 0-4-11, 0-5-10, 0-6-9, 0-7-8, 1-1-13, 1-2-12, 1-3-11, 1-4-10, 1-5-9, 1-6-8, 1-7-7, 2-2-11, 2-3-10, 2-4-9, 2-5-8, 2-6-7, 3-3-9, 3-4-8, 3-5-7, 3-6-6, 4-4-7, 4-5-6, 5-5-5; Possible explanation: I know I found them all because I systematically listed all the triples that included 0, then all that included 1 but not 0, and so on.

7b. 27

7c. $\frac{8}{27}$

8a. 20 teams; ABC, ABD, ABE, ABF, ACD, ACE, ACF, ADE, ADF, AEF, BCD, BCE, BCF, BDE, BDF, BEF, CDE, CDF, CEF, DEF

8b. $\frac{16}{20}$, or $\frac{4}{5}$

8c. $\frac{4}{20}$, or $\frac{1}{5}$

8d. $\frac{4}{20}$, or $\frac{1}{5}$

8e. $\frac{8}{20}$, or $\frac{2}{5}$; Amelia and Eduardo will be on the same team if both names are drawn or if neither name is drawn. So, we can add probabilities from Parts b and c.

9a. 25; Possible explanation: There are 5 possibilities for the seventh grader, and for each of these, there are 5 possibilities for the eighth grader. So, there are $5 \cdot 5 = 25$ pairs in all.

9b. $\frac{2}{25}$

9c. $\frac{20}{25}$, or $\frac{4}{5}$

9d. $\frac{25}{45}$, or $\frac{5}{9}$; Possible explanation: There are 45 possible pairs—25 that include one seventh grader and one eighth grader, 10 that include two seventh graders, and 10 that include two eighth graders. So, the probability that the pair will include one seventh grader and one eighth grader is $\frac{25}{45}$, or $\frac{5}{9}$.

10a. $3 \cdot 2 \cdot 4 = 24$

10b. $\frac{4}{24}$, or $\frac{1}{6}$

10c. $\frac{16}{24}$, or $\frac{2}{3}$

11a. 6 ways; ABC, ACB, BAC, BCA, CAB, CBA

11b. There are two ways.

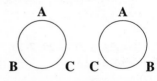

11c.

People	Row Arrangements	Circle Arrangements
1	1	1
2	2	1
3	6	2
4	24	6

11d. Possible answer: The number of row arrangements divided by the number of people equals the number of circle arrangements. The number of circle arrangements for n people is the same as the number of row arrangements for $n - 1$ people.

11e. 24

12. $20 \cdot 19 \cdot 18 \cdot 17 = 116{,}280$

13a.

Legs	Combinations	Number of Combinations
2	1C-0P	1
4	2C-0P, 0C1P	2
6	3C-01P, 1C-1P	2
8	4C-0P, 2C-1P, 0C-2P	3
10	5C-0P, 3C-1P, 1C-2P	3
12	6C-0P, 4C-1P, 2C-2P, 0C-3P	4
13	7C-0P, 5C-1P, 3C-2P, 1C-3P	4

13b. 5 combinations for each
for 16 legs: 8C-0P, 6C-1P, 4C-2P, 2C-3P, 0C-4P
for 18 legs: 9C-0P, 7C-1P, 5C-2P, 3C-3P, 1C-4P

13c. for multiples of 4: $\frac{L}{4} + 1$

for nonmultiples of 4: $\frac{L-2}{4} + 1$

13d. $\frac{42-2}{4} + 1 = \frac{40}{4} + 1 = 10 + 1 = 11$

11

14. $2y - 6 = {}^-7x + 1$
$2y = {}^-7x + 7$
$y = -\frac{7}{2}x + \frac{7}{2}$
Possible equation: $y = -\frac{7}{2}x$

15. $y = {}^-x - 2$
Possible equation: $y = {}^-x$

16. $2^{5 - 8 + 2p} = 2^{{}^-3 + 2p}$

17. $[({}^-1)3^{3m}]^6 = ({}^-1)^6 \times 3^{3m \cdot 6} = 1 \times 3^{18m} = 3^{18m}$

18. $(2k)^7$

19. $45 - 5x \le 4x + 72$
${}^-9x \le 27$
$x \ge {}^-3$

20. $7.5x < 15$
$x < 2$

21. ${}^-3(x^2 + x + 6)$
${}^-3(x + 2)(x - 3)$

22. $0.5(a^2 - 4 - 32)$
$0.5(a - 8)(a + 4)$

23. $(0.4 \div 2)^2 = 0.04$

24. $(12 \div 2)^2 = 36$

25a.

Time (h)	0	1	2	3	4	5
Cells	1	4	16	64	256	1,024

25b. $c = 4^t$

25c.

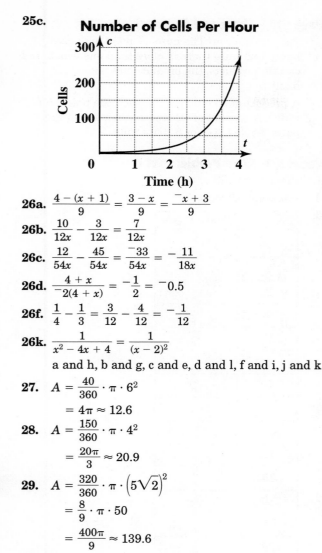

Number of Cells Per Hour

26a. $\dfrac{4 - (x + 1)}{9} = \dfrac{3 - x}{9} = \dfrac{^{-}x + 3}{9}$

26b. $\dfrac{10}{12x} - \dfrac{3}{12x} = \dfrac{7}{12x}$

26c. $\dfrac{12}{54x} - \dfrac{45}{54x} = \dfrac{^{-}33}{54x} = -\dfrac{11}{18x}$

26d. $\dfrac{4 + x}{^{-}2(4 + x)} = -\dfrac{1}{2} = {}^{-}0.5$

26f. $\dfrac{1}{4} - \dfrac{1}{3} = \dfrac{3}{12} - \dfrac{4}{12} = -\dfrac{1}{12}$

26k. $\dfrac{1}{x^2 - 4x + 4} = \dfrac{1}{(x - 2)^2}$

a and h, b and g, c and e, d and l, f and i, j and k

27. $A = \dfrac{40}{360} \cdot \pi \cdot 6^2$

$= 4\pi \approx 12.6$

28. $A = \dfrac{150}{360} \cdot \pi \cdot 4^2$

$= \dfrac{20\pi}{3} \approx 20.9$

29. $A = \dfrac{320}{360} \cdot \pi \cdot \left(5\sqrt{2}\right)^2$

$= \dfrac{8}{9} \cdot \pi \cdot 50$

$= \dfrac{400\pi}{9} \approx 139.6$

30. yes

31. yes

32. no

Page 563   In Your Own Words

Possible answer: One strategy to find the size of a sample space is to systematically list all of the possible outcomes using tables or tree diagrams. Another strategy is to begin a systematic list and look for a pattern that will help you find the size of the sample space without completing the list. Once all possible outcomes are shown, you can count them to find the size of the sample space.

9-2 | Probability Distributions

Pages 566–567   Problem Set A

1. Answers will vary.

2.

Die 1

$\times$	Even	Odd
Even	even	even
Odd	even	odd

3. even

4a. 3

4b. 1

5a. Predictions will vary.

5b. No; with both spinners you are more likely to spin an odd number. The table would work only if spinning an odd and spinning an even were equally likely.

5c.

Spinner 1

$\times$	1	2	3	4	5
1	1	2	3	4	5
2	2	4	6	8	10
3	3	6	9	12	15
4	4	8	12	16	20
5	5	10	15	20	25

probability of even: $\dfrac{16}{25}$

probability of odd: $\dfrac{9}{25}$

Page 568   Problem Set B

1. Predictions will vary.

2.

	Even Exponent	Odd Exponent
Even Base	even	even
Odd Base	odd	odd

3. The results are equally likely.

4a. $\dfrac{2}{4}$, or $\dfrac{1}{2}$

4b. $\dfrac{2}{4}$, or $\dfrac{1}{2}$

Page 568   Share and Summarize

Possible answer: Determine whether each of these combinations is odd or even: odd + odd, odd + even, even + odd, even + even. Determine the sum for each of the 16 possible number pairs, and compare the number of odd sums to the number of even sums.

Pages 569–570   Problem Set C

1. Predictions will vary.

2. Answers will vary.

3.

Player 2's roll

$-$	1	2	3	4	5	6
1	0	1	2	3	4	5
2	1	0	1	2	3	4
3	2	1	0	1	2	3
4	3	2	1	0	1	2
5	4	3	2	1	0	1
6	5	4	3	2	1	0

4. 2; 1 and 6, 6 and 1

5.

Difference	0	1	2	3	4	5
Probability	$\frac{6}{36}$	$\frac{10}{36}$	$\frac{8}{36}$	$\frac{6}{36}$	$\frac{4}{36}$	$\frac{2}{36}$

6.

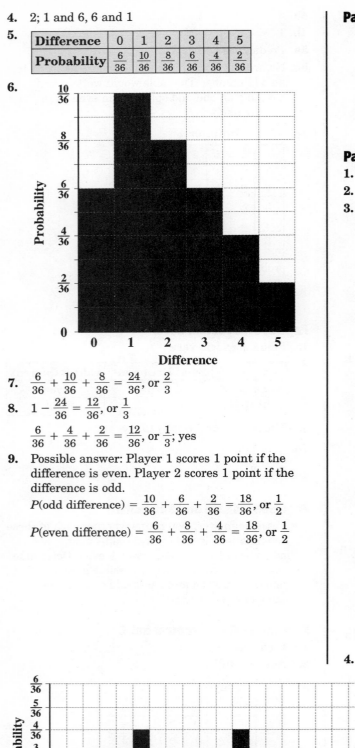

7. $\frac{6}{36} + \frac{10}{36} + \frac{8}{36} = \frac{24}{36}$, or $\frac{2}{3}$

8. $1 - \frac{24}{36} = \frac{12}{36}$, or $\frac{1}{3}$

$\frac{6}{36} + \frac{4}{36} + \frac{2}{36} = \frac{12}{36}$, or $\frac{1}{3}$; yes

9. Possible answer: Player 1 scores 1 point if the difference is even. Player 2 scores 1 point if the difference is odd.

$P(\text{odd difference}) = \frac{10}{36} + \frac{6}{36} + \frac{2}{36} = \frac{18}{36}$, or $\frac{1}{2}$

$P(\text{even difference}) = \frac{6}{36} + \frac{8}{36} + \frac{4}{36} = \frac{18}{36}$, or $\frac{1}{2}$

Page 570 Share and Summarize

Possible answer: The number pairs are equally likely, but since there is more than one way to roll certain products, the products are not equally likely.

A product of 25 only occurs when the pair 5-5 is rolled. A product of 12 occurs when any of the pairs 2-6, 3-4, 4-3, or 6-2 are rolled.

Pages 571–572 Problem Set D

1. Predictions will vary.

2. Answers will vary.

3.

Product	Probability
1	$\frac{1}{36}$
2	$\frac{2}{36}$
3	$\frac{2}{36}$
4	$\frac{3}{36}$
5	$\frac{2}{36}$
6	$\frac{4}{36}$
8	$\frac{2}{36}$
9	$\frac{1}{36}$
10	$\frac{2}{36}$
12	$\frac{4}{36}$
15	$\frac{2}{36}$
16	$\frac{1}{36}$
18	$\frac{2}{36}$
20	$\frac{2}{36}$
24	$\frac{2}{36}$
25	$\frac{1}{36}$
30	$\frac{2}{36}$
36	$\frac{1}{36}$

4.

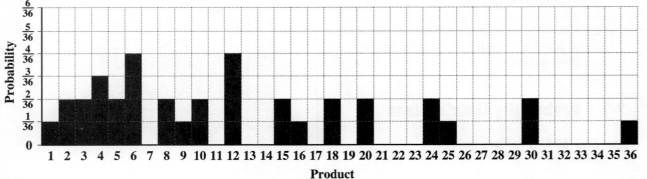

5. Plot A; each of the numbers 1, 9, 16, 25, and 36 can be made in only one way, so the probability of any one of them is only $\frac{1}{36}$. Most of the other numbers can be made in two ways, and 4, 6, and 12 can be made in more than two ways. B has many of the least likely: only 8 chances out of 36. C has 12 chances out of 36. And A has the remaining 16 chances.

Page 572   Share and Summarize

Possible Answer: You can see at a glance which outcomes are more likely than others, which are most likely, and whether some are not possible at all.

Pages 573–578   On Your Own Exercises

1a.

Die 1

+	1	2	3	4	5	6
1	2	3	4	5	6	7
2	3	4	5	6	7	8
3	4	5	6	7	8	9
4	5	6	7	8	9	10
5	6	7	8	9	10	11
6	7	8	9	10	11	12

1b. 11 sums; 2, 3, 4, 5, 6, 7, 8, 9, 10, 11, 12

1c. 7; $1 + 6, 2 + 5, 3 + 4, 4 + 3, 5 + 2, 6 + 1$

1d.

Die 1

+	Even	Odd
Even	even	odd
Odd	odd	even

1e. $\frac{1}{2}$

1f. no; Possible explanation: You're more likely to get odd numbers on the spinners, which might make a difference. Also, there are 9 combinations, so odd and even cannot have even chances-the closest they can come is $\frac{4}{9}$ and $\frac{5}{9}$.

2a. Predictions will vary.

2b.

+	1	3	5
1	1	3	5
2	2	6	10
3	3	9	15
4	4	12	20
5	5	15	25

probability of even: $\frac{6}{15}$ or $\frac{2}{5}$

probability of odd: $\frac{9}{15}$ or $\frac{3}{5}$

Conclusions will vary.

3a. $8 \cdot 8 = 64$

3b.

Die 1

+	1	2	3	4	5	6	7	8
1	2	3	4	5	6	7	8	9
2	3	4	5	6	7	8	9	10
3	4	5	6	7	8	9	10	11
4	5	6	7	8	9	10	11	12
5	6	7	8	9	10	11	12	13
6	7	8	9	10	11	12	13	14
7	8	9	10	11	12	13	14	15
8	9	10	11	12	13	14	15	16

3c. $\frac{32}{64}$, or $\frac{1}{2}$

3d. $\frac{23}{64}$

4a. $12 \cdot 12 = 144$

4b. $12 + 12 = 24$

4c.

+	1	2	3	4	5
1	2	3	4	5	6
2	3	4	5	6	7
3	4	5	6	7	8
4	5	6	7	8	9
5	6	7	8	9	10
6	7	8	9	10	11
7	8	9	10	11	12
8	9	10	11	12	13
9	10	11	12	13	14
10	11	12	13	14	15
11	12	13	14	15	16
12	13	14	15	16	17

+	6	7	8	9	10	11	12
1	7	8	9	10	11	12	13
2	8	9	10	11	12	13	14
3	9	10	11	12	13	14	15
4	10	11	12	13	14	15	16
5	11	12	13	14	15	16	17
6	12	13	14	15	16	17	18
7	13	14	15	16	17	18	19
8	14	15	16	17	18	19	20
9	15	16	17	18	19	20	21
10	16	17	18	19	20	21	22
11	17	18	19	20	21	22	23
12	18	19	20	21	22	23	24

$13; \frac{12}{144}$, or $\frac{1}{12}$

5a. $12 \times 8 = 96$

5b.

+	1	2	3	4	5	6	7	8
1	2	3	4	5	6	7	8	9
2	3	4	5	6	7	8	9	10
3	4	5	6	7	8	9	10	11
4	5	6	7	8	9	10	11	12
5	6	7	8	9	10	11	12	13
6	7	8	9	10	11	12	13	14
7	8	9	10	11	12	13	14	15
8	9	10	11	12	13	14	15	16
9	10	11	12	13	14	15	16	17
10	11	12	13	14	15	16	17	18
11	12	13	14	15	16	17	18	19
12	13	14	15	16	17	18	19	20

9, 10, 11, 12, and 13 all occur in eight ways; $\frac{8}{96}$, or $\frac{1}{12}$

5c. They are equally likely.

6a.

−	1	2	3	4	5	6
1	0	1	2	3	4	5
2	1	0	1	2	3	4
3	2	1	0	1	2	3
4	3	2	1	0	1	2
5	4	3	2	1	0	1
6	5	4	3	2	1	0
7	6	5	4	3	2	1
8	7	6	5	4	3	2

Difference	0	1	2	3	4	5	6	7
Probability	$\frac{6}{48}$	$\frac{11}{48}$	$\frac{10}{48}$	$\frac{8}{48}$	$\frac{6}{48}$	$\frac{4}{48}$	$\frac{2}{48}$	$\frac{1}{48}$

6b. P(Player 1 scores 1 point) $= \frac{6}{48} + \frac{11}{48} + \frac{10}{48} = \frac{27}{48}$, or $\frac{9}{16}$

P(Player 2 scores 1 point) $= \frac{8}{48} + \frac{6}{48} + \frac{4}{48} + \frac{2}{48} + \frac{1}{48} = \frac{21}{48}$, or $\frac{7}{16}$

No; Player 1 has 27 chances out of 48 to score a point, while Player 2 has only 21 chances out of 48 to score a point.

6c.

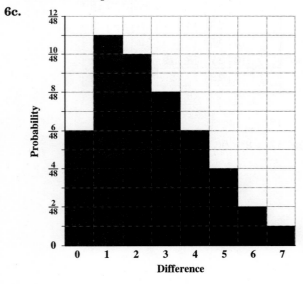

6d. This game; the probability that Player 2 will score a point is $\frac{12}{36}$, or $\frac{1}{3}$, or about 33%, with two ordinary dice, but improves to $\frac{21}{48}$, or almost 44%, with one die an octahedron.

7.

−	1	2	3	4	5	6	7	8
1	0	1	2	3	4	5	6	7
2	1	0	1	2	3	4	5	6
3	2	1	0	1	2	3	4	5
4	3	2	1	0	1	2	3	4
5	4	3	2	1	0	1	2	3
6	5	4	3	2	1	0	1	2
7	6	5	4	3	2	1	0	1
8	7	6	5	4	3	2	1	0

P(Player 1 scores 1 point) $= \frac{34}{64}$, or $\frac{17}{32}$

P(Player 2 scores 1 point) $= \frac{30}{64}$, or $\frac{15}{32}$

Player 1; Player 1 scores on 34 of the 64 possible rolls.

8a. Predictions will vary.

8b.

	R	B	Y	B
Y	YR	YB	YY	YB
R	RR	RB	RY	RB
Y	YR	YB	YY	YB
B	BR	BB	BY	BB

	R	B	Y	B
Y	O	G	Y	G
R	R	P	O	P
Y	O	G	Y	G
B	P	B	G	B

Mixture Color	Red	Yellow	Blue	Green	Orange	Purple
Probability	$\frac{1}{16}$	$\frac{2}{16}$	$\frac{2}{16}$	$\frac{5}{16}$	$\frac{3}{16}$	$\frac{3}{16}$

8c.

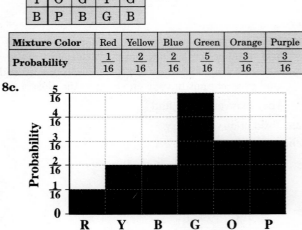

8d. Card 3 gives the best chance of winning because it has the most "high probability" colors. The probabilities of spinning the colors on Card 3 are $\frac{2}{16}$, $\frac{5}{16}$, $\frac{3}{16}$, and $\frac{3}{16}$. On Card 1, each color has only a $\frac{2}{16}$ chance of being spun. Card 2 has the same probabilities as Card 3 for three of its colors, but the fourth color, red, has only a $\frac{1}{16}$ probability of being spun compared to $\frac{5}{16}$ for green on Card 3.

Card 4 has sections with probabilities $\frac{1}{16}, \frac{2}{16}, \frac{2}{16},$ and $\frac{5}{16}$, which are less than Card 3's.

9a. $6^3 = 216$

9b. Possible method: Determine whether each of these possible combinations is odd or even: odd × odd × odd, odd × odd × even, odd × even × odd, odd × even × even, even × even × even, even × even × odd, even × odd × even, even × odd × odd.

9c. Of the 8 possible combinations, only one, odd × odd × odd, results in an odd product. Therefore, rolling an even product is more likely.

10a. There are 6 possible rolls for each die, so there are $6^5 = 7,776$ possible outcomes.

10b. all 1s, all 2s, all 3s, all 4s, all 5s, and all 6s
6

10c. $\frac{6}{6^5}$, or $\frac{1}{6^4}$, or $\frac{1}{1,296}$

10d. There are 36 possible outcomes, and rolling two 3s occurs only once out of these 36.
$\frac{1}{36}$

11.

−	1	2	3	4	5	6
1	0	1	2	3	4	5
2	1	0	1	2	3	4
3	2	1	0	1	2	3
4	3	2	1	0	1	2
5	4	3	2	1	0	1
6	5	4	3	2	1	0

$P(\text{Player 2 scores}) = \frac{12}{36}$, or $\frac{1}{3}$

$P(\text{Player 1 scores}) = \frac{24}{36}$, or $\frac{2}{3}$

$2\left(\frac{1}{3}\right) = 1\left(\frac{2}{3}\right)$

$\frac{2}{3} = \frac{2}{3}$

Both players have the same chances of winning because Player 2 receives 2 points to make up for having only half as many ways to score.

12a.

+	1	2	3	4	5	6
1	2	3	4	5	6	7
2	3	4	5	6	7	8
3	4	5	6	7	8	9
4	5	6	7	8	9	10
5	6	7	8	9	10	11
6	7	8	9	10	11	12

Sum	2	3	4	5	6	7	8	9	10	11	12
Probability	$\frac{1}{36}$	$\frac{2}{36}$	$\frac{3}{36}$	$\frac{4}{36}$	$\frac{5}{36}$	$\frac{6}{36}$	$\frac{5}{36}$	$\frac{4}{36}$	$\frac{3}{36}$	$\frac{2}{36}$	$\frac{1}{36}$

12b. $P(\text{Player 1 scores}) = \frac{2}{36} + \frac{5}{36} + \frac{4}{36} + \frac{1}{36} = \frac{12}{36}$, or $\frac{1}{3}$

12c. $P(\text{Player 2 scores}) = 1 - \frac{1}{3} = \frac{2}{3}$

$2\left(\frac{2}{3}\right) = x\left(\frac{1}{3}\right)$

$\frac{4}{3} = \frac{1}{3}x$

$x = 4$

4 points

13a.

+	1	2	3	4	5	6
1	2	3	4	5	6	7
2	3	4	5	6	7	8
3	4	5	6	7	8	9
4	5	6	7	8	9	10
5	6	7	8	9	10	11
6	7	8	9	10	11	12

Step	1	2	3	4	5	6
Probability	$\frac{4}{36}$	$\frac{3}{36}$	$\frac{5}{36}$	$\frac{6}{36}$	$\frac{4}{36}$	$\frac{3}{36}$

Step	1	2	3	4	5	6
Probability	$\frac{4}{36}$	$\frac{3}{36}$	$\frac{5}{36}$	$\frac{6}{36}$	$\frac{5}{36}$	$\frac{4}{36}$

Step	1	2	3	4	5	6
Probability	$\frac{4}{36}$	$\frac{3}{36}$	$\frac{5}{36}$	$\frac{5}{36}$	$\frac{3}{36}$	$\frac{2}{36}$

13b. the South Face

13c. the East Face

14. Possible answer: This plot uses both of the numbers with a $\frac{4}{36}$ probability and the one with a $\frac{3}{36}$ probability, and no $\frac{1}{36}$ probabilities. No plot will give a better chance of winning than this one.

4	6
3	2
12	5

15a.

Sum	Die 1	Die 2
12	6	6
11	5	6
	6	5
10	5	5
	4	6
	6	4
9	4	5
	5	4
	3	6
	6	3
8	4	4
	3	5
	5	3
	2	6
	6	2
7	1	6
	6	1
	2	5
	5	2
	3	4
	4	3

15b.

Sum	Die 1	Die 2
2	1	1
3	1	2
	2	1
4	2	2
	1	3
	3	1
5	1	4
	4	1
	2	3
	3	2
6	3	3
	1	5
	5	1
	2	4
	4	2
7	1	6
	6	1
	2	5
	5	2
	3	4
	4	3

15c.

Number	1	2	3	4	5	6
Appearances	2	4	6	8	10	12

$6, \dfrac{12}{42} = \dfrac{11}{21}$

15d.

Number	1	2	3	4	5	6
Appearances	12	10	8	6	4	2

$1, \dfrac{12}{42} = \dfrac{11}{21}$

15e. 2 possibilities, 5 and 6

15f. A 1 appears only with a 6, so you can win the game by using your second guess.

15g. A 1 appears in only 2 of 21 possible number pairs.

15h. Guessing 6 gives you the best chance of scoring a point in your turn but it leaves open all six (1–6) possibilities for the other die; that is, you have only a 1 out of 6 chance for a "quick" victory.

16a. Since the x^2 coefficient is negative, the graph opens downward.

Graph B

16b. $y = 2x^2$

Since the x^2 coefficient is positive, the graph opens upward. When $x = 0$, $y = 0$, so the graph passes through the origin.

Graph C

16c. $y = 0.5x^2 - 3$

Since the x^2 coefficient is positive, the graph opens upward. When $x = 0$, $y = {}^-3$, so the graph passes through $(0, {}^-3)$.

Graph A

17. $K = 0.4^n$

18. $\sqrt[3]{{}^-4}, \sqrt[5]{{}^-4}, \sqrt[7]{{}^-4}, \sqrt[9]{{}^-4}, \sqrt[11]{{}^-4}$

19.
$$4x + 3y = 31$$
$$3y = {}^-4x + 31$$
$$y = -\frac{4}{3}x + 10\frac{1}{3}$$

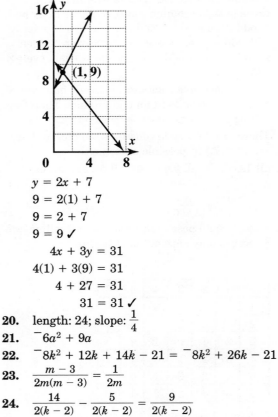

$$y = 2x + 7$$
$$9 = 2(1) + 7$$
$$9 = 2 + 7$$
$$9 = 9 \checkmark$$
$$4x + 3y = 31$$
$$4(1) + 3(9) = 31$$
$$4 + 27 = 31$$
$$31 = 31 \checkmark$$

20. length: 24; slope: $\dfrac{1}{4}$

21. ${}^-6a^2 + 9a$

22. ${}^-8k^2 + 12k + 14k - 21 = {}^-8k^2 + 26k - 21$

23. $\dfrac{m - 3}{2m(m - 3)} = \dfrac{1}{2m}$

24. $\dfrac{14}{2(k - 2)} - \dfrac{5}{2(k - 2)} = \dfrac{9}{2(k - 2)}$

Page 579   In Your Own Words

Possible answer: To decide whether a game was fair, I would find the probabilities of various events involved in the game and how they are distributed among each possible outcome. If the game is unfair, I can use the probability distribution to make the game fair, and their probabilities equal, by assigning points to the outcomes.

9-3 | Probability Investigations

Pages 583–584   Problem Set A

1. Answers will vary.

2. Answers will vary.

3. 1-2, 1-3, 1-4, 1-5, 1-6, 2-3, 2-4, 2-5, 2-6, 3-4, 3-5, 3-6, 4-5, 4-6, 5-6; 15 pairs

4a. 6

4b. 5

4c.

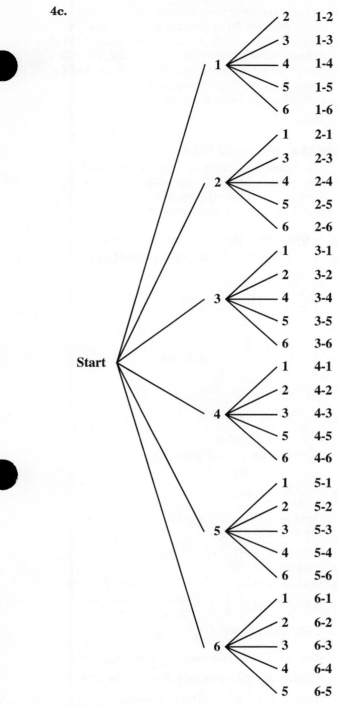

1	2	1-2
	3	1-3
	4	1-4
	5	1-5
	6	1-6
2	1	2-1
	3	2-3
	4	2-4
	5	2-5
	6	2-6
3	1	3-1
	2	3-2
	4	3-4
	5	3-5
	6	3-6
4	1	4-1
	2	4-2
	3	4-3
	5	4-5
	6	4-6
5	1	5-1
	2	5-2
	3	5-3
	4	5-4
	6	5-6
6	1	6-1
	2	6-2
	3	6-3
	4	6-4
	5	6-5

Start

30 pairs

4d. There are 6 choices for the first number, and each of those has 5 choices, so there are 30 in all.

4e. 15; the results are the same.

5. 15

6. Answers will vary.

Page 585   Problem Set B

1a. 7

1b. 6

1c. 5

1d. $7 \cdot 6 \cdot 5 = 210$

1e. 3

1f. 2

1g. 1

1h. $3 \cdot 2 \cdot 1 = 6$

1i. $210 \div 6 = 35$

2. 1 out of 35

3. Answers will vary.

Page 586   Share and Summarize

1. $\frac{49 \cdot 48 \cdot 47 \cdot 46 \cdot 45 \cdot 44}{6 \cdot 5 \cdot 4 \cdot 3 \cdot 2 \cdot 1} = 13{,}983{,}816$, so the probability is $\frac{1}{13{,}983{,}816}$.

2. $\frac{13{,}983{,}816}{2(52)} \approx 134{,}460$, so about once every 134,460 yr

Pages 587–588   Problem Set C

1. Team A: $\frac{1}{2}$; Team B: $\frac{1}{2}$

2. Answers will vary.

3. Answers will vary. Most groups will find that Team A wins the most. Team A has an advantage because they must win only one game to be champions; Teams B and C each must win two games in a row.

4a. $8 \cdot \frac{1}{2} = 4$

4b. $4 \cdot \frac{1}{2} = 2$

4c. $\frac{2}{8}$, or $\frac{1}{4}$

4d. $8 \cdot \frac{1}{2} = 4$

Team A can be expected to win the final game 4 out of 8 times

Team A: $\frac{4}{8} = \frac{1}{2}$

$8 \cdot \frac{1}{2} = 4$

Team C can be expected to beat Team C in the first game 4 out of 8 times.

$4 \cdot \frac{1}{2} = 2$

Team C can be expected to beat Team A in the final game 2 out of 4 times.

Team C: $\frac{2}{8} = \frac{1}{4}$

5. Answers will vary. Many students will consider the three-team structure unfair and therefore inappropriate. Others may suggest that the unequal chances of winning could be used to balance other influences such as playing the series "away from home." Still others may think that if Team A finished the season with the best record, it "deserves" an advantage in the playoffs.

Pages 588–589   Problem Set D

1. Answers will vary.

2. Answers will vary. Each team should win about the same number of times.

3. Answers will vary.

4. Answers will vary. Students should find that Teams A and B win a significantly greater number of times than Teams C and D.

5. Possible answer: The first structure would be good for a sports league that has four divisions, because it does not give advantage to one division winner over another.

6. *Structure 1:*

Team A can be expected to win its first game 4 out of 8 times. After winning its first game, Team A can be expected to win its second game 2 out of 4 times. So Team A can be expected to win the championship 2 out of 8 times.

Team A: $\frac{2}{8} = \frac{1}{4}$

Team B can be expected to win its first game 4 out of 8 times. After winning its first game, Team B can be expected to win its second game 2 out of 4 times. So Team B can be expected to win the championship 2 out of 8 times.

Team B: $\frac{2}{8} = \frac{1}{4}$

Team C can be expected to win its first game 4 out of 8 times. After winning its first game, Team C can be expected to win its second game 2 out of 4 times. So Team C can be expected to win the championship 2 out of 8 times.

Team C: $\frac{2}{8} = \frac{1}{4}$

Team D can be expected to win its first game 4 out of 8 times. After winning its first game, Team D can be expected to win its second game 2 out of 4 times. So Team D can be expected to win the championship 2 out of 8 times.

Team D: $\frac{2}{8} = \frac{1}{4}$

Structure 2:

Team A can be expected to win its first game 4 out of 8 times. After winning its first game, Team A can be expected to win its second game 2 out of 4 times. In addition, if Team A loses its first game, it can be expected to win its second game 2 out of 4 times, and then win its third game 1 out of 2 times. So Team A can be expected to win the championship 3 out of 8 times.

Team A: $\frac{3}{8}$

Team B can be expected to win its first game 4 out of 8 times. After winning its first game, Team B can be expected to win its second game 2 out of 4 times. In addition, if Team B loses its first game, it can be expected to win its second game 2 out of 4 times, and then win its third game 1 out of 2 times. So Team B can be expected to win the championship 3 out of 8 times.

Team B: $\frac{3}{8}$

Team C can be expected to win its first game 4 out of 8 times. After winning its first game, Team C can be expected to win its second game 2 out of 4 times. After winning its second game, Team C can be expected to win its third game 1 out of 2 times So Team C can be expected to win the championship 1 out of 8 times.

Team C: $\frac{1}{8}$

Team D can be expected to win its first game 4 out of 8 times. After winning its first game, Team D can be expected to win its second game 2 out of 4 times. After winning its second game, Team D can be expected to win its third game 1 out of 2 times So Team D can be expected to win the championship 1 out of 8 times.

Team D: $\frac{1}{8}$

Page 589   Share and Summarize

The teams that didn't have to play as many games had a better chance. Also, the teams that were given an opportunity to play more even if they lost a game had a better chance.

Pages 590–595   On Your Own Exercises

1a. W1-W2, W1-W3, W1-O, W2-W3, W2-O, W3-O

1b. $\frac{3}{6} = \frac{1}{2}$

2a. $\frac{10 \cdot 9 \cdot 8}{3 \cdot 2 \cdot 1} = 120$

2b. $\frac{1}{120}$

3a. $\frac{30 \cdot 29 \cdot 28 \cdot 27 \cdot 26}{5 \cdot 4 \cdot 3 \cdot 2 \cdot 1} = 142{,}506$

3b. $\frac{1}{142{,}506}$

3c. $\frac{142{,}506}{3} = 47{,}502$

once every 47,502 weeks

47502 weeks = 913.5 years

about once every 913 yr

3d. $\frac{142{,}506}{300} = 475.02$

about once every 475 weeks

475 weeks ≈ 9 years

about once every 9 yr

4a. Answers will vary.

4b. Answers will vary.

4c. Teams A and D: $\frac{1}{2} \cdot \frac{1}{2} = \frac{1}{4}$

Teams B, C, E, and F: $\frac{1}{2} \cdot \frac{1}{2} \cdot \frac{1}{2} = \frac{1}{8}$

Teams A and D each have a $\frac{1}{4}$ probability of winning the championship. Each of the other teams has a $\frac{1}{8}$ probability of winning.

5. Possible answer:

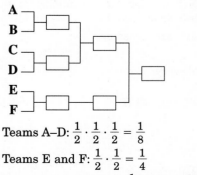

Teams A–D: $\frac{1}{2} \cdot \frac{1}{2} \cdot \frac{1}{2} = \frac{1}{8}$

Teams E and F: $\frac{1}{2} \cdot \frac{1}{2} = \frac{1}{4}$

Teams A–D: Each has $\frac{1}{8}$ chance of winning;

Teams E and F: Each has $\frac{1}{4}$ chance of winning.

6a. $20 \cdot 19 \cdot 18 = 6{,}840$

6b. $10 \cdot 9 \cdot 8 = 720$

6c. $6{,}840 \cdot 720 = 4{,}924{,}800$

7a. Worse; there are more possible pairs.

7b. 36; There are 6 ways to choose each number, so there are $6 \cdot 6$ or 36 possible pairs.

7c. 1-1, 1-2, 1-3, 1-4, 1-5, 1-6,
2-1, 2-2, 2-3, 2-4, 2-5, 2-6,
3-1, 3-2, 3-3, 3-4, 3-5, 3-6,
4-1, 4-2, 4-3, 4-4, 4-5, 4-6,
5-1, 5-2, 5-3, 5-4, 5-5, 5-6,
6-1, 6-2, 6-3, 6-4, 6-5, 6-6

7d. 21

7e. No; there are 2 ways to get a pair in which the numbers are different but only 1 way to get a pair in which both numbers are the same.

7f. P(a certain pair made up of different numbers)
$= \frac{2}{36} = \frac{1}{18}$
P(a certain pair made up of the same number)
$= \frac{1}{36}$
A pair in which the numbers are different has a $\frac{2}{36}$ or $\frac{1}{18}$ chance of winning, while a pair in which the numbers are the same has a $\frac{1}{36}$ chance of winning.

8a. 343; There are 7 ways to choose each number so there are $7 \cdot 7 \cdot 7$ or 343 possible pairs.

8b. No; there are 6 ways to get a triple in which none of the numbers are the same; 3 ways to get a triple in which two number are the same, but the third number is different; and only 1 way to get a triple in which all of the numbers are the same.

8c. P(a certain triple made up of three different numbers) $= \frac{6}{343}$
P(a certain triple made up of a number repeated exactly two times) $= \frac{3}{343}$
P(a certain triple made up of a number repeated three times) $= \frac{1}{343}$
A triple in which none of the numbers are the same has a $\frac{6}{343}$ chance of winning; a triple in which two numbers are the same has a $\frac{3}{343}$ chance of winning; and a triple in which all of the numbers are the same has a $\frac{1}{343}$ chance of winning.

9a. There are $7 \cdot 6 \cdot 5 \cdot 4$ possible groups of 4 numbers.
There are $4 \cdot 3 \cdot 2 \cdot 1$ possible ways a group of 4 numbers can be ordered.
$\frac{7 \cdot 6 \cdot 5 \cdot 4}{4 \cdot 3 \cdot 2 \cdot 1} = 35$, so the probability is $\frac{1}{35}$.

9b. It is the same.

9c. *5 of 7:*
There are $7 \cdot 6 \cdot 5 \cdot 4 \cdot 3$ possible groups of 5 numbers.
There are $5 \cdot 4 \cdot 3 \cdot 2 \cdot 1$ possible ways a group of 5 numbers can be ordered.
$\frac{7 \cdot 6 \cdot 5 \cdot 4 \cdot 3}{5 \cdot 4 \cdot 3 \cdot 2 \cdot 1} = 21$, so the probability is $\frac{1}{21}$.
2 of 7:
There are $7 \cdot 6$ possible groups of 2 numbers.
There are $2 \cdot 1$ possible ways a group of 5 numbers can be ordered.
$\frac{7 \cdot 6}{2 \cdot 1} = 21$, so the probability is $\frac{1}{21}$.
They're the same, $\frac{1}{21}$.

9d. Possible answer: To find the probability for the *4-of-7* game, do this calculation: $\frac{7 \cdot 6 \cdot 5 \cdot 4}{4 \cdot 3 \cdot 2 \cdot 1}$. To find the probability for the *3-of-7* game, do this calculation: $\frac{7 \cdot 6 \cdot 5}{3 \cdot 2 \cdot 1}$. Factoring out $\frac{4}{4}$ in the first calculation shows that the results are the same. For the *5-of-7* game, the probability is $\frac{7 \cdot 6 \cdot 5 \cdot 4 \cdot 3}{5 \cdot 4 \cdot 3 \cdot 2 \cdot 1}$. For the *2-of-7* game, it's $\frac{7 \cdot 6}{2 \cdot 1}$. Factoring out $\frac{5 \cdot 4 \cdot 3}{5 \cdot 4 \cdot 3}$ in the first calculation shows that the results are the same.

9e. the *2-of-6* game; Possible explanation: You have the higher four numbers in the numerator and the lower four in the denominator. Since there are only six numbers, the middle two are in both numerator and denominator, so you can take them out. That leaves only two numbers in both parts of the calculation, which is what you have for the *2-of-6* game.

10a. There is 1 possible route to the movie theater. 4 out of 8 times he can be expected to drive to D. From D, 2 out of 4 times he can be expected to drive to F. From F, 1 out of 2 times he can be expected to drive to the movie theater. So he can be expected to go to the theater 1 out of 8 times.
$\frac{1}{8}$

10b. There are 3 possible routes to the park.
route 1:
4 out of 8 times he can be expected to drive to C. From C, 4 out of 4 times he can be expected to drive to E. From E, 2 out of 4 times he can be expected to drive to the park.
route 2:
4 out of 8 times he can be expected to drive to D. From D, 2 out of 4 times he can be expected to drive to E. From E, 1 out of 2 times he can be expected to drive to the park.
route 3:
4 out of 8 times he can be expected to drive to D. From D, 2 out of 4 times he can be expected to drive toward F. From F, 1 out of 2 times he can be expected to drive to the park.
So he can be expected to go to the park 4 out of 8 times.
$\frac{4}{8}$, or $\frac{1}{2}$

10c. There are 2 possible routes to the ice cream store.

route 1:

4 out of 8 times he can be expected to drive to C. From C, 4 out of 4 times he can be expected to drive to E. From E, 2 out of 4 times he can be expected to drive to the ice cream store.

route 2:

4 out of 8 times he can be expected to drive to D. From D, 2 out of 4 times he can be expected to drive to E. From E, 1 out of 2 times he can be expected to drive to the ice cream store.

So he can be expected to go to the ice cream store 3 out of 8 times.

$\frac{3}{8}$

11a. Possible answers:

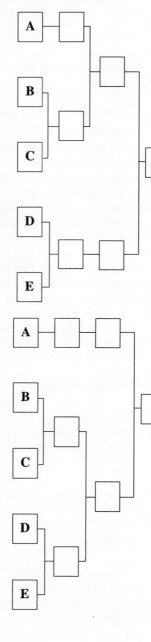

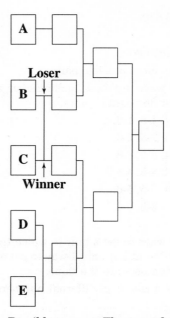

11b. Possible answer: The second structure shown in the answer to Part a, in which Team A does not have to play the first two rounds, might be more appropriate if Team A has a record that indisputably sets it above the other teams, as it gives the other teams a more equal chance to get to the final game.

12a. P(Team A) = 0.6; P(Team B) = 0.4

12b.

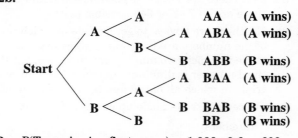

12c. P(Team A wins first game) = 1,000 · 0.6 = 600

P(Team A wins second game) = 600 · 0.6 = 360

12d. AA: 360

ABA: 1,000 · 0.6 · 0.4 · 0.6 = 144

ABB: 1,000 · 0.6 · 0.4 · 0.4 = 96

BAA: 1,000 · 0.4 · 0.6 · 0.6 = 144

BAB: 1,000 × 0.4 × 0.6 × 0.4 = 96

BB: 1,000 × 0.4 × 0.4 = 160

144 + 96 + 144 + 144 + 160 = 1,000

12e. Team A: 360 + 144 + 144 = 648

Team B: 96 + 96 + 160 = 352

P(Team A wins the tournament) = $\frac{648}{1,000}$

= 64.8%

12f. P(B in 1-game tournament) = 40%

P(B in best-two-out-of-three tournament) = 1 − 64.8% = 35.2%

1-game

13a. The value of m is ⁻5.

13b. $y = {}^-5x$

13c. $y = {}^-5x - 2$

13d. $y = {}^-5x + b, (3, 0)$
$0 = {}^-5(3) + b$
$b = 15$
$y = {}^-5x + 15$

14. $p = 5^h$

15.

16. $0 > 35 - 5x + 12x$
${}^-35 > 7x$
$x < {}^-5$

```
◄──┼──┼──┼──○──┼──┼──┼──┼──┼──┼──►
  ⁻8 ⁻7 ⁻6 ⁻5 ⁻4 ⁻3 ⁻2 ⁻1  0  1  2
```

17. $2h(2h - 1)$

18. $(3a + b)({}^-2a + b)$

19. ${}^-(k + j)(4k + j)$

20. $(m + 3)(2m - 3)$

21. $y = \dfrac{-b \pm \sqrt{b^2 - 4ac}}{2a}$

$y = \dfrac{2 \pm \sqrt{4 + 72}}{6}$

$y = \dfrac{2 \pm \sqrt{76}}{6}$

$y = \dfrac{2 \pm 2\sqrt{19}}{6}$

$y = \dfrac{1 \pm \sqrt{19}}{3}$

22. ${}^-6a^2 + 3a + 4 = 0$

$y = \dfrac{-b \pm \sqrt{b^2 - 4ac}}{2a}$

$y = \dfrac{{}^-3 \pm \sqrt{9 + 96}}{{}^-12}$

$y = \dfrac{3 \pm \sqrt{105}}{12}$

23. $4k^2 - 5k - 2 = 0$

$y = \dfrac{-b \pm \sqrt{b^2 - 4ac}}{2a}$

$y = \dfrac{5 \pm \sqrt{25 + 32}}{8}$

$y = \dfrac{5 \pm \sqrt{57}}{8}$

24. $2m^2 - 6m - 12 = 0$

$y = \dfrac{-b \pm \sqrt{b^2 - 4ac}}{2a}$

$y = \dfrac{6 \pm \sqrt{36 + 96}}{4}$

$y = \dfrac{6 \pm \sqrt{132}}{4}$

$y = \dfrac{6 \pm \sqrt{132}}{4}$

$y = \dfrac{6 \pm 2\sqrt{33}}{4}$

$y = \dfrac{3 \pm \sqrt{33}}{2}$

25. $(x - 5)^2 = 49$
$(x - 5) = 7$
$x = 12$
${}^-(x - 5) = 7$
$5 - x = 7$
${}^-x = 2$
$x = {}^-2$
$12, {}^-2$

26. $6x^2 - 30x + 36 = 0$
$6(x^2 - 5x + 6) = 0$
$6(x - 3)(x - 2) = 0$
$2, 3$

Page 592　In Your Own Words

Possible answer: To make a given lottery game more difficult to win, I would increase the number of matches required to win if the number of choices stayed the same. The chances of winning decrease as the number of matches increases up to a point. In a lottery, the number of matches that produces the lowest probability of winning is one half the number of choices. For example, matching 6 balls correctly in a lottery of 12 balls (*6-of-12* game) produces a 1 in 924 chance of winning. All other matches produce higher chances of winning.

Review and Self-Assessment

Pages 596–598　Strategies and Applications

1. 10 games; AB, AC, AD, AE, BC, BD, BE, CD, CE, DE

2a.

A First	B First	C First	D First
ABCD	BACD	CABD	DABC
ABDC	BADC	CADB	DACB
ACBD	BCAD	CBAD	DBAC
ACDB	BCDA	CBDA	DBCA
ADBC	BDAC	CDAB	DCAB
ADCB	BDCA	CDBA	DCBA

2b. 24

3a. Possible explanation: Nine different players could bat first, leaving eight different players to bat second, seven different players to bat third, and so on, so you can multiply $9 \cdot 8 \cdot 7 \cdot 6 \cdot 5 \cdot 4 \cdot 3 \cdot 2 \cdot 1$; 362,880 orders.

3b. $8 \cdot 7 \cdot 6 \cdot 5 \cdot 4 \cdot 3 \cdot 2 \cdot 1 = 40,320$

4. Possible explanation: There are $12 \cdot 11 \cdot 10 \cdot 9 \cdot 8 = 95,040$ ways to order 5 players chosen from a team of 12, but since order is unimportant, divide by the number of ways to order 5 players, which is $5 \cdot 4 \cdot 3 \cdot 2 \cdot 1 = 120$. The result is $95,040 \div 120 = 792$.

5a. $\frac{1}{10}$

5b. $\frac{7}{10}$

5c. $1 - \frac{7}{10} = \frac{3}{10}$

6a. $\frac{12}{24}$, or $\frac{1}{2}$

6b. $\frac{13}{24}$

7a.

+	1	2	3	4	5	6
1	2	3	4	5	6	7
2	3	4	5	6	7	8
3	4	5	6	7	8	9
4	5	6	7	8	9	10
5	6	7	8	9	10	11
6	7	8	9	10	11	12

No; the probability that Player 1 will win is $\frac{16}{36}$, and the probability that Player 2 will win is $\frac{20}{36}$.

7b. No; the probability that Player 1 will win is $\frac{16}{36}$, and the probability that Player 2 will win is $\frac{20}{36}$.

7c. $P(\text{Player 1 scores}) = \frac{3}{36} = \frac{1}{12}$

$P(\text{Player 2 scores}) = \frac{9}{36} = \frac{1}{4}$

$3\left(\frac{1}{12}\right) = 1\left(\frac{1}{4}\right)$

$\frac{1}{4} = \frac{1}{4}$

yes; Possible explanation: Although Player 2 is three times as likely to score on a given roll, Player 1 receives 3 times as many points, so in 36 games they are both expected to get 9 points.

8a. If the die shows a 1, 2, 3, or 4, the sum will be lower than 7.

If the die shows a 6 or 7, the sum will be higher than 7.

lower; $\frac{4}{6}$, or $\frac{2}{3}$

8b. If the die shows a 4, 5, or 6, the sum will be higher than 7.

If the die shows a 1 or 2, the sum will be lower than 7.

higher; $\frac{3}{6}$; or $\frac{1}{2}$

Page 599   Demonstrating Skills

9. $7 \cdot 6 \cdot 5 \cdot 4 \cdot 3 \cdot 2 \cdot 1 = 5,040$

10. 0 condiments: 1

1 condiment: 7

2 condiments: $\frac{7 \cdot 6}{2 \cdot 1} = 21$

3 condiments: $\frac{7 \cdot 6 \cdot 5}{3 \cdot 2 \cdot 1} = 35$

4 condiments: $\frac{7 \cdot 6 \cdot 5 \cdot 4}{4 \cdot 3 \cdot 2 \cdot 1} = 35$

5 condiments: $\frac{7 \cdot 6 \cdot 5 \cdot 4 \cdot 3}{5 \cdot 4 \cdot 3 \cdot 2 \cdot 1} = 21$

6 condiments: $\frac{7 \cdot 6 \cdot 5 \cdot 4 \cdot 3 \cdot 2}{6 \cdot 5 \cdot 4 \cdot 3 \cdot 2 \cdot 1} = 7$

7 condiments: 1

$1 + 7 + 21 + 35 + 35 + 21 + 7 + 1 = 128$

11. $\frac{21 \cdot 20 \cdot 19 \cdot 18 \cdot 17}{5 \cdot 4 \cdot 3 \cdot 2 \cdot 1} = 20,349$

Chapter 10 Modeling with Data

10-1 Data Patterns in Tables and Graphs

Pages 603–604 Problem Set A

1. Possible table:

Northtown Scores	Southtown Scores
54	44
58	55
66	59
66	59
68	60
69	62
69	63
72	66
72	70
73	73
74	74
76	79
77	88
81	90
81	92
82	94
84	94
85	100
87	100
89	100
90	100
94	100

2. entire group: $3{,}389 \div 44 \approx 77.02$

   Northtown: $1{,}667 \div 22 \approx 75.77$

   Southtown: $1{,}722 \div 22 \approx 78.27$

   Southtown's mean is 2.5 points higher than Northtown's.

3. entire group: The two middle numbers are 74 and 76.

   $(74 + 76) \div 2 = 75$

   Northtown: The two middle numbers are 74 and 76.

   $(74 + 76) \div 2 = 75$

   Southtown: The two middle numbers are 74 and 79.

   $(74 + 79) \div 2 = 76.5$

   Southtown's median is 1.5 points higher than Northtown's.

4a. Northtown: $94 - 54 = 40$

   Southtown: $100 - 44 = 56$

   Southtown has a wider range.

4b. Northtown: 11

   Southtown: 11

   Yes; they both have 11 students above the class median.

4c. All five are from Southtown.

4d. Southtown

   $54 - 44 = 10$

4e. Answers will vary. Southtown may provide stronger opportunities for top students, since their best scorers all got perfect scores. Northtown may provide stronger opportunities for low and average students, since their lowest score was 10 points above Southtown's lowest score.

Page 604 Problem Set B

1. Possible table:

Morning	Afternoon
44	54
55	58
59	59
62	60
66	63
68	66
69	66
70	69
73	72
73	72
74	74
79	76
81	77
81	82
85	84
87	88
90	89
90	92
94	94
100	94
100	100
100	100

2. Possible answer: Although the morning class has a higher mean and median, the classes are close in these measures, so the results don't seem particularly conclusive. The morning class has more top scorers, but it also includes the lowest scorer. The classes have the same number of students above and below the overall median.

Page 604 Share and Summarize

1. Possible answer: I thought about what I was trying to find out about the data and ignored the extra information.

2. Possible answer: Advantage: The single table gives all the information without having to repeat the scores. Disadvantage: You can't really sort the information in a way that makes both town and class easy to compare.

3. Possible answer: mean, mode, range, the high and low scorers in each case

1.

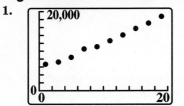

linear

Use a graphing calculator to find the regression line for the data.

Possible equation: $y = 702x + 5,254$

2. Possible answer:

For 2005, $x = 25$.

$y = 702(25) + 5,254 = 22,804$

For 2007, $x = 27$.

$y = 702(27) + 5,254 = 24,208$

$24,208 - 22,804 = 1,404$

If the current year is 2005, the price would be about \$22,804, which is \$1,404 less than the 2007 estimated price of \$24,208.

Page 606   Problem Set D

1. miles for the year: $135,135 - 119,982 = 15,153$

average miles per month: $15,153 \div 12 = 1,262.75$

2. July: $122,564 - 121,142 = 1,422$

$1,422 \div 36.6 \approx 38.9$ miles per gallon

November: $128,919 - 128,106 = 813$

$813 \div 34.7 \approx 23.4$

3.

Month	Miles Driven	Fuel Economy (mpg)
Jun	1,160	27.1
Jul	1,422	38.9
Aug	3,790	27.1
Sep	1,105	26.3
Oct	647	24.4
Nov	813	23.4
Dec	1,020	24.6
Jan	1,113	25.0
Feb	642	23.6
Mar	735	24.8
Apr	1,684	28.1
May	1,021	28.9

4. Nov, Feb, Oct, Dec

Page 607   Problem Set E

1. Answers will vary, perhaps depending on where a student lives or has lived. In many parts of the country, the mean temperature for June will look low and that for December will look high.

2.

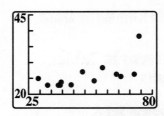

Possible answer: There may be a connection but not much of one. There are some low-fuel-economy months when it wasn't that cold.

3.

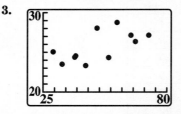

Possible answer: Although there may be a slight connection, there doesn't seem to be much of one.

Page 607   Problem Set F

1. A possible table (months are sorted by number of miles driven) is shown. Possible answer: It's hard to tell from the table whether months in which fewer miles were driven have lower fuel economy.

Month	Gas Bought	Miles Driven	Fuel Economy
Feb	27.2	643	23.6
Oct	26.5	647	24.4
Mar	29.6	735	24.8
Nov	34.7	813	23.4
Dec	41.5	1,020	24.6
May	35.3	1,021	28.9
Sep	42.0	1,105	26.3
Jan	44.6	1,113	25.0
Jun	42.8	1,160	27.1
Jul	36.6	1,422	38.9
Apr	60.0	1,684	28.1
Aug	139.7	3,790	27.1

2.

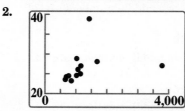

Possible answer: There seems to be a connection but not much of one. Two points seem really far from the general trend.

Page 608   Share and Summarize

1. Possible answer: In Problem Set E, I had to use my calculation of fuel economy; in Problem Set F, I had to use my calculations of both miles driven and fuel economy. It was necessary because the variables I needed to graph weren't given in the tables; I had to make the calculations to get the data I needed.

2. Possible answer: It's difficult to say. The graph of miles driven seems to show a stronger connection but not by much.

3. Yes; the best months for fuel economy were in the summer (plus April).

Pages 610–612   Problem Set G

1a. boys' names: Michael (42 years) and John (27 years)

girls' names: Mary (56 years) and Jennifer (15 years)

1b. Mary; her name was most popular 14 years more than Michael's.

1c. Answers will vary. Likely guesses for top boys' names (with scores) are James (92), John (128), Michael (141), and Robert (90), so Michael and John are still the most popular, though Michael is only slightly ahead of John. Likely guesses for top girls' names are less clear but might include Ashley (27), Dorothy (26), Helen (45), Jennifer (48), Jessica (43), Linda (30), and Mary (187), so Mary and Jennifer are still the most popular, with Mary far ahead.

2. Possible answer: There are by far more girls' names in total, so they must change more frequently.

3. John and Mary, with streaks of 53 and 65 years, respectively.

4. No boys' names show this kind of short-term popularity, but several girls' names do. Without the nineteenth-century data we can't tell about Anna, and without future data we can't tell about Alexis, Madison, and Samantha; but Brittany, Deborah, Debra, Karen, Kimberly, Sarah, Shirley, and Taylor all had short-lived popularity. Explanations will vary, but entertainers and other famous people by those names seem like probable sources.

5. Possible answers: For Problem 1a, the first table makes it easier because you see immediately that Mary spent several 10-year intervals in first place. With the second table it's even easier; you just find the greatest number in the first column.

For Problem 1c, the first table is a little easier than the original, but the second table is a lot easier because the number of years are already counted; you just multiply each by its point value and add the products.

For Problem 3, it's a little easier to tell that Mary is first because that name is in first place for several 10-year intervals in a row. Using the second table, it's very easy; you just look at the "Maximum Consecutive Years" columns.

For Problem 4, the original table is easier than this first table, because you can look across a row for a name and see if it is only on the list for a few years; with the first table here, you have to look around for other places the name might be. The second table is easiest, though, because you can look at the results for one name and don't have to count.

6. Possible answer: Jacob, Joshua, and Matthew have clearly become more popular for boys in recent years, and Michael since the mid-century, but otherwise boys' names haven't changed very much. Popular girls' names have changed radically, with a totally different set at the end of the century than at the beginning.

7. Possible answer: The most popular boys' names in recent years have been Jacob, Matthew, and Michael, so these three should be included. The only other listed names popular since 1990 have been Christopher and Joshua, which leaves one name open. The most popular girls' names in recent years have been Ashley, Jessica, Emily, Hannah, Madison, Samantha, Sarah, and Taylor, so those are the most likely names from which to choose.

8. Possible answer: For boys, John, William, and probably James are logical choices; from 1900 to 1917, John had first place, William had second, and James had third, so it seems likely the three would have been popular in 1899 as well. For girls, Mary and maybe Helen and Anna are good choices, because these were most popular from 1900 to 1902.

Page 612   Share and Summarize

1. Possible answer: The table organized by 10-year intervals is relatively compact, and it was easier to use for some of the questions. The table giving year totals was easy to use to answer all of the questions, but it gives no information about when a particular name was most popular; the other two do. The original table gives the most information, although it isn't easy to read.

2. Possible questions: What are the actual numbers of babies with each name? What names were in fourth place?

Pages 613–615   Problem Set H

1. Possible answer: There are many in the center of the map and fewer near the edges.

2.
0	25	50	75	100	125	150	175	200

3. See student work.

4. Answers will vary, depending on the location of the center of the rings and judgment calls about deaths that occur on their borders. There are approximately 120 deaths within Ring 3. The victims lived from 50 m to 75 m from the pump.

5. Possible table:

Ring	Victims
1	45
2	100
3	120
4	110
5	110
6	40
7	15
8	5

6. Possible histogram:

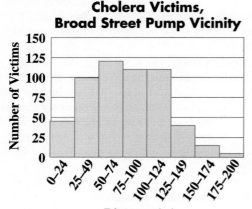

Cholera Victims, Broad Street Pump Vicinity

7. Possible answer: No; there are more deaths in Ring 3 than any other, and the first ring (closest to the pump) has relatively few deaths.

8. Answers will vary, but most students should realize that they don't reveal anything particularly useful.

9a. $A = \pi \cdot 25^2 \approx 1{,}963$

about $1{,}963 \text{ m}^2$

9b.

Ring	Victims	Area (m²)
1	45	1,963
2	100	5,890
3	120	9,817
4	110	13,744
5	110	17,671
6	40	21,598
7	15	25,525
8	5	29,452

9c.

Ring	Victims	Area (m²)	Population Density of Victims
1	45	1,963	0.0229
2	100	5,890	0.0170
3	120	9,817	0.0122
4	110	13,744	0.0080
5	110	17,671	0.0062
6	40	21,598	0.0019
7	15	25,525	0.0006
8	5	29,452	0.0002

9d. Yes; the density increases as you move through the rings toward the pump.

10.

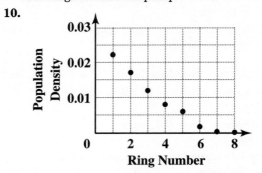

Page 615   Share and Summarize

1. Possible answer: The map supports the conclusion, because it seems obvious that there are more victims living close to the pump.

The table is revealing only when the population density is included; the other information doesn't show the pattern.

The mean, median, and mode don't help you see the overall trend.

The histogram is a little helpful because after a point the bars aren't as tall, but the shorter first couple of bars might hurt the argument for the conclusion.

The population-density plot supports the conclusion, because it makes it clear that there are more victims closer to the pump.

2. Arguments can be made for either the original map, which gives a lot of information at just a glance, or the population-density plot, which supports the conclusion with numbers.

Pages 616–630   On Your Own Exercises

1. Possible answer: Some stores charge a wide variety of prices, while others have prices that are about the same, except for Aviva, whose CD is higher in all stores. It also seems that some artists' CDs are priced relatively lower at all the stores and that other artists' CDs, Aviva's in particular, are more expensive.

2a. Possible answer:

Store	Artist	Price
Castle	A K Mango	$12.19
Castle	Screaming Screamers	12.50
Castle	Front Street Girls	13.09
Castle	Out of Sync	14.29
Castle	Aviva	19.00
InstantMusic	A K Mango	13.25
InstantMusic	Front Street Girls	13.25
InstantMusic	Screaming Screamers	13.49
InstantMusic	Out of Sync	13.59
InstantMusic	Aviva	15.00
GLU Sounds	Front Street Girls	13.95
GLU Sounds	A K Mango	14.50
GLU Sounds	Out of Sync	15.49
GLU Sounds	Screaming Screamers	15.50
GLU Sounds	Aviva	16.75
Pineapples	A K Mango	14.99
Pineapples	Screaming Screamers	15.99
Pineapples	Front Street Girls	16.00
Pineapples	Out of Sync	16.25
Pineapples	Aviva	18.89

2b. Castle: $71.07 \div 5 \approx \$14.21$
InstantMusic: $68.58 \div 5 \approx \$13.72$
GLU Sounds: $76.19 \div 5 \approx \$15.24$
Pineapples: $82.12 \div 5 \approx \$16.42$

2c. Possible answer: Castle, because they have the lowest price for all but the most expensive CD; or InstantMusic, because they have the lowest mean price.

3a. Possible answer:

Store	Artist	Price
Castle	A K Mango	$12.19
InstantMusic	A K Mango	13.25
GLU Sounds	A K Mango	14.50
Pineapples	A K Mango	14.99
Castle	Screaming Screamers	12.50
InstantMusic	Screaming Screamers	13.49
GLU Sounds	Screaming Screamers	15.50
Pineapples	Screaming Screamers	15.99
Castle	Front Street Girls	13.09
InstantMusic	Front Street Girls	13.25
GLU Sounds	Front Street Girls	13.95
Pineapples	Front Street Girls	16.00
Castle	Out of Sync	14.29
InstantMusic	Out of Sync	13.59
GLU Sounds	Out of Sync	15.49
Pineapples	Out of Sync	16.25
Castle	Aviva	19.00
InstantMusic	Aviva	15.00
GLU Sounds	Aviva	16.75
Pineapples	Aviva	18.89

3b. A K Mango: $54.93 \div 4 \approx \$13.73$
Screaming Screamers: $57.48 \div 4 = \$14.37$
Front Street Girls: $56.29 \div 4 \approx \$14.07$
Out of Sync: $59.62 \div 4 \approx \$14.91$
Aviva: $69.64 \div 4 = \$17.41$

4a. $\dfrac{67.7 - 5.6}{5.6} \approx 11.09$, or 1,109%
about 1,100%

4b.

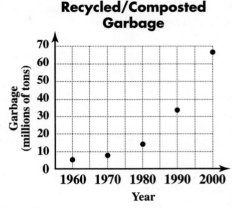

Recycled/Composted Garbage

4c. Possible answer: There does seem to have been a dramatic improvement.

4d. 1960: $5.6 \div 88.1 \approx 0.0636$
1970: $8.0 \div 121.1 \approx 0.0661$
1980: $14.5 \div 151.6 \approx 0.0956$
1990: $33.2 \div 205.2 \approx 0.1618$
2000: $67.7 \div 232.0 \approx 0.2918$

Year	Ratio of Waste Recycled or Composted to Total Generated
1960	0.064
1970	0.066
1980	0.096
1990	0.162
2000	0.292

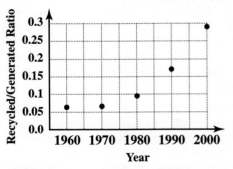

4e. Possible answer: People have been recycling increasing portions of their garbage each year.

5. In every case, for boys and girls, when a name dropped out of first place it appeared in second or third place the following year.

6a. Answers will vary; there were more Republicans elected.

6b. Possible answer: Instead of listing the years for each state, list the states who voted for each party, by year.

Year	Democratic	Republican	Other
1948	AZ, AR, CA, CO, FL, GA, ID, IL, IA, KY, MA, MN, MO, MT, NV, NM, NC, OH, OK, RI, TN, TX, UT, VA, WA, WV, WI, WY	CT, DE, IN, KS, ME, MD, MI, NE, NH, NJ, NY, ND, OR, PA, SD, VT	AL, LA, MS, SC

6c. Possible answer: Add a column listing the number of electoral votes for each state.

6d. Answers will vary. There is no easy way to do this with so many states and so many years; however, students might suggest reordering the table according to the number of electoral votes or repeating a year for every *x* electoral votes a state has. (For example, a student repeating years for every 5 electoral votes would repeat each of MO's entries twice for its 11 electoral votes.)

7a. Democrat: DC, HI, MN; Republican: AK, AZ, CO, ID, IN, KS, MS, NE, NH, ND, OK, SD, UT, VT, WY

7b. Republican: 1964; Democrat: no year

7c. Answers will vary. Sorting the data by the number of times Republicans (or Democrats) won each state might help. The given table seems good because you can just scan the entries for low numbers of years won, although trying to find which years are common to most is a little more difficult with the states in question spread out like this.

8a. Alabama, Georgia, Louisiana, Mississippi, and South Carolina; 1948, 1960, and 1968

8b. Possible answer: Most of the states choosing the "other" candidate in 1948 also chose the "other" candidate in 1960; all five states choosing "other" candidates were Southern states, four east of the Mississippi River.

8c. Answers will vary. Because there were so few of these states, the given table works as well as any other, although the fact that all the states are Southern would have been immediately obvious if the table were organized by region.

9a. Boston

9b. Westwood

9c. Answers will vary. Luna's reasoning seems more solid; it's likely that Boston sends more just because it has so many seventh and eighth graders. However, there are many reasons Westwood might have a greater fraction: some special arrangement between Westwood and Aftermath; the program has become popular there and spread by word of mouth; the schools have no extra-help programs of their own, or perhaps it's an affluent city whose citizens can more easily afford to send their children to such a program.

10a. Cambridge is farthest north, Mansfield is farthest south, Medfield is farthest west, and Duxbury is farthest east.

10b. Possible answer: Braintree or Quincy

10c. It removes Medfield and Duxbury from their positions as farthest west and east, respectively, making Needham farthest west and Norwell farthest east. Braintree or Quincy is still in the middle.

10d. If a town sends only one or two students, it might not mean anything statistically or geographically. They might be children of faculty members, for example.

10e. Possible answer: Braintree or Quincy because they are the most central.

11a. "return immediately"

11b. In this version the two rows have been interchanged, since it's conventional to work from top to bottom.

A	B	C	D	E	F	G	H	I	J	K	L	M	N	O	P	Q	R	S	T	U	V	W	X	Y	Z
i	r	a	j	s	b	k	t	c	l	u	d	m	v	e	n	w	f	o	x	g	p	y	h	q	z

11c. "you are correct"

12a. "this is not an easy example to figure out"

12b. Possible answer: You can find the frequency of each letter in the coded message and compare it to the letter-frequency table; all the letters in the coded message may not appear with exactly the same frequency, but you can get some helpful information.

12c. Possible answer: The sources from which the data were gathered probably differ.

12d. Possible answer: Specific texts vary in their letter frequencies (for example, a short passage might include no e's but would still contain vowels), use of words in a particular context (for example, a discussion of zoos might have more z's than is typical), and even deliberate efforts to confuse (for example, if you knew your message might be intercepted, you might intentionally write something with unusual letter frequencies).

13. Possible answer: Yes; they have been (or even have more than made up for it), but the assumptions for the future are that they will not continue to do so.

14. $750,000,000 \cdot 17 = 12,750,000,000$

$3,150,000,000 \cdot 0.5 = 1,575,000,000$

Possible answer: Paul; in 1960, there were approximately 750 billion vehicle miles with emissions of about 17 g/mi, for about 12.8 trillion grams of hydrocarbon; in 2010, there were approximately 3.15 trillion miles at about 0.5 g/mi, for about 1.6 trillion grams of hydrocarbon. So, there is less hydrocarbon expected in 2010 than there was in 1960.

15a. Note: Values in table are approximations.

Year	Average per-Vehicle Emissions (grams of hydrocarbon per mile)	Vehicle Miles Traveled (billions)	Total Emissions (billions of grams of hydrocarbon)
1960	17	750	12,750
1965	15.5	950	14,725
1970	13	1,150	14,950
1975	10.5	1,250	13,125
1980	7.5	1,500	11,250
1985	5.5	1,500	8,250
1990	3	2,000	6,000
1995	1.5	2,300	3,450
2000	1	2,600	2,600
2005	0.75	2,850	2,138
2010	0.5	3,150	1,575
2015	0.5	3,400	1,700

15b. Possible graph:

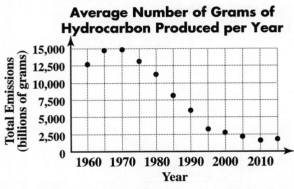

Average Number of Grams of Hydrocarbon Produced per Year

15c. It increased and then decreased, and from the graph we expect it to be about the same (slight increase) from 2010 to 2015.

15d. Possible answer: Per-vehicle emissions could stay at about 0.5 g/mi; assuming vehicle miles traveled is increasing linearly, the miles traveled would be about 4,150 billion.

15e. $4,150,000,000 \cdot 0.5 = 2,075,000,000$

Possible answer: Using 0.5 g/mi emission and 4,150 billion miles traveled, about 2,075 billion grams.

16. Possible answer: Her hypothesis is not very reasonable. Large earthquakes are more newsworthy and probably not more frequent.

17a. no

17b.

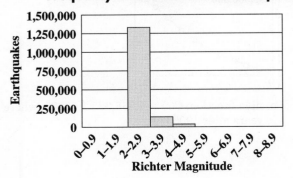

Frequency of Occurrence of Earthquakes

17c. If the histogram is on a sheet of paper of reasonable size, the bars for earthquakes of magnitude greater than 4 will be so short they can't be read.

17d. Possible answer: Although you can see from looking at the table that decreasing magnitude results in a very sharp increase in the average number of earthquakes, the histogram makes the pattern more dramatic.

18a. Possible answers: It does seem like there have been more earthquakes towards the end of the 20th century than might be expected. In general, though, the figures are slightly below the century-long averages.

18b. 1992, 1995, 1996, 1999

18c. All magnitudes under 4; according to Table 1, these low magnitudes should be registering thousands, hundreds of thousands, even millions of quakes for the lowest magnitudes, but Table 2 shows hundreds down to single digit for the lowest magnitudes.

18d. Possible answer: Earthquakes with magnitudes under 4 are probably not strong enough for their locations to be determined by an instrument that is not close by.

19. Answers will vary.

20. $2n(n - 3)$

21. $(2a + 1)(2a - 1)$

22. $3(x^2 - 3x - 10) = 3(x + 2)(x - 5)$

23. $2(2g^2 - g - 21) + 2g^3 + 3g$
$= 4g^2 - 2g - 42 + 2g^3 + 3g$
$= 2g^3 + 4g^2 + g - 42$

24. $x + 2 - (3x^2 + 7x + 4) + 16 - 2x$
$= x + 2 - 3x^2 - 7x - 4 + 16 - 2x$
$= {}^-3x^2 - 8x + 14$

25. $0.5t + 3t - 1.5(7t^2 + 8t + 1)$
$= 0.5t + 3t - 10.5t^2 - 12t - 1.5$
$= {}^-10.5t^2 - 8.5t - 1.5$

26.

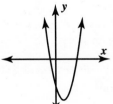

27.

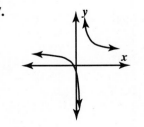

28.

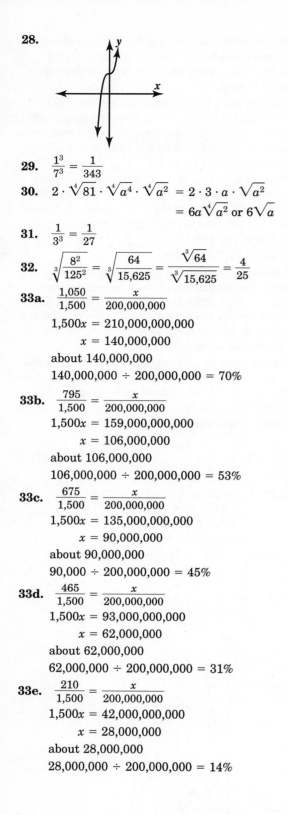

29. $\dfrac{1^3}{7^3} = \dfrac{1}{343}$

30. $2 \cdot \sqrt[4]{81} \cdot \sqrt[4]{a^4} \cdot \sqrt[4]{a^2} = 2 \cdot 3 \cdot a \cdot \sqrt[4]{a^2}$
$= 6a\sqrt[4]{a^2}$ or $6\sqrt[4]{a}$

31. $\dfrac{1}{3^3} = \dfrac{1}{27}$

32. $\sqrt[3]{\dfrac{8^2}{125^2}} = \sqrt[3]{\dfrac{64}{15,625}} = \dfrac{\sqrt[3]{64}}{\sqrt[3]{15,625}} = \dfrac{4}{25}$

33a. $\dfrac{1,050}{1,500} = \dfrac{x}{200,000,000}$
$1,500x = 210,000,000,000$
$x = 140,000,000$
about 140,000,000
$140,000,000 \div 200,000,000 = 70\%$

33b. $\dfrac{795}{1,500} = \dfrac{x}{200,000,000}$
$1,500x = 159,000,000,000$
$x = 106,000,000$
about 106,000,000
$106,000,000 \div 200,000,000 = 53\%$

33c. $\dfrac{675}{1,500} = \dfrac{x}{200,000,000}$
$1,500x = 135,000,000,000$
$x = 90,000,000$
about 90,000,000
$90,000 \div 200,000,000 = 45\%$

33d. $\dfrac{465}{1,500} = \dfrac{x}{200,000,000}$
$1,500x = 93,000,000,000$
$x = 62,000,000$
about 62,000,000
$62,000,000 \div 200,000,000 = 31\%$

33e. $\dfrac{210}{1,500} = \dfrac{x}{200,000,000}$
$1,500x = 42,000,000,000$
$x = 28,000,000$
about 28,000,000
$28,000,000 \div 200,000,000 = 14\%$

Page 625   In Your Own Words

Possible answer: The Web site www.census.gov has official population figures for the United States that are shown in tables and in different types of graphs. For example, a table has population figures for all fifty states as well as for the nation as a whole. It also breaks up the population figures into age bands: under 5 years, 5 to 13 years, 14 to 17 years, etc. From historical tables and graphs, you can analyze trends and predict the population of different sectors of the United States using demographic, social, economic, and housing data.

10-2   Models, Data, and Decisions

Page 632   Problem Set A

1.

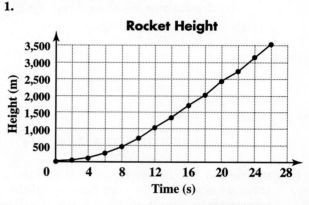

Rocket Height

2a. First differences are 48, 96, 144, 192, 240, 288, 336; all second differences are 48; quadratic.

2b. $h = 6t^2 + 12t$

3a. linear

3b. $h = 180t - 1,176$

4. times up to 14 s, times beyond 14 s

5. $h(3) = 6(3)^2 + 12(3) = 90$ ft
$h(15) = 180(15) - 1,176 = 1,524$ ft
$h(23) = 180(23) - 1,176 = 2,964$ ft

Page 633   Problem Set B

1. Possible answer: Yes; it starts out rising slowly and ends up rising rapidly.

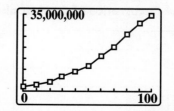

2. Possible function: $C(t) = 1,868,788(1.0322^t)$, where t is years after 1900

3. Possible answer: It does a fairly good job; most of the points are close to the curve.

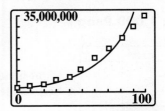

4. $C(^-10) = 1,868,788(1.0322^{-10}) = 1,361,198.586$

$C(110) = 1,868,788(1.0322^{110}) = 61,035,717.93$

Possible answer: about 1,360,000 and about 61,000,000

5. Possible answer: It's a little less (about 12% difference, which is relatively close).

Page 634   Share and Summarize

1. Possible answer: You can use them to make predictions for where other data points might be. For example, with the population data, we predicted the population for years before and after the times in the data set. We could also have predicted the population for years between those given, such as 1983.

2. Possible answer: Graph the data to see if they have a particular shape so you can choose a type of equation to use. Then use a graphing calculator to find an equation for that type of relationship.

Pages 634–635   Problem Set C

1. $120 \div 5 = 24$ hr

2. $24 \cdot \$3 = \$72$

3. $30 \div 5 = 6$ hr

4. $6 \cdot \$9 = \$54$

Each earned $18 per month less.

5. $60 \div 5 = 12$ hr each

$12 \cdot \$7 = \$84$

This is their highest income yet.

6.

Hourly Rate	Income per Baby-sitter
$3	$72
7	84
9	54

7. Possible answer: quadratic (parabola)

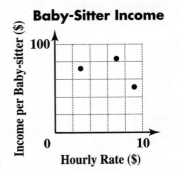

Baby-Sitter Income

8a. the number of hours lost by raising the rate $1

8b. the number of hours they get when they charge nothing at all

8c. quadratic; Possible answer: yes

9. $i = {}^-3r^2 + 33r$

10. rate: $5.50; income: $90.75

Page 636   Share and Summarize

1. Possible answer: In all cases, we chose a curve type and fit a curve of that type to the data (sometimes using a graphing calculator).

2. Possible answer: In Investigation 1, we chose a type of curve based on the shape of the data points. In Investigation 2, we used an assumption about the situation to choose the type of curve.

Pages 636–637   Problem Set D

1. Year 1: $600 + $1,000 = $1,600

Year 2: $1,000

Year 3: $1,000 + $200 = $1,200

Year 4: $1,200 + $200 = $1,400

Year 5: $1,400 + $200 = $1,600

2. Year 1: 7

Year 2: $7 \cdot 1.5 = 10.5$

Year 3: $10 \cdot 1.5 = 15$

Year 4: $15 \cdot 1.5 = 22.5$

Year 5: $22 \cdot 1.5 = 33$

Possible answer: 7, 10, 15, 22, 33; since a fractional number of bicycles can't be sold and can't easily be turned into a full bicycle, I rounded down.

3. build:

Year 1: 12

Year 2: 12 + 10 = 22

Year 3: 22 + 10 = 32

Year 4: 32 + 10 = 42

Year 5: 42 + 10 = 52

on hand:

Year 1: 12 − 7 = 5

Year 2: 5 + 22 − 10 = 17

Year 3: 17 + 32 − 15 = 34

Year 4: 34 + 42 − 22 = 54

Year 5: 54 + 52 − 33 = 73

4. Year 1: $250.00

Year 2: $250 \cdot 1.1 = \$275.00$

Year 3: $275 \cdot 1.1 = \$302.50$

Year 4: $302.50 \cdot 1.1 = \$332.75$

Year 5: $332.75 \cdot 1.1 = \$366.03$

5. Answers will vary slightly, depending on how students round.

gross income:

Year 1: 7 · $250 = $1,750

Year 2: 10 · $275 = $2,750

Year 3: 15 · $302.50 = $4,537.50

Year 4: 22 · $332.75 = $7,320.50

Year 5: 33 · $366.03 = $12,078.99

net profit:

Year 1: $1,750 − $1,600 = $150

Year 2: $2,750 − $1,000 = $1,750

Year 3: $4,537.50 − $1,200 = $3,337.50

Year 4: $7,320.50 − $1,400 = $5,920.50

Year 5: $12,078.99 − $1,600 = $10,478.99

Year	Costs	Bikes Sold	Price per Bike	Gross Income	Net Profit
1	$1,600	7	$250.00	$1,750.00	$ 150.00
2	1,000	10	275.00	2,750.00	1,750.00
3	1,200	15	302.50	4,537.50	3,337.50
4	1,400	22	332.75	7,320.50	5,920.50
5	1,600	33	366.03	12,078.99	10,478.99

6. Possible answer:

$150 + $1,750 + $3,337.50 + $5,920.50 + $10,478.99 = $21,636.99

Page 637 Share and Summarize

1. Possible answer: They might reconsider or have to reevaluate the number of bikes they will build per year (due to demand, storage, time and resources, and their interest); the cost of parts (it may be that discarded parts appear less frequently or are on the side of the road for a reason!); and the price of the bikes (which they could reevaluate after they have some data about how well the bikes sell).

2a.

Year	Net Profit
1	⁻$350.00
2	1,250.00
3	2,837.50
4	5,420.50
5	9,978.99

2b. Possible answer:

⁻$350 + $1,250 + $2,837.50 + $5,420.50 + $9,978.99 = $19,136.99

Pages 638–639 Problem Set E

1. Possible graphs:

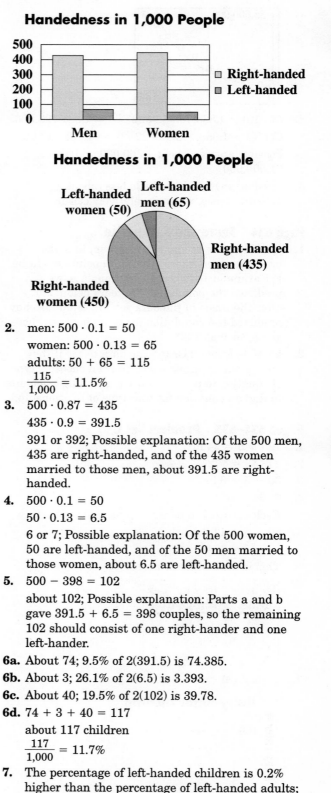

Handedness in 1,000 People

Handedness in 1,000 People

2. men: 500 · 0.1 = 50

women: 500 · 0.13 = 65

adults: 50 + 65 = 115

$\frac{115}{1,000}$ = 11.5%

3. 500 · 0.87 = 435

435 · 0.9 = 391.5

391 or 392; Possible explanation: Of the 500 men, 435 are right-handed, and of the 435 women married to those men, about 391.5 are right-handed.

4. 500 · 0.1 = 50

50 · 0.13 = 6.5

6 or 7; Possible explanation: Of the 500 women, 50 are left-handed, and of the 50 men married to those women, about 6.5 are left-handed.

5. 500 − 398 = 102

about 102; Possible explanation: Parts a and b gave 391.5 + 6.5 = 398 couples, so the remaining 102 should consist of one right-hander and one left-hander.

6a. About 74; 9.5% of 2(391.5) is 74.385.

6b. About 3; 26.1% of 2(6.5) is 3.393.

6c. About 40; 19.5% of 2(102) is 39.78.

6d. 74 + 3 + 40 = 117

about 117 children

$\frac{117}{1,000}$ = 11.7%

7. The percentage of left-handed children is 0.2% higher than the percentage of left-handed adults; a very long time from now, there may be just as many left-handed people as right-handed people.

Pages 640–641   Problem Set F

$(56 \cdot 27 + 54 \cdot 3) \div 30 = 55.8$

Green Room

	Girls	Boys	Total
Students	27	3	30
Average Height (in.)	56	54	55.8

Possible answers are given in the Blue Room table.

$(58 \cdot 3 + 55 \cdot 27) \div 30 = 55.3$

Blue Room

	Girls	Boys	Total
Students	3	27	30
Average Height (in.)	58	55	55.3

Page 641   Share and Summarize

1. Possible answer: It makes it easier, since I'm able to find percentages and add with real numbers rather than just percentages. Without the model, I would have had to find percentages of percentages and try to add them. It would have been a lot more difficult to keep track of what the numbers meant.

2a. Possible answers: Equal number of men and women; not likely for a large population (it certainly won't be exact) but may be reasonable. Every person gets married; definitely won't be true for a real population. Handedness of a potential spouse is not a factor; this is debatable, as some people might meet spouses at a support group for left-handed people, or something like that. However, the assumption is more likely to be true than, say, a similar assumption for very tall or short people. Every couple has exactly two children; this is not likely to be true.

2b. Possible answer: Not a lot, because much of it will probably balance out. Being left-handed isn't likely to make you not marry or not have children. Left-handers might be a little more likely to seek out other left-handers, and their children would have the greatest chance of being left-handed; that might increase the number of left-handed children by a little, but probably not by much. The number of men and women aren't exactly even, but probably close enough that it won't have a big effect either. If couples have more or fewer children, the percentage of left-handers might change at a different rate.

3. Possible answer: When you first consider the situation, you probably assume there are about the same number of boys as girls in each room. If that's not true, it's easy for a few girls (or boys) to be really tall or really short without affecting the average by a whole lot.

Pages 642–651   On Your Own Exercises

1a.

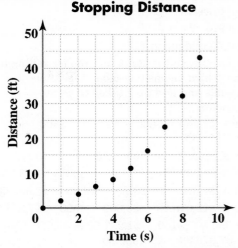

Stopping Distance

1b. The car travels at a constant speed for the first 4 s and then speeds up over the next 5 s.

1c. around 4 s

1d. $0 \cdot 2 = 0$
$1 \cdot 2 = 2$
$2 \cdot 2 = 4$
$3 \cdot 2 = 6$
$4 \cdot 2 = 8$
$d = 2t$

1e. first differences: 3, 5, 7, 9, 11
second differences: 2, 2, 2, 2
quadratic; Possible explanation: The second differences are all 2.

1f. $d = t^2 - 6t + 16$

2a.

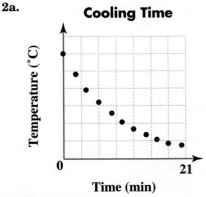

Cooling Time

2b. exponential

2c. From 50°C, about 12 min; from 100°C, about 18 min. No; water at 100°C will lose more heat in a minute than water at 50°C, but water at 100°C still has to fall to 50°C before it can freeze, and from that point it takes just as much time to freeze as water that started at 50°C.

2d. $T = 120(0.9^t)$

3a. Day 1: $30 \cdot 0 = \$0$
Day 2: $20 \cdot 10 = \$200$
Day 3: $10 \cdot 20 = \$200$

3b. quadratic

3c. $15; Possible explanation: Since $10 and $20 gave the same revenue, the vertex is halfway between these prices.

4a. $9 or $10, about $105

4b. about $5 and about $16

4c. $16; she'll earn the same revenue for selling fewer items, which means less money spent on materials and less time taken to create the ornaments.

5. Year 1: $1,750 − $600 − $2,000 − $500 = ⁻$1,350

Year 2: $2,750 − $2,400 − $500 = ⁻$150

Year 3: $4,537.50 − $2,800 − $500 = $1,237.50

Year 4: $7,320.50 − $3,200 − $500 = $3,620.50

Year 5: $12,078.99 − $3,600 − $500 = $7,978.99

⁻$1,350 + ⁻$150 + $1,237.50 + $3,620.50 + $7,978.99 = $11,336.99

6. Possible answer: They might not be able to sell as many bikes as they thought, because most people would rather buy a new one. The $250 price seems high. Assuming they can sell only 5 the first year and each year after sell 2 more than the previous year, and a price of $150 the first year and an additional 5% each year after that, and $500 advertising costs each year, gives this table:

Year	Costs	Bikes Sold	Price	Gross Income	Cumulative Net Profit
1	$2,100	5	$150,00	$ 750.00	⁻$1,350.00
2	1,500	7	157.50	1,102.50	⁻1,747.50
3	1,700	9	165.38	1,488.42	⁻1,959.08
4	1,900	11	173.64	1,910.04	⁻1,949.04
5	2,100	13	182.33	2,370.29	⁻1,678.75

7a. Answers will vary.

7b. $1,000 \cdot 0.04 = 40$

$40 \cdot 0.1 = 4$

4 will test negative.

7c. $1,000 − 40 = 960$

$960 \cdot 0.05 = 48$

48 will test positive.

7d.

	Population	Tests Positive	Tests Negative
Has Disease	40	36	4
Doesn't Have Disease	960	48	912
Total	1,000	84	916

7e. $\frac{36}{84}$, or about 42.9%

7f. $\frac{912}{916}$, or about 99.6%

8a. Answers will vary.

8b. **i.** exponential curve

ii. line

8c. The exponential equation; answers will vary.

8d. $y(1890) = 0.0022(1.0129^{1890}) = 72,986,430.19$

about 72,986,000

$y(2010) = 0.0022(1.0129^{2010}) = 339,805,699.2$

about 339,806,000

8e. Possible answer: It's lower but still fairly close (about 14% lower than the estimate).

9a. reciprocal, $y = \frac{A}{x}$

9b. quadratic, $y = Ax^2$

9c. reciprocal, $y = \frac{-A}{x} + B$

9d. **a.** $15.4 = \frac{A}{50}$

$A = 770$

$7.9 = \frac{A}{100}$

$A = 790$

$5.2 = \frac{A}{150}$

$A = 780$

Possible answer: $y = \frac{780}{x}$

b. $16 = A \cdot 20^2$

$A = 0.04$

$25 = A \cdot 25^2$

$A = 0.04$

$36 = A \cdot 30^2$

$A = 0.04$

Possible answer: $y = 0.04x^2$

c.

$60 = \frac{^-A}{3} + B \qquad 90 = \frac{^-A}{4} + B$

$180 = {}^-A + 3B \qquad 360 = {}^-A + 4B$

$360 = {}^-A + 4B$

$\underline{-180 = {}^-A + 3B}$

$180 = \qquad B$

$180 = {}^-A + 3(180)$

$A = 360$

Possible answer: $y = \frac{-360}{x} + 180$

9e. Possible answers:

a. $y = \frac{780}{350} \approx 2.2$

b. $y = 0.04(35)^2 = 49$

c. $y = \frac{-360}{25} + 180 = 165.6$

$y = \frac{-360}{30} + 180 = 168$

10a. Graph A

10b. **i.** Graph C

ii. Graph A

iii. Graph B

10c. $P(0) = 1,000(5)(1) = 5,000$

$P(^-4) = 1,000(1)(17) = 17,000$

$P(2) = 1,000(7)(5) = 35,000$

10d. Possible answer: For Graph C: The profit in the first year was $0, and a bad series of commercials kept people from trying the new restaurant. After a couple of years, a new ad firm was able to interest people, and although the company was still losing money, they weren't losing as much. By year 4, the company was breaking even and actually began making a profit. Unfortunately, a popular TV news magazine just reported unhealthy conditions at 90% of the chain's restaurants, and the manager's TV interview didn't go well, so they expect to experience a large drop in profits that will be very difficult to recover from.

11a. distance run and time

11b. The time will be the same for the first 100 m as for every other 100 m.

11c. linear

11d. No; it's not easy to keep up that pace for more than a few seconds.

12a. number of people and cost to get in

12b. each person's ticket costs the same

12c. linear

12d. Yes; unless one of them is a lot younger or a lot older, the price for each will be the same.

13a. size of pizza and number of students it will feed

13b. the students each eat about the same amount

13c. quadratic

13d. No; if one of the students is an athlete, he or she might eat a lot more than a smaller or a younger student.

14a. amount in bank and time after initial deposit

14b. Interest is based only on the original amount (simple interest, not compound).

14c. linear

14d. probably not, because most bank accounts use compound interest

15a. Possible answer:

total sample population: 1,000

has condition: $1,000 \cdot 0.1 = 100$

doesn't have condition: $1,000 - 100 = 900$

false-positives: $900 \cdot 0.3 = 270$

false-negatives: $100 \cdot 0.1 = 10$

true-positives: $100 - 10 = 90$

true-negatives: $900 - 270 = 630$

total positives: $270 + 90 = 360$

total negatives: $630 + 10 = 640$

	Population	Tests Positive	Tests Negative
Doesn't Have Condition	900	270	630
Has Condition	100	90	10
Total	1,000	360	640

15b. $\frac{630}{640}$, or about 98.4%

15c. $\frac{90}{360}$, or 25%

15d. Possible answer:

total sample population: 1,000

has condition: $1,000 \cdot 0.1 = 100$

doesn't have condition: $1,000 - 100 = 900$

false-positives: $900 \cdot 0.1 = 90$

false-negatives: $100 \cdot 0.3 = 30$

true-positives: $100 - 30 = 70$

true-negatives: $900 - 90 = 810$

total positives: $90 + 70 = 160$

total negatives: $810 + 30 = 840$

	Population	Tests Positive	Tests Negative
Doesn't Have Condition	900	90	810
Has Condition	100	70	30
Total	1,000	160	840

15e. $\frac{810}{840}$, or about 96.4%

15f. $\frac{70}{160}$, or 43.8%

15g. Possible answer: The new one, because although there's a slightly lower percentage who test negative correctly with the new test than with the old, there's a much greater percentage who test positive correctly with the new test than with the old.

16. $\frac{2}{7}t + \frac{48}{7}$

17. $4x - 13x^2$

18. $14.4v - 0.6$

19. $3.582 \times 10^6 = 3,582,000$

$n = 6$

20. $0.0034001 \times 10^7 = 34,001$

$n = 0.0034001$

21. $n = 82,882$

22. $n = 0.0281$

23.

Possible values: $^-3$, 0, 6.9

24. $7! = 7 \cdot 6 \cdot 5 \cdot 4 \cdot 3 \cdot 2 \cdot 1 = 5,040$

25. $y = 16x + b, (3, {}^-14)$

$^-14 = 16(3) + b$

$b = {}^-62$

$y = 16x - 62$

26. $m = \frac{9 - 3}{^-8 + 1} = \frac{-6}{7}$

$y = \frac{-6}{7} + b, ({}^-1, 3)$

$3 = \frac{-6}{7}({}^-1) + b$

$b = \frac{15}{7}$

$y = \frac{-6}{7}x + \frac{15}{7}$

27. $y = b, (2, 0.5)$

$0.5 = b$

$y = 0.5$

28a. 1 bit: 2 series

2 bits: $2^2 = 4$ series

3 bits: $2^3 = 8$ series

4 bits: $2^4 = 16$ series

5 bits: $2^5 = 32$ series

6 bits: $2^6 = 64$ series

6 bits, 64 series

28b. 2^8 or 256

28c. 2^{10}

28d. $2^{10} \cdot 8 = 2^{10} \cdot 2^3 = 2^{10+3} = 2^{13}$

Page 648   In Your Own Words

Possible answer: Creating mathematical models can be helpful to someone starting a business because it can show her whether or not it can be successful. By placing all of the assumptions into a table and estimating costs, units sold, incomes, and profits for several scenarios, she can make predictions of what may happen in the future. A good bit of advice I would give to her would be to make sure her assumptions are as accurate as possible. Since assumptions are the base of the model, she can make better decisions with regards to the business if the assumptions are accurate.

Review and Self-Assessment

Pages 652–657   Strategies and Applications

1a. Answers will vary. Based on just the number of runs, the AL looks better. The mean number of runs for the AL is 788, but only 747 for the NL. The median for the AL is 793, but the median for the NL is only 737.5.

1b. Possible Answer: Split it into two tables, one for the AL and one for the NL, still sorted by the number of runs.

2. Possible answer: Make three tables, one for each region.

3a. Possible answer: Plots i and ii both show some connection; Plot ii shows no connection. For Plot i, except for one outlier the points seem to decrease from left to right, though they don't fall on a line. For Plot ii, the points seem to decrease from left to right. For Plot iii, the points seem completely random.

3b. Possible answer: Plot i

4a. Possible answer: The most farmland is in the center of the country, and a little to the west, although most of the western states (except California) are on the lower end. Montana and Texas may be the most important farming states.

4b. Possible answer: The most farmland is in the center of the country; as you move away (in either direction), less land is used for farming. The only exceptions seem to be Delaware (which is high for the East Coast) and Nevada (which is a little low for the western states). The most important farming states seem to be the Dakotas, Nebraska, Kansas, and Iowa.

4c. Possible answer: The percentage map because, for example, Texas and Montana are fairly large states. They can use a lot of land for farming and still have a lot more left over. But for a smaller state to have a greater percentage, farming must be more important to the majority of the people who live there.

5a. exponential (decay)

5b. Possible answer:

$y = 32.737425(0.999954)^x$, where y is pressure and x is altitude.

5c. Possible answer:

$y(20,320) = 32.737425(0.999954)^{20,320} \approx 12.86$

about 12.86 in. of mercury

5d. Possible answers:

$y(85,068.997) = 32.737425(0.999954)^{85,068.997}$
≈ 0.65

$y(123,523.58) = 32.737425(0.999954)^{123,523.58}$
≈ 0.11

about 0.65 and 0.11 in. of mercury, respectively

6a. Co-Efficiency: $1{,}000 \cdot 0.25 = 250$

Diagon: $1{,}000 \cdot 0.1 = 100$

6b. Co-Efficiency: $250 \cdot 0.4 = 100$

Diagon: $100 \cdot 0.3 = 30$

6c. $1{,}000 \cdot 0.5 = 500$

$500 + 30 + 100 + 30 = 660$

6d. $\frac{660}{1,000} = 66\%$

Page 658   Demonstrating Skills

7.

Effective Date	Minimum Wage	Annual Income
Jan 1, 1978	$2.65	$5,300
Jan 1, 1979	2.90	5,800
Jan 1, 1980	3.10	6,200
Jan 1, 1981	3.35	6,700
Apr 1, 1990	3.80	7.600
Apr 1, 1991	4.25	8,500
Oct 1, 1996	4.75	9,500
Sep 1, 1997	5.15	10,300

8a. inverse variation

8b. linear

8c. quadratic

8d. exponential growth

8e. exponential decay

Appendix: Trigonometric Ratios

Page 662   Problem Set A

1. Yes, because they all have a right angle and one other angle that is congruent. Since two of the three angles are congruent, the triangles must be similar.

2a. The same. About 0.84.

2b. $\frac{\text{shorter leg}}{\text{longer leg}} = 0.84$

shorter leg $= 0.84 \cdot$ longer leg

shorter leg $= 0.84 \cdot 14 = 11.76$ in.

About $0.84 \cdot 14$ or about $11\frac{3}{4}$ in.

3a. $\frac{f}{e}$

3b. $\frac{c}{f}$ and $\frac{a}{d}$

3c. $\frac{c}{a}$

Pages 662–663   Problem Set B

1. Possible triangle:

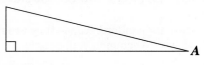

$m\angle A \approx 14°$

2. Possible triangle:

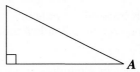

$m\angle A \approx 27°$

3. Possible triangle:

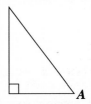

$m\angle A \approx 53°$

4. Possible triangle:

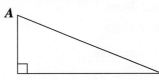

$m\angle A \approx 68°$

5. $\angle A$ increases. If the length of the adjacent leg is fixed and the length of the opposite leg is increased, the ratio of the leg opposite $\angle A$ to the leg adjacent $\angle A$ increases. As the opposite leg gets longer, $\angle A$ must increase.

Page 663   Share and Summarize

1. The reason all the ratios are approximately the same is that all the right triangles are similar. Since the triangles are similar, the ratios of the lengths of their sides will be equivalent. Writing the ratio as a decimal is another way to write a ratio in reduced form. So if all those equivalent ratios are written in reduced form, they should all be the same.

2. The ratio of legs is $\frac{a}{b}$. If a is 0, there is no triangle. So $\frac{a}{b}$ can be as small as one wants, but must always be greater than 0. There is no "smallest" ratio because any thin triangle can be beaten by a still thinner triangle. The same is true of the "largest." There is no largest ratio because any large ratio can be beaten by a still larger ratio. Students can imagine a very tall skinny triangle with a very tall opposite leg and a tiny adjacent leg. As the opposite leg gets taller and taller, and the adjacent leg gets smaller and smaller, the ratio will get extremely large, but there is always a larger one possible. We say that the ratios "approach" zero and "approach" infinity, but no *triangle* corresponds to either limiting case.

3. The ratio of legs in a right triangle depends only on one of the two acute angles.

Pages 665–666   Problem Set C

1.
$$\tan 40° = \frac{x}{5.2}$$
$$0.8391 = \frac{x}{5.2}$$
$$0.8391 \cdot 5.2 = x$$
$$4.36 \approx x$$

2.
$$\tan 62° = \frac{22.7}{x}$$
$$1.8807 = \frac{22.7}{x}$$
$$1.8807 \cdot x = 22.7$$
$$x = \frac{22.7}{1.8807}$$
$$x \approx 12.07$$

3.
$$\tan 18° = \frac{3}{x}$$
$$0.3249 = \frac{3}{x}$$
$$0.3249 \cdot x = 3$$
$$x = \frac{3}{0.3249}$$
$$x \approx 9.23$$

4.
$$\tan 32° = \frac{x}{18}$$
$$0.6249 = \frac{x}{18}$$
$$0.6249 \cdot 18 = x$$
$$11.25 \approx x$$

5.
$$\tan 3° = \frac{x}{1{,}000}$$
$$0.0524 = \frac{x}{1{,}000}$$
$$0.0524 \cdot 1{,}000 = x$$
$$52.4 = x$$
52 ft

6a.
$$\tan 34° = \frac{x}{52}$$
$$0.6745 = \frac{x}{52}$$
$$0.6745 \cdot 52 = x$$
$$35.074 = x$$
35 ft

6b. She forgot to add the distance from the ground up to her eye. That distance plus 35 feet would give her the height of the flagpole.

7.
$$\tan 60° = \frac{x}{2{,}640}$$
$$1.73205 = \frac{x}{2{,}640}$$
$$1.7321 \cdot 2{,}640 = x$$
$$4{,}572.744 = x$$
About 4,570 feet or a little less than $\frac{7}{8}$ of a mile

8a.
$$\tan 75° = \frac{25}{x}$$
$$3.73205 = \frac{25}{x}$$
$$3.7321 \cdot x = 25$$
$$x = \frac{25}{3.7321}$$
$$x \approx 6.699$$
6.7 ft or about $6\frac{3}{4}$ ft

8b.
$$a^2 + b^2 = c^2$$
$$6.7^2 + 25^2 = c^2$$
$$44.89 + 625 = c^2$$
$$669.89 = c^2$$
$$\sqrt{669.89} = \sqrt{c^2}$$
$$25.88 \approx c$$
at least a 26-foot ladder

9a. Possible answer: The tree and its shadow form a similar triangle to the triangle that Luisa creates. Because the triangles are similar, Luisa knows that the angle formed by the tree and the imaginary line to the top of the shadow is also 36°. She measures the length of the tree's shadow. Then she sets up the equation
$$\tan 36° = \frac{\text{tree's shadow}}{\text{height of tree}}.$$

9b.
$$\tan 36° = \frac{42.5}{x}$$
$$0.7265 = \frac{42.5}{x}$$
$$0.7265 \cdot x = 42.5$$
$$x = \frac{42.5}{0.7265}$$
$$x \approx 58.4997$$
58.5 ft

Page 667 Share and Summarize

1. The two legs are the same length. (Also, the two acute angles each measure 45°.)

2. If the tangent of one of the angles is 1, then the ratio of the length of the opposite leg to the length of the adjacent leg is $\frac{1}{1}$. That means the legs must be the same length.

Page 668 Problem Set D

1. They are both calculated as a ratio of AC to OC.

2. $\frac{AC}{OC} = \frac{0.4}{2} = 0.2$
Mosi traveled 0.4 mile in 2 minutes at an average rate of 0.2 mile a minute.
$\frac{BD}{OD} = \frac{0.8}{4} = 0.2$
Mosi traveled 0.8 mile in 4 minutes at an average rate of 0.2 mile a minute.
Both represent the ratio of distance traveled to time.

3. $\frac{AC}{OC} = \frac{0.4}{2} = 0.2$
$\frac{BD}{OD} = \frac{0.8}{4} = 0.2$
Yes, because these ratios are equal.

4. Yes, because the graph is a straight line starting at the origin.

5. These triangles are similar because they are right triangles and have a common acute angle.

Pages 668–669 Problem Set E

1. $\frac{AC}{OC} = \frac{0.4}{2} = 0.2$
Mosi and Sancha each traveled 0.4 mile in 2 minutes at an average rate of 0.2 mile a minute.
$\frac{ED}{OD} = \frac{0.6}{4} = 0.15$
Sancha traveled 0.6 miles in 4 minutes at an average rate of 0.15 miles a minute.
Both represent the ratio of distance traveled to time.

2. $\frac{AC}{OC} = \frac{0.4}{2} = 0.2$
$\frac{ED}{OD} = \frac{0.6}{4} = 0.15$
You can't make a proportion because the ratios are not equal.

3. No, because she didn't ride at a constant speed. Some students may comment that the relationships before and after Sancha changed speed are linear and direct.

4a. $\frac{0.4 - 0}{2 - 0} = \frac{0.4}{2} = 0.2$ mi/min

4b. $\frac{0.6 - 0.4}{4 - 2} = \frac{0.2}{2} = 0.1$ mi/min

5. $\tan \angle AOC = \frac{AC}{OC} = \frac{0.4}{2} = 0.2$
$\tan \angle EAF = \frac{EF}{AF} = \frac{0.2}{2} = 0.1$

6. $\frac{0.4 - 0}{2 - 0} = \frac{0.4}{2} = 0.2$
$\frac{0.6 - 0.4}{4 - 2} = \frac{0.2}{2} = 0.1$
No; for the first 2 minutes the slope of her graph is $\frac{0.4}{2}$ or 0.2, but over the next 2 minutes, the slope of her graph is $\frac{0.2}{2}$ or 0.1.

7. The average speed for the first two minutes should be equal to the average speed for the first four minutes.

Page 669   Problem Set F

1. $5 per hour
2. $\dfrac{30 - 20}{2 - 0} = \dfrac{10}{2} = 5$
3. The hourly rate and the slope are expressed by the same number.
4. $\dfrac{AC}{OC} = \dfrac{30}{2} = 15$
   Hannah is paid $30 for 2 hours of work for an average rate of $15 an hour.
   $\dfrac{ED}{OD} = \dfrac{40}{4} = 10$
   Hannah is paid $40 for 4 hours of work for an average rate of $10 an hour.
   Both represent the ratio of total pay to time.
5. $\dfrac{AC}{OC} = \dfrac{30}{2} = 15$
   $\dfrac{ED}{OD} = \dfrac{40}{4} = 10$
   No; the ratios are not equivalent.
6. No; the graph does not start at the origin.

Page 670   Share and Summarize

1. $\tan \angle ASE = \dfrac{10}{2} = 5$
   $\tan \angle BSF = \dfrac{20}{4} = 5$
   Hannah's hourly rate of pay is $5. The slope of the graph is 5. This is the tangent of $\angle ASE$ and also of $\angle BSF$ in the graph.
2a. $\tan 40° \approx 0.84$
2b. $(2, 0)$, $(8, 5)$
   $\dfrac{5 - 0}{8 - 2} = \dfrac{5}{6} = 0.8\overline{3}$
   Students will choose different points, but the $\dfrac{\text{rise}}{\text{run}}$ between these points should be reasonably close to 0.84.
2c. They are nearly equal because they are both measures of the slope of the same line. They are not exactly equal because both are approximations.

Page 671   Problem Set G

1a. Answers will vary.
1b. Answers will vary. The decimal ratio should be approximately 0.91.
1c. It is approximately the same for each of the triangles.
1d. Yes; since all right triangles that have one angle measuring 65° must be similar to each other, the ratio of their corresponding sides is proportional.
2. Since the sum of the two acute angles in a right triangle is 90°, the measure of the other acute angle in each of these triangles is $(90 - 65)°$ or 25°. To approximate sin 25°, find the ratio of the length of the side opposite this 25° angle to the length of the hypotenuse for one of the triangles. Approximations should be close to 0.42.

Pages 671–672   Problem Set H

1a. Answers will vary.
1b. Answers will vary. The decimal ratio should be approximately 0.42.
1c. It is approximately the same for each of the triangles.
1d. Yes; since all right triangles that have one angle measuring 65° must be similar to each other, the ratio of their corresponding sides is proportional.
2. Marcus is correct. If the cosine of an angle is the ratio of the length of the adjacent leg to the hypotenuse, the cosine can never be greater than 1 since the hypotenuse is always the largest side.
3. The ratio must be larger than 0, but can get as close to 0 as you like. The opposite or adjacent leg can get very small, approaching 0, and the hypotenuse can be any length. The ratio must be smaller than 1, but can get arbitrarily close to 1 as the opposite leg or adjacent leg approaches the length of the hypotenuse.

Pages 672–673   Problem Set I

1. $\cos 52° = \dfrac{x}{136}$
   $0.6157 = \dfrac{x}{136}$
   $0.6157 \cdot 136 = x$
   $84 \approx x$
   $\sin 52° = \dfrac{y}{136}$
   $0.7880 = \dfrac{y}{136}$
   $0.7880 \cdot 136 = y$
   $107 \approx y$
2. $\sin 4° = \dfrac{x}{1,500}$
   $0.0698 = \dfrac{x}{1,500}$
   $0.0698 \cdot 1,500 = x$
   $104.7 = x$
   about 105 ft
3. $\cos \angle A = \dfrac{\text{adjacent}}{\text{hypotenuse}}$
   $0.2 = \dfrac{\text{adjacent}}{\text{hypotenuse}}$
   Let the adjacent side be 2 units long.
   $0.2 = \dfrac{2}{\text{hypotenuse}}$
   $\text{hypotenuse} = \dfrac{2}{0.2} = 10$
   Use the Pythagorean theorem to find the third side.
   $a^2 + b^2 = c^2$
   $a^2 + 2^2 = 10^2$
   $a^2 + 4 = 100$
   $a^2 = 96$
   $\sqrt{a^2} = \sqrt{96}$
   $a \approx 9.8$

Let the adjacent side be 1 unit long.

$0.2 = \dfrac{1}{\text{hypotenuse}}$

hypotenuse $= \dfrac{1}{0.2} = 5$

Use the Pythagorean theorem to find the third side.

$a^2 + b^2 = c^2$

$a^2 + 1^2 = 5^2$

$a^2 + 1 = 25$

$a^2 = 24$

$\sqrt{a^2} = \sqrt{24}$

$a \approx 4.9$

Possible answers: 2, 9.8, 10; 1, 4.9, 5; an infinite number

4. Yes, Anson is correct. The leg adjacent to one of the acute angles is the opposite leg for the other acute angle. Therefore, their sines and cosines are equal.

Page 673　Share and Summarize

1. The reason all the ratios are constant for any given angle in a right triangle is that all the right triangles are similar. Since the triangles are similar, the ratios of the lengths of their sides will be equivalent.

2. Only the tangent ratio can be greater than 1, when the opposite leg is greater than the adjacent leg. The sine and cosine can never be greater than 1, since the hypotenuse has to be the longest side of the triangle, and the hypotenuse is in the denominator of each of these ratios.

3. If the sin 30° is 0.5, that means the ratio of the leg opposite the 30° angle to the hypotenuse is $\dfrac{1}{2}$.

   Therefore, the sides could be 1 and 2, 2 and 4, 5 and 10, etc., as long as the leg opposite is half the hypotenuse.

Pages 674–680　On Your Own Exercises

1a. $\dfrac{1}{5} = \dfrac{a}{2.4}$

$5a = 2.4$

$a = 0.48$ in.

1b. 0.2

1c. $\dfrac{a}{b} = \dfrac{x}{y} = \dfrac{1}{5} = 0.2$

2a. $0.25 = \dfrac{19.6}{y}$

$0.25 \cdot y = 19.6$

$y = \dfrac{19.6}{0.25}$

$y = 78.4$ m

2b. $\dfrac{x}{y} = \dfrac{a}{b} = 0.25$

3.

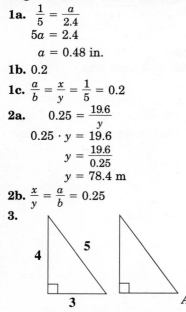

4.

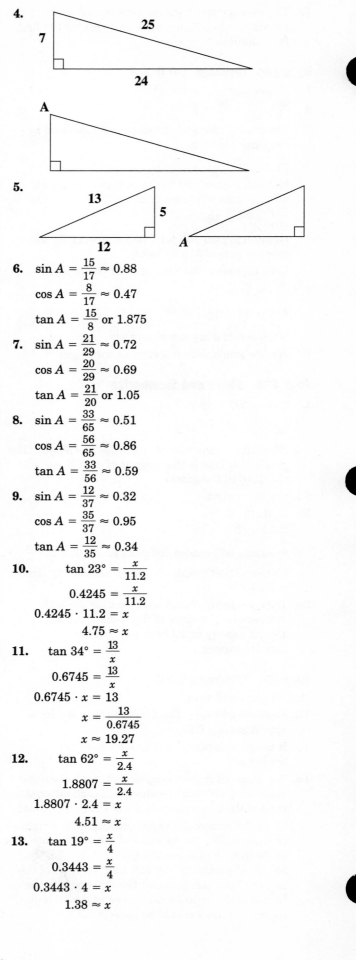

5.

6. $\sin A = \dfrac{15}{17} \approx 0.88$

$\cos A = \dfrac{8}{17} \approx 0.47$

$\tan A = \dfrac{15}{8}$ or 1.875

7. $\sin A = \dfrac{21}{29} \approx 0.72$

$\cos A = \dfrac{20}{29} \approx 0.69$

$\tan A = \dfrac{21}{20}$ or 1.05

8. $\sin A = \dfrac{33}{65} \approx 0.51$

$\cos A = \dfrac{56}{65} \approx 0.86$

$\tan A = \dfrac{33}{56} \approx 0.59$

9. $\sin A = \dfrac{12}{37} \approx 0.32$

$\cos A = \dfrac{35}{37} \approx 0.95$

$\tan A = \dfrac{12}{35} \approx 0.34$

10. $\tan 23° = \dfrac{x}{11.2}$

$0.4245 = \dfrac{x}{11.2}$

$0.4245 \cdot 11.2 = x$

$4.75 \approx x$

11. $\tan 34° = \dfrac{13}{x}$

$0.6745 = \dfrac{13}{x}$

$0.6745 \cdot x = 13$

$x = \dfrac{13}{0.6745}$

$x \approx 19.27$

12. $\tan 62° = \dfrac{x}{2.4}$

$1.8807 = \dfrac{x}{2.4}$

$1.8807 \cdot 2.4 = x$

$4.51 \approx x$

13. $\tan 19° = \dfrac{x}{4}$

$0.3443 = \dfrac{x}{4}$

$0.3443 \cdot 4 = x$

$1.38 \approx x$

14.
$$\cos 23° = \frac{x}{21.5}$$
$$0.9205 = \frac{x}{21.5}$$
$$0.9205 \cdot 21.5 = x$$
$$19.79 \approx x$$
$$\sin 23° = \frac{y}{21.5}$$
$$0.3907 = \frac{y}{21.5}$$
$$0.3907 \cdot 21.5 = y$$
$$8.40 \approx y$$

15.
$$\sin 65° = \frac{x}{8}$$
$$0.9063 = \frac{x}{8}$$
$$0.9063 \cdot 8 = x$$
$$7.25 \approx x$$
$$\cos 65° = \frac{y}{8}$$
$$0.4226 = \frac{y}{8}$$
$$0.4226 \cdot 8 = y$$
$$3.38 \approx y$$

16.
$$\sin 27° = \frac{1.4}{x}$$
$$0.4540 = \frac{1.4}{x}$$
$$0.4540 \cdot x = 1.4$$
$$x = \frac{1.4}{0.4540}$$
$$x \approx 3.08$$

17.
$$\cos 50° = \frac{6.4}{x}$$
$$0.6428 = \frac{6.4}{x}$$
$$0.6428 \cdot x = 6.4$$
$$x = \frac{6.4}{0.6428}$$
$$x \approx 9.96$$

18.
$$\tan 52° = \frac{x}{6}$$
$$1.2799 = \frac{x}{6}$$
$$1.2799 \cdot 6 = x$$
$$7.68 \approx x$$
$$\cos 52° = \frac{6}{y}$$
$$0.6157 = \frac{6}{y}$$
$$0.6157 \cdot y = 6$$
$$y = \frac{6}{0.6157}$$
$$y \approx 9.75$$

19.
$$\tan 73° = \frac{10.5}{x}$$
$$3.2709 = \frac{10.5}{x}$$
$$3.2709 \cdot x = 10.5$$
$$x = \frac{10.5}{3.2709}$$
$$x \approx 3.21$$
$$\sin 73° = \frac{10.5}{y}$$
$$0.9563 = \frac{10.5}{y}$$
$$0.9563 \cdot y = 10.5$$
$$y = \frac{10.5}{0.9563}$$
$$y \approx 10.98$$

20a.

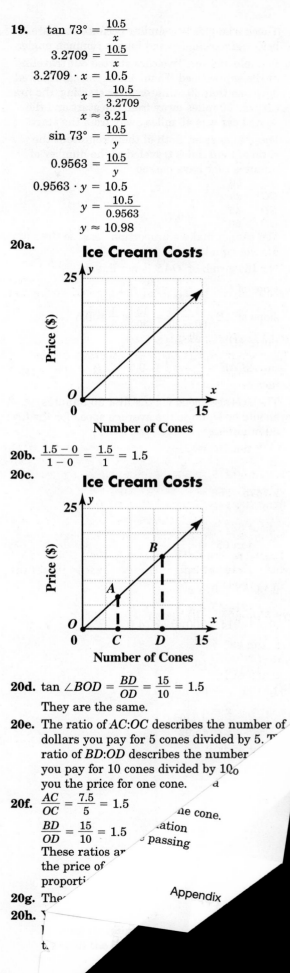

Ice Cream Costs

20b. $\frac{1.5 - 0}{1 - 0} = \frac{1.5}{1} = 1.5$

20c.

Ice Cream Costs

20d. $\tan \angle BOD = \frac{BD}{OD} = \frac{15}{10} = 1.5$
They are the same.

20e. The ratio of $AC{:}OC$ describes the number of dollars you pay for 5 cones divided by 5. T~~he~~ ratio of $BD{:}OD$ describes the number ~~of dollars~~ you pay for 10 cones divided by 10~~, giving~~ you the price for one cone.

20f. $\frac{AC}{OC} = \frac{7.5}{5} = 1.5$ ~~one cone.~~
$\frac{BD}{OD} = \frac{15}{10} = 1.5$ ~~...ation~~ ~~... passing~~
These ratios a~~re...~~
the price of ~~...~~
proporti~~...~~

20g. The~~...~~

20h. ~~...~~

Appendix

235

20i. These triangles are similar because they are both right triangles and have a common angle.

21a. Possible answer: Two cars started out traveling at the same speed. Then, one of the cars slowed down, so that 60 minutes after starting, the first car was 60 miles away from the start and the second car was 45 miles away from the start.

21b. Possible answer: Both of them represent the ratio of total miles traveled to the number of minutes that have passed.

21c. $\dfrac{AC}{OC} = \dfrac{30}{30} = 1$

$\dfrac{ED}{OD} = \dfrac{45}{60} = \dfrac{3}{4} = 0.75$

You cannot make a proportion because the ratios are not equal.

21d. No; the graph of OAE is not linear.

21e. slope of $\overrightarrow{OA}$: $\dfrac{30-0}{30-0} = \dfrac{30}{30} = 1$

slope of $\overrightarrow{AE}$: $\dfrac{45-30}{60-30} = \dfrac{15}{30} = \dfrac{1}{2} = 0.5$

21f. $\tan \angle AOC = \dfrac{30}{30} = 1$

$\tan \angle EAF = \dfrac{15}{30} = \dfrac{1}{2} = 0.5$

21g. no

21h. The average speed for the first 30 minutes should be equal to the average speed for the first 60 minutes.

22. $\tan 70° = \dfrac{x}{250}$

$2.7475 = \dfrac{x}{250}$

$2.7475 \cdot 250 = x$

$686.875 = x$

about 687 ft

23. $\tan 65° = \dfrac{x}{100}$

$2.1445 = \dfrac{x}{100}$

$2.1445 \cdot 100 = x$

$214.45 = x$

about $(214 - 200)$ ft or 14 ft

24. $\tan 48° = \dfrac{50}{x}$

$1.1106 = \dfrac{50}{x}$

$1.1106 \cdot x = 50$

$x = \dfrac{50}{1.1106}$

$x \approx 45.02$

about 45 ft

25. $\cos 35° = \dfrac{20}{x}$

$0.8192 = \dfrac{20}{x}$

$0.8192 \cdot x = 20$

$x = \dfrac{20}{0.8192}$

≈ 24.41

26. $\sin 15° = \dfrac{2}{x}$

$0.2588 = \dfrac{2}{x}$

$0.2588 \cdot x = 2$

$x = \dfrac{2}{0.2588}$

$x \approx 7.73$

about 7.7 ft

27a. unit rise = 7 ft ÷ 9 stairs = $0.\overline{7}$ ft = $9.\overline{3}$ in. $\approx$ 9.3 in.

unit run = 9 ft ÷ 9 stairs = 1 ft = 12 in.

27b. No; the unit rise is 9.3 in., which is not between 6 and 8 in. In addition, the unit rise plus the unit run is 21.3 in., which is not between 17 and 18 in.

27c. 9.3:12 or 0.78

27d. slope of $\overrightarrow{AB} = \dfrac{7}{9} = 0.\overline{7} \approx 0.78$

This ratio is equal to the slope of $\overrightarrow{AB}$.

27e. $\dfrac{7}{9} = 0.\overline{7} \approx 0.78$

This ratio is also equal to the slope of $\overrightarrow{AB}$.

27f. $\dfrac{9.3}{12} = \dfrac{7}{9} = 0.\overline{7} \approx 0.78$

These ratios are equal and both equal to the slope of the staircase. Therefore, you can form a proportion with these ratios.

27g. $\tan \angle BAC = \dfrac{7}{9} = 0.\overline{7} \approx 0.78$

These ratios are equal to the tangent of $\angle$BAC. You can calculate the tangent by dividing the total rise by the total run.

27h.

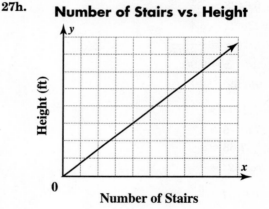

Number of Stairs vs. Height

y-axis: Height (ft)

x-axis: Number of Stairs

27i. slope $= \dfrac{7-0}{9-0} = \dfrac{7}{9}$ or about 0.78

They are all equal.

28a. $2x$

28b. Since the diagonals bisect each other, $EB = 0.5x$ and $EC = x$. The diagonals are also perpendicular, so $\triangle BEC$ is a right triangle with $\angle E$ as its right angle. The tangent of $\angle CBE$, is equal to the ratio $\dfrac{EC}{BE}$ or $\dfrac{x}{0.5x}$. This ratio simplifies to $\dfrac{1}{0.5}$ or 2. Thus, the tangent of $\angle CBE$ is 2. Derrick can use the trigonometric table to find an angle measure whose tangent is about 2.

28c. $\tan \angle CBE = \dfrac{6}{3} = 2$

Answers will vary but should be between 60° and 65°.

Page 678   In Your Own Words

Possible answer: Slope is found by calculating the ratio of the vertical change (rise) to the horizontal change (run) between two points on a line or $\dfrac{\text{rise}}{\text{run}}$. The segment joining these two points can also be seen as the hypotenuse of a right triangle with one leg equal in measure to the rise between the two points and the other equal in measure to the run between the two points. By definition, the tangent of the angle formed by the horizontal leg of this right trianble and its hypotenuse is found by calculating the ratio of the leg opposite this angle to the leg adjacent this angle or $\dfrac{\text{opposite leg}}{\text{adjacent leg}}$. Since the leg opposite this angle hs the same measure as the rise between the two points, and the leg adjacent this angle has the same measure as the run between the two points, $\dfrac{\text{rise}}{\text{run}} = \dfrac{\text{opposite leg}}{\text{adjacent leg}}$. Therefore, the slope of a line and the tangent of the angle that line forms with another horizontal line describe the same ratio.